THE ORAL HISTORY COLLECTION

The Oral History Collection

OF COLUMBIA UNIVERSITY

Edited by
ELIZABETH B. MASON
and
LOUIS M. STARR

NEW YORK

ORAL HISTORY RESEARCH OFFICE

1973

A New York Times Company Publication
produced and sold
by
Microfilming Corporation of America

Library of Congress Card No. 73-78480

Printed in the United States of America

Contents

Introduction

THIS CATALOGUE describes the largest hoard of unpublished reminiscence in the world. More significantly, the Oral History Collection is the largest and most diversified memory bank of its kind on 20th Century American life, a collection unique in that it has been created, bit by bit over the last quarter century, through a method developed at Columbia and known, for want of a better term, as "oral history." The term is misleading. The end product of oral history, as we practice it, is not a tape but a typewritten transcript, generally edited for accuracy by the oral author. This third edition of *The Oral History Collection* is a guide to 360,000 pages of such transcript.

"I am willing to wager," our interviewers heard time and again in our early years, "that no one will ever lay eyes on a word I have told you." Some who spoke in this vein have lived to see their Oral History memoirs cited and quoted in modest monographs published by university presses, others in histories large and small, in biographies on best-seller lists, in learned journals, in mass circulation magazines, in textbooks and anthologies, in a few instances even in children's readers and on radio and television programs. Still others among the skeptics survived to see both this kind of dissemination and the acquisition of their Oral History memoirs, with their permission, by other libraries around the country, purchased in microform that scholars everywhere might have access to them.

The development of this new kind of primary source material—one that has both enriched historical writing and complicated the scholar's task—stems from the work of a single man, Allan Nevins. Sensing that manuscript sources were drying up in the age of the telephone, the airliner, and the automobile, Professor Nevins had the faith and persistence to pursue his vision. He conducted our first interview (see McANENY, George) on May 18, 1948. His wisdom, *élan*, and high resolve carried the venture through its difficult formative years. When he retired, in 1958, Oral History had amassed over 100,000 pages of memoirs and (as he had predicted) was sprouting elsewhere.

The slender first edition of *The Oral History Collection*

vii

opened a door. Significant use of the Collection by scholars dates from its publication in 1960, a point documented in our annual reports.

Four years later the second edition, more voluminous and better dressed, stimulated both use and emulation of the oral history idea in this country and abroad.

The present edition, long awaited because supplements to the second went out of print several years ago, calls itself a milestone on the following impeccable grounds:

- ✔ It appears (fortuitously, in light of unavoidable delays) on our 25th anniversary;

- ✔ It is the first to emanate from a trade publisher, freeing us of the tasks of production and sales;

- ✔ It is the first to be offered in both hardcover and soft;

- ✔ It is the first to utilize computer tape, so that both text and index may ingest new entries, facilitating future editions and eliminating the awkward supplements.

More broadly, this last accomplishment lights the way toward up-to-date catalogues for manuscript collections of all kinds.*

Appropriately, this advance was made possible by a grant from the Lucius N. Littauer Foundation of New York. Modest in resources by foundation standards, Littauer was the first to respond with outside support for Oral History almost a quarter of a century ago—a classic instance of what is meant by seed money. We salute its President, Harry Starr (no relation to the writer), and his associates for their perceptive help, then and now.

Like its catalogue, the Oral History Collection itself, which represents the investment of over a million dollars, to say nothing of equivalents in sweat and tears, has been financed largely by outside funds. Gifts and bequests from individuals, grants from public and private agencies, plus support from the Libraries' Bancroft fund and our own endowment, have fueled us. Not a penny has come from the general income of

*The pressing need for progress in this area is set forth in "Finding Aids and the Historian," American Historical Association *Newsletter*, May, 1972, pp. 15–19.

the University, a point to note at a time when universities are too constricted to afford activities as central to their purpose as creating, processing, and disseminating primary source materials. In this catalogue, the sponsors are credited in a line of italic at the end of the entry describing the work they underwrote. May they, as well as our oral authors and the many friends who have contributed to the Oral History Endowment Fund, share our pride in what has been done, our zest for what lies ahead.

We borrow from Bruce Catton for our preroration:

> I suspect most people never give a thought to the importance of source materials, for, after all, most people don't use them. The simplest way to put it is that civilization is built on them. The building keeps going on as knowledge expands, is stored, evaluated, refined, redefined and passed along through myriad channels from generation to generation.
>
> By *creating* source materials on a broad scale for the first time, the oral historians are performing work that, it seems to me, is just as significant and maybe a lot more enduring than any number of doings that catch the fancy, and the fancy money, of the big foundations that pour millions into education.... One meaningful measure of a society is the value it places on enriching and preserving its own heritage, on conserving human experience.*

Conserving human experience is what oral history is all about.

Notes on Use

This edition organizes the whole Collection into a single alphabet. All 2,697 persons represented in it, whether by a full-length biographical memoir, by a brief contribution to a special project, or (in a few instances) by a speech or lecture deemed worth preserving, have been placed in this one se-

*Think, March-April, 1965, p. 23.

quence, as have the project descriptions. Memoirs of broad interest done in connection with special projects have been accorded brief individual entries; more commonly, the searcher is referred to the project to which the person contributed, where related memoirs are listed.

The year given at the end of each entry is that of the concluding interview.

"NYT (Part I)" indicates that in addition to being available in Butler Library, where the entire Collection is housed, the memoir is among the 200 obtainable on microfiche from the New York Times Oral History Program (c/o Microfilming Corporation of America, Glen Rock, N. J. 07452.) Researchers interested in such a memoir should check the nearest major library to see if it has this series, now widely held. If not, it may be ordered individually from the address given, along with a catalogue and price list. "NYT (Part II)" means that the memoir will be included in the second such offering by the Times, anticipated for 1974.

Tapes: Many memoirs, in general those done since 1962, may be heard on tape, restrictions permitting, but it is well to give us at least a week's advance notice.

Access: Our oral authors know before they begin that they will be able to decide upon access to their material when it is ready for submission to the Collection. (Micropublication is an option that, restrictions permitting, is considered later, after both parties have gained perspective.) There are four categories of restriction:

✓ Memoirs designated *Open* may be read upon presentation of credentials to the Oral History Research Office, 221-M Butler Library. Quotation from such memoirs for publication requires permission, but one may cite and paraphrase, in moderation, without this formality. Consult us when in doubt.

✓ Those specifying *Permission required to cite or quote* are equally accessible, the scholar pledging himself to observe the requirement.

✓ Where the stipulation reads *Permission required*, it must be obtained in writing from the memoirist or the person he has designated before access can be granted. The researcher should write us, specifying his interest as explicitly as possible, for assistance in obtaining such permissions. Often as not, they are readily granted.

Closed means literally that. One should draw no inference from the fact that material is closed. (In some instances, we have imposed the restriction ourselves, in the absence of word from the memoirist.)

Since provisions regarding access change with the passage of time, we invite inquiry.

Finding aids: Supplementing the text of this catalogue, which is itself a listing of all persons interviewed, is an index limited to (1) broad groupings that appeared useful, *e.g.,* Agriculture, Art, Book Publishing, and a list of all Special Projects; (2) names of persons mentioned in the entries. The absence of a name from this index, it should be emphasized, is far from conclusive as to the Collection itself.*

Each memoir carries its own biographical index.

The Office maintains a master biographical card index to the entire Collection. We search it in response to inquiries and report without charge. For those unable to come here, we arrange for research in the Collection itself in response to precise instructions, a nominal sum being charged per hour.

The ultimate finding aid, a multiple-access name, subject and topical index, is on the horizon, but it will be limited to memoirs released for micropublication. The computerized first edition of this, an index to NYT Part I memoirs, is in preparation.

Citation: The standard form of citation is, *"The Reminiscences of Norman Thomas,* Part II (1965), p. 151, in The Oral History Collection of Columbia University, hereafter Thomas, OHC." Citations from memoirs related to special projects should include the name of the project.

We maintain a permanent exhibit of books drawing upon the Collection, authors and publishers kindly contributing them in recognition of services rendered. We appreciate hearing from readers alerting us to instances of use of which we were unaware, in both books and periodicals.

---

*For example, the catalogue index refers to six memoirs that touch upon the life of Walter Reuther. Our master biographical index turns up 77 others that speak of him, some at length.

Fifteen to twenty-five thousand pages of new materials are added to the Collection each year. These are summarized in our annual reports, obtainable without charge, and also available in many libraries. Reports deal with developments of current interest in the field of oral history, at Columbia and elsewhere.

This volume, complete to February 1, 1973, describes memoirs totaling 364,650 pages, of which 55,338 are *Open*, 114,-424 *Permission required to cite or quote*, 122,593 *Permission required*, 63,752 *Closed*, and 8,543 *In process*. It is worth noting from these figures that less than one fifth of the Collection, at this writing, remains closed, the impression having got abroad in our early years that much of it was inaccessible. That becomes progressively less true with each passing year.

Seventy-two special projects and 549 biographical memoirs are included in this edition, many of them for the first time. One thousand and thirty-eight memoirs are individually described.

To repeat a standing invitation, scholars interested in any phase of American history from the 1880's to the present are invited to inquire of us for material of possible interest in the Oral History Collection. We welcome visitors.

ACKNOWLEDGEMENTS

The task of putting together a publication of this dimension has been arduous. An irony with which we live is the assumption, far and wide, that Oral History at Columbia has become a vast organization—a Department, at very least, our mail tells us. This delusion perhaps reflects the city and the institution we represent as perceived elsewhere. It also reflects the fact that the Collection is indeed vast—in pages of transcription, for example, nearly equal to other oral history programs in the United States taken together.* A long headstart had much to do with this. The office itself is no larger than it ever was, so that keeping all wheels turning while at the same time writing and checking hundreds of

*See *Oral History in the United States*, A Directory, compiled by Gary Shumway, which we edited and published for the Oral History Association in 1971. At the rate oral history is growing, this ratio, of course, will not obtain much longer.

Introduction

entries for the catalogue has been a challenge. That it was met is due largely to the cheerful persistence of the Associate Director, Mrs. Elizabeth B. Mason, for whom this was the third (and by far the most complicated) time around. As in previous editions, her mastery of detail, her enthusiasm and her sound judgement, were indispensable. We had the willing help, first of Christine Erazo, more recently of Carol Hertzberg, both of whom deserve warm thanks. Others who helped in spare time with descriptions and preparing copy for the printer were Dr. Mary-Jo Kline and Russell Schoch. In the offices of Arno Press, the indefatigible Leslie Pap and his lieutenant, Mrs. Marie Iversen, were valuable collaborators.

Thanks are due also to members of our University Advisory Committee, individually and collectively, and to President William McGill and his associates. Continuing interest and support throughout the University reassure us as we embark upon a second quarter century. While none of us may see it out ourselves, Oral History at Columbia surely will, and by then what a Collection it will be!

Finally, we salute here the many interviewers and transcribers who have served us across the years. They are credited on the front page of every memoir; their devotion to the cause will merit the thanks of scholars for years to come.

Oral History Research Office
February, 1973

LOUIS M. STARR
Director

xiii

ABBREVIATIONS

AAA	Agricultural Adjustment Administration
ACLS	American Council of Learned Societies
ACLU	American Civil Liberties Union
ADA	Americans for Democratic Action
AEC	Atomic Energy Commission
AFL	American Federation of Labor
AHA	American Historical Association
AHR	*The American Historical Review*
AID	Agency for International Development
AMA	American Medical Association
AP	Associated Press
BAE	Bureau of Agricultural Economics
BEW	Board of Economic Warfare
CARE	Cooperative for American Remittances to Europe
CBI	China, Burma, India Theater of War
CCC	Civilian Conservation Corps
CCNY	College of the City of New York
CG	Commanding General
CIA	Central Intelligence Agency
CIO	Congress of Industrial Organizations
CO	Commanding Officer
CORE	Congress on Racial Equality
CPA	certified public accountant
DAB	*Dictionary of American Biography*
EDC	European Defense Community
EFC	Emergency Fleet Corporation
EPIC	End Poverty in California
FAO	Food and Agriculture Organization
FCC	Federal Communications Commission
FEAF	Far Eastern Air Force
FEPC	Fair Employment Practices Committee
FERA	Federal Emergency Relief Administration
FHA	Federal Housing Administration
FSA	Farm Security Administration
FTC	Federal Trade Commission
HEW	Department of Health, Education, and Welfare
HIP	Health Insurance Plan
HQMC	Marine Corps Headquarters

ICA	International Cooperation Administration
ICFTU	International Confederation of Free Trade Unions
IFC	International Finance Corporation
IGY	International Geophysical Year
IHB	International Health Board
ILO	International Labor Office
IPR	Institute of Pacific Relations
IRO	International Relief Organization
IWW	International Workers of the World
MGH	Massachusetts General Hospital
MIT	Massachusetts Institute of Technology
MSA	Mutual Security Administration
NAACP	National Association for the Advancement of Colored People
NAM	National Association of Manufacturers
NDRC	National Defense Research Committee
NEA	National Education Association
NIH	National Institutes of Health
NLRB	National Labor Relations Board
NRA	National Recovery Administration
NSC	National Security Council
NYA	National Youth Administration
NYU	New York University
OCD	Office of Civilian Defense
ODT	Office of Defense Transportation
OES	Office of Economic Stabilization
OFRRO	Office of Foreign Relief and Rehabilitation Operations
ONI	Office of Naval Intelligence
OPA	Office of Price Administration
OPM	Office of Production Management
OSRD	Office of Scientific Research and Development
OSS	Office of Strategic Services
OTC	Officers Training Corps
OWI	Office of War Information
PAC	Political Action Committee
P&S	College of Physicians and Surgeons
PUMC	Peking Union Medical College
PWA	Public Works Administration
RA	Resettlement Administration
RAF	Royal Air Force

Abbreviations

REA	Rural Electrification Administration
RFC	Reconstruction Finance Administration
ROTC	Reserve Officers Training Corps
SCAP	Supreme Commander Allied Powers
SEATO	South East Asia Treaty Organization
SEC	Securities and Exchange Commission
SHAEF	Supreme Headquarters, Allied Expeditionary Force
SNCC	Student Non-violent Coordinating Committee
SPAB	Supply Priorities and Allocations Board
SSRC	Social Science Research Council
TC	Teachers College
TIAA	Teachers Insurance and Annuity Association
TNEC	Temporary National Economic Committee
TVA	Tennessee Valley Authority
UAW	United Automobile Workers
UJA	United Jewish Appeal
UMW	United Mine Workers
UNESCO	United Nations Educational, Scientific and Cultural Organization
UNICEF	United Nations International Children's Emergency Fund
UNRRA	United Nations Relief and Rehabilitation Administration
USAF	United States Air Force
USHA	United States Housing Authority
USIA	United States Information Agency
USIS	United States Information Service
USMC	United States Marine Corps
USO	United Service Organizations
USSB	United States Shipping Board
WCTU	Woman's Christian Temperance Union
WFA	War Food Administration
WFC	War Finance Corporation
WFTU	World Federation of Trade Unions
WHO	World Health Organization
WIB	War Industries Board
WLB	National War Labor Board
WPA	Works Progress Administration
WPB	War Production Board
WWI	World War I
WWII	World War II.

The Oral History Collection

ABAD DE SANTILLAN, Diego. Journalist.
ARGENTINA IN THE 1930's.
Discussion of labor organizations in Argentina during 1920's and 1930's: political tendencies and affiliations, general strikes, factionalism, philosophy of labor.
20 pp. *Open.* 1970.

ABBOTT, Paul (1898–1971) *See* McGraw-Hill.

ABEL, Elie (1920–) Journalist.
EISENHOWER ADMINISTRATION.
Recollections of the Eisenhower administration, 1953–59; Washington correspondent, *NY Times,* 1949–59; press conferences, information leaks; Vietnam War. Impressions of John Foster Dulles, Richard M. Nixon, and Charles Wilson.
45 pp. *Permission required to cite or quote.* 1970.

ABEL, Walter Charles (1898–) *See* Popular Arts.

ABERBACH, Jean. *See* Popular Arts.

ABERBACH, Julius. *See* Popular Arts.

ABRAMS, Charles (1901–1970) Housing expert.

Urban renewal, social reform; National Committee Against Discrimination; First Houses, NYC; Morris Strunsky, Langdon W. Post.
78 pp. *Permission required to cite or quote.* 1964.

ABRAMS, Frank Whittemore (1889–) Executive.

Early life and education; career with Standard Oil of New

Jersey; responsibilities of management; Council on Financial Aid to Education.
48 pp. *Closed during lifetime.* 1954.

ABT, John J. (1904–   ) *See* La Follette Civil Liberties Committee.

ACHESON, Dean (1893–1971) *See* Journalism Lectures *and* Marshall Plan.

ACKERMAN, Lauren V. *See* Occupation of Japan.

ADAMS, John Charles (–1952) *See* Benedum and the Oil Industry.

ADAMS, Sherman (1899–   ) Presidential aide.
EISENHOWER ADMINISTRATION

Eisenhower's decision to run for the Presidency; 1952 convention and campaign; Richard Nixon fund; Korea speech; Cabinet and White House staff; NSC; Council of Economic Advisors; foreign policy; congressional-executive relations; economic controls. Recollections of John Foster Dulles, Herbert Brownell, Thomas E. Dewey, Earl Warren, Emmett Hughes, Gabriel Hauge, Arthur F. Burns.
268 pp. *Permission required to cite or quote.* 1970.

ADKINS, Bertha (1906–   ).
EISENHOWER ADMINISTRATION

Republican National Committee; 1952 convention; women in government; impressions of President and Mrs. Eisenhower.
72 pp. *Permission required to cite or quote.* 1967.

AGHNIDES, Thanassos (1889–   ) Greek diplomat.
LEAGUE OF NATIONS

Education, University of Constantinople; League of Nations, 1919–41; Sir Eric Drummond, Joseph Avenol as Secretaries General; preparatory commission and disarmament

conference, 1932; Under Secretary General, 1938; discussion of League Secretariat and degree of national influence on Secretariat members; political pressures in Europe with rise of Nazis; effects of Munich, Albania, Danzig, outbreak of WWII; Greek government-in-exile, 1942; UN organization meeting in San Francisco, drafting charter; chairman of advisory committee on administration and finance; review of 21 years of UN: description of major crises, recollections of Trygve Lie, Dag Hammarskjold, U Thant, many other League and UN staff members.
506 pp. *Permission required.* 1966.

AIKEN, George David (1892–) Senator.
EISENHOWER ADMINISTRATION

Agricultural policies from late 1940's through 1950's; impressions of President Eisenhower.
31 pp. *Open.* 1967.

AIR FORCE ACADEMY PROJECT

In 1968, the faculty of the USAF Academy initiated a series of oral history interviews with significant figures in military aviation. The major topics discussed include strategy and tactics in WWI and WWII and Korea, the establishment of the Air Force Academy, and inter-service relationships.

Participants and pages: John Allison, 54; Charles P. Cabell and Haywood Hansell, 133; Charles I. Carpenter, 72; Benjamin W. Chidlaw, 23; Jarred V. Crabb, 150; Laurence C. Craigie, 81; Howard C. Davidson, 35; Charles Dolan, 25; Charles D'Olive, 58; James H. Doolittle, 56; Wendell H. Fertig, 18; Harold L. George and Haywood Hansell, 60; Haywood Hansell, 52; Edwin Lansdale, 83; Curtis Le May, 107; Grover Loening, 9;

John P. McConnell, 31; Robert McDermott, 207; S.L.A. Marshall, 70; Joseph O. Mauborgne, 79; Thomas Moorman, 134; Oliver K. Niess, 43; Emmett O'Donnell, 48; Joseph Reich, 29; Edward V. Rickenbacker, 19; Reginald Sinclair, 58; Jesse Smith, 37; Carl Spaatz, 26; Dean C. Strother, 76; Herbert B. Thatcher, 122; Thayer Tutt, 35; Nathan Twining, 54; John F. Victory, 114; Albert C. Wedemeyer, 90.

2,288 pp. *Subject to individual restrictions.* 1969–71.
Contributed by the USAF Academy, Colorado Springs, Colorado; copy also available there.

3

AITCHISON, A. E. *See* Weyerhaeuser Timber Company.

ALASKAN PIONEERS

This project gathers the reminiscences of pioneer settlers in Alaska, providing accounts of gold prospecting, mining, cattle driving, homesteading, and travel by trail and river. Included are descriptions of the social life of the pioneers, as well as accounts of the depression of 1893 and the Klondike strike.

Participants and pages: Jack Brooks, 7; Nat Browne, 33; Edward Crawford, 57; George Gasser, 23; Bobby Sheldon, 36; William R. Sherwin, 40; Sam White, 39; Oscar Winchell, 159.

394 pp. *Open.* 1959–62.
Contributed by Mrs. Sandy Jensen of Fairbanks, Alaska.

ALBEE, Edward (1928–) *See* Popular Arts.

ALBERTSON, Ralph (1866–1951) Clergyman.

Christian Commonwealth Movement, co-workers; Walter Lippmann; Russia, 1918–19.
53 pp. *Open.* 1950. Papers (microfilm).

ALBRIGHT, Horace Marden (1890–) Conservationist.

Department of the Interior, 1913; National Park Service, 1916–33; Superintendent of Yellowstone, 1919–33; conservation problems; maintenance of park facilities, establishment of new parks, acquisition of lands; historical areas and national monuments; organization of CCC; Capital Parks and Planning Commission; borax mining and potash producing, US Potash Company; chemical code under NRA; labor problems; international cartel and price war; impressions of Franklin K. Lane, Woodrow Wilson, Albert B. Fall, Warren G. Harding, Owen Brewster, Gifford Pinchot, Calvin Coolidge, Herbert Hoover, John D. Rockefeller, Jr., Hiram Johnson, Franklin D. Roosevelt, Harold Ickes.
851 pp. *Permission required to cite or quote.* 1960. NYT (Part I). Papers.

REFER TO "NOTES ON USE" IN INTRODUCTION

Comments on conservation, 1900–60: a joint interview with Newton Drury.
49 pp. *Permission required to cite or quote.* 1961. *Contributed by the Regional Oral History Office, University of California, Berkeley. See also* Jackson Hole Preserve.

ALCORN, Hugh Meade, Jr. (1907–   ) Lawyer.
EISENHOWER ADMINISTRATION

Account of Republican Conventions, 1952 and 1964; Republican National Committee; Senatorial Campaign Committee and Congressional Campaign Committee; Operation Dixie. Recollections of Sherman Adams, John Foster Dulles, Richard Nixon, Harold Stassen, Leonard Hall, and Barry Goldwater.
159 pp. *Permission required to cite or quote.* 1967.

ALDERMAN, Sidney Sherrill (1892–   ) Lawyer.

Early life; Trinity College (now Duke University); law school and teaching; military training and WWI; law practice in North Carolina; General Solicitor, General Counsel and Vice President of the Southern Railway System; Nuremberg War Crimes trials.
1,817 pp. *Closed until 5 years after death.* 1953. Papers.

ALDERSON, Harold B. *See* Robert A. Taft Project.

ALDERWERELD, Siem (1909–   ) *See* World Bank.

ALDRICH, Winthrop Williams (1885–   ) *See* Eisenhower Administration.

ALEXANDER, Will Winton (1884–1956) Authority on race relations.

Childhood and education; Vanderbilt University; ministry, Methodist Church South, 1901–17; WWI; race riots; beginning work in race relations, Commission in Interracial Cooperation, 1919–30; lynching; Ku Klux Klan; Atlanta University merger; Dillard University, Acting President, 1931–35; RA, 1935–36; Greenbelt towns; Great Plains; subsistence homesteads; Bankhead-Jones Farm Tenant Act, FSA, 1937; Julius Rosenwald Fund; FEPC; organizing the American Council on Race Relations; impressions of C. B. Baldwin, John Fischer, Sidney Hillman, President and Mrs. Franklin D. Roosevelt, Julius Rosenwald, Frank Tannenbaum, Mr. and Mrs. Rexford G. Tugwell, Henry Wallace, and others.

756 pp. *Permission to cite or quote.* 1952. NYT (Part I).

ALEXANDER, Willard. *See* Popular Arts.

ALEXANDERSON, Ernst F. W. (1878–   ) *See* Radio Pioneers.

ALFORD, Dale. *See* Eisenhower Administration.

ALGER, George William (1872–1967) Lawyer.

Law practice in NYC at the turn of the century; Moreland commission; NY prisons; Moreland commissioner to investigate NY superintendent of insurance in the guaranteed mortgage companies debacle on nearly two billion issues of bonds, 1933; NYC garment industry; Vermont boyhood. Observations on social reformers, including Lillian Wald and Florence Kelley; Theodore Roosevelt.

538 pp. *Permission required to cite or quote.* 1952. NYT (Part I).

ALISON, John Richardson (1912–   ).

AVIATION

Pre-WWII training and experience in Army Air Corps; demonstrating P-40's in England; London during the Blitz; duty in Russia, Lend-Lease program with Russian Air Force; combat assignments in CBI; kamikaze attacks on Pacific Fleet; Assistant Secretary of Commerce for Air; Northrop Corporation. Recollections of Harry Hopkins,

Gens. Henry H. Arnold, Claire Chennault, and Orde Wingate.
132 pp. *Permission required to cite or quote.* 1960.

ALLEN, Chester Robinson (1905–1972) Marine Corps officer.

Education, University of Florida, 1925–29; early USMC training, sea and barracks duty; Shanghai, 1938–39; barrage balloon program, 1941–43; quartermaster duties, 1943–46; occupation of Japan; Supply Depot, Barstow, California, 1947–51; 1st Marine Division, Korea, 1951–52; duty at HQMC successively as Head of Supply Department, Director of Marksmanship Training Division, and USMC Quartermaster General, 1954–60.
383 pp. *Open.* 1969.

ALLEN, Ed. *See* Radio Pioneers.

ALLEN, Ernest Mason (1904–   ) *See* Health Science.

ALLEN, George Venable (1903–1970) Diplomat.

US Foreign Service, 1930; consular service, Shanghai, Greece; Middle East Division, State Department, 1938–46; Potsdam, 1945.
77 pp. *Permission required.* 1962.
                              EISENHOWER ADMINISTRATION
Ambassador to India; Director of USIA; recollections of John Foster Dulles and other Secretaries of State; Korea; Greece; US exhibition in Moscow and "Kitchen Debate"; Brussels Fair, 1958.
136 pp. *Permission required.* 1967.

ALLEN, James E., Jr. (1911–1971) Educator.

Early work in West Virginia and at Princeton, Harvard, and Syracuse Universities; executive assistant to NY Commissioner of Education, later Commissioner; Presidential Commission on Higher Education.
55 pp. *Permission required.* 1966.

7

ALLEN, Netta Powell (1890–   ) *See* China Missionaries.

ALLEN, William Harvey (1874–1963) Civic worker.

Youth and education; Universities of Chicago and Pennsylvania; Association for Improving the Condition of the Poor, 1903–07; Bureau of Municipal Research, 1907–14; Rockefeller Foundation and Carnegie Foundation; Training School for Public Service, 1911–14; University of Wisconsin Survey; Dr. Charles Van Hise; Institute for Public Service; NYC Municipal Civil Service Commission, 1934–37; NY politics; Mayors Fiorello La Guardia and James Walker, Thomas E. Dewey.
532 pp. *Permission required to cite or quote.* 1950. NYT (Part I). Papers.

ALLISON, John M. *See* International Negotiations.

ALLISON, John. *See* Air Force Academy.

ALMARZA, Camilo (1904–   ) Labor leader.
ARGENTINA IN THE 1930'S
Early work experience on railroad; development from section leader of local union to officer of General Confederation of Workers (CGT), 1936–43; organization of local: political beliefs and effect on policy, degree of independence; analysis of general economic and social conditions in Argentina in 1930 with examples: regional differences, ethnic make-up, foreign influences, wages and housing, health and sanitation; effect of unions, especially in construction, meat-packaging, railroads, textiles; labor gains and union growth, largely after 1936; strikes, factionalism, deportations; effects of WWII.
160 pp. *Open.* 1971.

ALSOP, Joseph Wright (1910–   ) *See* Eisenhower Administration.

ALTER, Gerald (1919–   ) *See* World Bank.

REFER TO "NOTES ON USE" IN INTRODUCTION

ALTMEYER, Arthur Joseph (1891–1972) Administrator.
SOCIAL SECURITY
Education, background in health insurance movement,
John R. Commons; Committee on Economic Security,
1934–35; Assistant Secretary of Labor, 1934; Advisory
Council, National Conference on Health, 1938; adminis-
trative problems and policies in Social Security: training,
relations with Congress, Treasury Department, Internal
Revenue Service; influence of organized labor and
professional associations. Impressions of Frances Perkins,
Edwin Witte, Wilbur Cohen, Isidore Falk, and others.
231 pp. *Permission required to cite or quote.* 1967.

ALTSCHUL, Helen (Mrs. Frank) (1887–   ) *See* Herbert H.
Lehman Project.

AMEN, John Harlan (1898–1960) Lawyer.

Harvard Law School; Departments of Justice and of War;
Nuremberg War Crimes trials.
36 pp. *Permission required to cite or quote.* 1951. NYT
(Part I).

AMERICAN ASSOCIATION OF PHYSICS TEACHERS

Founding members discuss the formation of the American
Association of Physics Teachers in 1930 and describe its
relations with the American Physical Society and the
American Institute of Physics. Efforts to improve teaching
methods and to achieve a balance between teaching and
research; anecdotes and appraisals of leading American
physicists, including Karl Compton, Arthur Compton, and
F. K. Richtmyer.

Participants and pages: Homer L. Dodge, 47; Paul Klopsteg, 42; Frederic
Palmer, 36; M. N. States, 31; D. L. Webster, 37.

193 pp. *Permission required to cite or quote.* 1963.
*Underwritten by the American Association of Physics
Teachers and the American Institute of Physics of New*

9

The Oral History Collection

AMERICAN CULTURAL LEADERS

This series of interviews was conducted by Joan Simpson Burns to provide material for a study of patterns in American cultural life. Mrs. Burns's interest centered on her subjects' family backgrounds and early exposure to the arts as well as on their later contributions to American culture. Her interviewing method, frankly experimental, encouraged free association and frequent digressions. The principals' memoirs are supplemented by conversations with their professional associates.

Participants and pages: William Arrowsmith and Roger Shattuck, 16; Mody Boatwright, 12; Robert Brustein, 17; Turner Catledge, 35; Hedley Donovan, 184; Ronnie Dugger, 33; Lloyd Goodrich, 86; John Hawkes, 51; Barnaby Keeney, 23; Goddard Lieberson, 95; W. McNeil Lowry, 296; Robert McCord, 50; Harry Ransom, 89; Gordon Ray, 18; Frank Stanton, 330; Frank Thompson, 138; Mrs. Marshall Thompson, 37.

1,510 pp. *Closed pending publication of a study.* 1968. *Contributed by Joan Simpson Burns, Williamstown, Massachusetts.*

AMERICAN HISTORIANS

A series of interviews with leading historians, conducted by Professor John Garraty, dealing with such topics as westward expansion and economic change to 1860; slavery in the US; American nationalism, social and cultural changes in the US between the Civil War and WWI; Reconstruction period; the US in world affairs from 1918 to 1945; and problems of interpretation of history.

Participants and pages: Bernard Bailyn, 83; Ray Allen Billington, 103; Stuart Bruchey, 92; Henry Steele Commager, 81; Robert D. Cross, 122; George Dangerfield, 82; Sigmund Diamond, 109; David Donald, 88; Clement Eaton, 89; Stanley Elkins, 87; Robert Ferrell, 111; Jack P. Greene, 161; Robert Heilbroner, 86; Richard Hofstadter, 58; Alfred Kazin, 82; Edward C. Kirkland, 67; Richard W. Leopold, 87; William E. Leuchtenburg, 99; Arthur S. Link, 96; Ernest R. May, 104; Richard B. Morris, 133; Robert K. Murray, 114; Roy F. Nichols, 81; Russell B. Nye, 101; David M.

Columbia University

Potter, 82; Arthur M. Schlesinger, Jr., 73; T. Harry Williams, 103; C. Vann Woodward, 86.

2,660 pp. *Permission required to cite or quote.* 1968–69. *Contributed by John A. Garraty, New York.*

ANDERSON, Carl D. (1905–   ) *See* Nobel Laureates.

ANDERSON, Dillon (1906–   ) Lawyer.

EISENHOWER ADMINISTRATION

Pre-convention and election campaigns, 1952; Tidelands issue; NSC; Draper Committee; Vietnam; Laos; Quemoy and Matsu; Open Skies proposal; Geneva Summit Conference; impressions of President Eisenhower and John Foster Dulles.

130 pp. *Open.* 1969.

ANDERSON, Florence (1910–   ) Foundation officer.

CARNEGIE CORPORATION

Detailed account of her experiences with the Carnegie Corporation from 1934; relationships, functions and organizations of the various Carnegie enterprises; description of major programs undertaken by Carnegie Corporation with particular emphasis on philosophy, policy, restrictions, procedures, follow-up, and impact; trustees and staff members; relationship with federal government, Congressional investigations; impressions of Andrew Carnegie, Frederick Keppel, Charles Dollard, John Gardner, Nicholas Murray Butler, Alan Pifer, and many other educators and public figures.

656 pp. *Permission required.* 1967.

ANDERSON, Frank Maloy (1871–1961) Historian.

AHA politics and policies; *AHR*; Mississippi Valley Historical Association and its *Review*.

24 pp. *Open.* 1955.

ANDERSON, Gilbert M. (1883–   ) *See* Popular Arts.

11

ANDERSON, M. O. *See* Independence Park.

ANDERSON, Maxwell (1888–1959) Author, playwright.

Experiences with the NY *World*; writing *Winterset* and other plays.
34 pp. *Permission required to cite or quote.* 1956. NYT (Part I).

ANDERSON, Orvil A. (1895–   ).
HENRY H. ARNOLD PROJECT

Recollections of Gen. Arnold from 1938; War Department policy on planes; fighters vs. bombers; Lend-Lease; expansion of forces, 1941–42; problems of allocation and division of appropriations; organization of USAF; Joint Chiefs and Joint Planning Staff; Pearl Harbor attack; Ploesti raid, 1942. Impressions of President Franklin D. Roosevelt, Gen. George C. Marshall, Adm. Ernest J. King, and others.
113 pp. *Permission required.* 1959.
See also Aviation.

ANDERSON, Russell. *See* McGraw-Hill.

ANDERSON, Walter Stratton (1881–   ) Naval officer.

Childhood and education; Naval Academy; Naval War College; teaching at Naval Academy and St. John's; NY Harbor Supervisor; sea commands; Naval attaché, London, 1934–37; Director of Naval Intelligence, 1939–41; Pearl Harbor attack; Board of Inspections; Commander, Gulf Sea Frontier; Automatic Electric Company, 1946–56. Impressions of Adms. Ernest King, Chester Nimitz, and Hugo Osterhaus and of Josephus Daniels and Frank Knox.
290 pp. *Permission required to cite or quote.* 1962. NYT (Part I).

ANDERSON, Mr. and Mrs. Warwick. *See* Adlai E. Stevenson Project.

REFER TO "NOTES ON USE" IN INTRODUCTION

ANDERSON, William Hamilton (1874–1959) Prohibitionist.

Organization, personnel and activities of Anti-Saloon League; Prohibition and NY politics, 1915–24; trial of Mr. Anderson.
148 pp. *Open.* 1950. Papers.

ANDREW, Geoffrey C. *See* Carnegie Corporation.

ANDREWS, Dana (1909–   ) *See* Popular Arts.

ANGELL, Sir Norman (1872–1967) Author.

Peace movements, British and American politics, and personal reflections, 1900–50; Lord Northcliffe and his newspaper empire. An informal memoir accompanied by an annotated bibliography of his work.
278 pp. *Permission required to cite or quote.* 1951. NYT (Part I). Papers.

ANNAN, Robert. *See* Mining Engineers.

ANNETT, Fred A. (1879–1959) *See* McGraw-Hill.

ANNIS, Edward Roland (1913–   ) Physician.

The President of the AMA (1963–64) discusses debates with Hubert Humphrey, Walter Reuther, John Kennedy, Lyndon Johnson and George Smathers; King-Anderson and Kerr-Mills bills.
84 pp. *Closed during lifetime.* 1967.

ANSORGE, Martin Charles (1882–1967) Lawyer, congressman.

Columbia University, 1903; NYC politics, 1914–32; WWI; national politics during Warren Harding administration.
74 pp. *Permission required to cite or quote.* 1949. NYT (Part I). Papers.

APPLEBY, Paul Henson (1891–1963) Political scientist.

Family background; Grinnell College; newspaper experiences; assistant to Secretary of Agriculture Henry A. Wallace, including detailed description of important New Deal leaders, agencies, politics and policies; trip to London and experiences with Lend-Lease; Department of State.
360 pp. *Permission required to cite or quote.* 1952. NYT (Part I).

APPLEMAN, Roy E. *See* Independence Park.

ARAM, John Lorenzo (1912–   ) *See* Weyerhaeuser Timber Company.

ARENDS, Leslie Cornelius (1895–   ) *See* Robert A. Taft Project.

ARGENTINA IN THE 1930'S

This series of interviews provides a broad general view of Argentina at a critical period in that country's development. A joint effort of the Instituto Torcuato Di Tella in Buenos Aires and the Oral History Research Office of Columbia University, the project began in 1970 with a grant from the Tinker Foundation.

While the memoirs focus primarily on the 1930's, there is much background information from prior years, and a number of the memoirists deal with events in the succeeding two decades. The institute plans to continue the project, concentrating next on the 1940's and the rise to power of Juan D. Peron.

Taken together, the memoirs offer a richly detailed panorama of political, sociological, and economic developments unobtainable elsewhere. A group of labor leaders highlight the transition from craft to industrial unions, the factional and partisan conflicts within the labor movement, and attitudes toward ethnic and regional concentrations. Argentine industrial and manufacturing figures describe technological changes, relationships with foreign enter-

REFER TO "NOTES ON USE" IN INTRODUCTION

prises, and attitudes toward organized labor. Political leaders discuss internal organization and practices of political groups, with examples from municipal and national campaigns. The interviews, conducted by staff members of the institute, are in Spanish. The project is a continuing one.

Participants and pages: Diego Abad de Santillan, 20; Camilo Almarza, 160; Cecilio Benitez de Castro, 13; Lucio Bonilla, 103; Andres Cabona, 116; Guido Clutterbuck, 20; Luis Danussi, 87; Jorge del Rio, 41; Jose Domenech, 192 *(certain pages closed)*; Hector Duarte, 40; Carlos Emery, 33; Jesus Fernandez, 31; Alfredo Fidanza, 21; Manuel Fossa, 39; Mateo Fossa, 77; Luis F. Gay, 107; Americo Ghioldi, 50; Rafael Ginocchio, 67; Roberto Giusti, 59; Ricardo Guardo, 62; Esteban Habiague, 147; Carlos Ibarguren, 48; Julio Irazusta, 51; Ernesto Janin, 57; Arturo Jauretche, 221; Emilio Jofre, 40;

Julio A. Lagos, 31; Roberto Lobos, 55; Juan Maggi, 123; Ernesto Malaccorto, 64 *(closed until 1980)*; Luciano F. Molinas, 25; Alberto Morello, 30; Francisco Muro de Nadal, 59; Maria Rosa Oliver, 57; Jose Luis Pena, 74; Francisco Perez Leiros, 180 *(permission required to cite or quote)*; Jorge Walter Perkins, 3; Federico Pinedo, 84 *(permission required to cite or quote)*; Pedro Pistarini, 46; Jose Luis Portos, 47; Luis Ramicone, 43; Juan Rodriguez, 70; Luis Maria Rodriguez, 21; Julian Sancerni Gimenez, 7; Silvano Santander, 81; Dario Sarachaga, 21; Fernando Sola, 50; Diogenes Taboada, 25; Mariano Tedesco, 78; Adolfo Vicchi, 173.

3,349 pp. *Open except as noted.* 1971–
Underwritten by the Tinker Foundation, New York City.

ARMSTRONG, Barbara (1890–   ) Lawyer.
                                            SOCIAL SECURITY

Social Insurance Commission, California, 1915–19; attempts to get social and health insurance; *Insuring the Essentials,* 1932; consultant on unemployment insurance and old age insurance, Committee on Economic Security, 1934; detailed account of preparatory work for Social Security legislation: effect of Depression, Wisconsin plan, separation of taxing and spending provisions, constitutionality, relationship with insurance industry and Treasury, Edwin Witte, J. Douglas Brown, Arthur Altmeyer, Senator Robert LaFollette, and others.

317 pp. *Permission required.* 1965.

ARMSTRONG, James Sinclair (1915–   ) *See* Eisenhower Administration.

ARNER, Fred. *See* Social Security.

ARNOLD, Eleanor (Mrs. Henry H.).

HENRY H. ARNOLD PROJECT

Family background of Henry H. Arnold; early meetings; engagement and marriage, 1913; Gen. Arnold's experiences in Army Air Corps: Washington in WWI, planning and production problems, forest patrols, air mail; Mitchell trial, reprimand and exile; Morrow Board; Command and General Staff School; effects of Depression. Impressions of Gens. Douglas MacArthur, George C. Marshall, William L. Mitchell, Wendell Westover, and others.

108 pp. *Permission required.* 1959.

ARNOLD, Frank Atkinson (1867–1958).

RADIO PIONEERS

Early advertising experiences; first contacts with radio; broadcasting and advertising; Director of Development for NBC; pre-recorded programs; early radio advertisers; *Broadcast Advertising: the Fourth Dimension;* advertising agencies, independent radio counsel; technical advances in radio; television and its problems.

101 pp. *Open.* 1951.

HENRY H. ARNOLD PROJECT

The life of the late Gen. Henry H. Arnold (1886–1950), first Commander of the Army Air Forces, as related by his associates. Included are interviews with veteran Air Force officers throughout the country and with retired RAF officers in Great Britain who worked with Gen. Arnold during WWII. Primary emphasis is upon Arnold's role in the Air Forces, his relations with his associates, the types of problems he met, and his contributions to the development of military aviation, including a wealth of material of value to Air Force historians. The material deals with Arnold as a student at West Point, as infantry officer in the Philippines, as student pilot under Orville Wright, as close associate of Gen. William Mitchell, as

Chief of the Army Air Corps, and as Commanding General of the Air Forces and member of the Combined Chiefs of Staff during WWII.

Participants and pages: Orvil A. Anderson, 113; Eleanor Pool (Mrs. Henry H.) Arnold, 108; John Leland Atwood, 26; Eugene Beebe, 80; James Henry Burns, 26; Charles P. Cabell, 59; Benjamin Castle, 78; Frederick Warren Conant, 28; Donald Wills Douglas, 137; Ira C. Eaker, 184; Grandison Gardner, 54; Robert Ellsworth Gross, 29; W. Averell Harriman, 60; Sir Arthur Harris, 85;

James Howard Kindelberger, 57; Frank P. Lahm, 31; Robert Abercrombie Lovett, 69; Leroy Lutes, 32; Thomas D. Milling, 100; A. C. Peterson, 31; Elwood Quesada, 18; Arthur Emmons Raymond, 24; Sir Henry Self, 56; Sir John Slessor, 38; Carl Spaatz, 81; Henry Wyman Strangman, 38; Hayden Wagner, 35; Kenneth B. Wolfe, 49.

1,726 pp. *Permission required.* 1959–60.
Underwritten by friends of General Arnold. Also available at USAF Academy Library, Colorado Springs, Colorado.

ARNOLD, Leslie Philip (1894–   ) *See* Aviation.

ARNOLD, Thurman Wesley (1891–1970) Lawyer.

New Deal economic theories; NRA, TNEC; Assistant Attorney General, 1938–43; antitrust cases.
46 pp. *Permission required.* 1962.
See also James Lawrence Fly Project *and* Journalism Lectures.

ARNOLD, William W. (1878–1957) *See* Benedum and the Oil Industry.

ARONSON, A. Henry

SOCIAL SECURITY

Director of personnel, Social Security Board; selection of administrators; field assistants; personnel problems in public assistance and unemployment insurance; merit system; recruitment; Bureau of Research and Statistics; authority of Civil Service Commission over Social Security Adminis-

tration; Bureau of Old Age and Survivors Insurance; patronage problems; federal-state relationships in personnel administration. Recollections of Arthur Altmeyer, Vincent Miles, and John Winant.
173 pp. *Closed during lifetime.* 1965.

ARROWSMITH, William (1924–) *See* American Cultural Leaders.

ARTHUR, George K. (1899–) *See* Popular Arts.

ARVEY, Jacob M. (1895–) *See* Adlai E. Stevenson Project.

ASCHER, Charles (1899–) Urban planner.

Family history; boyhood, West Side NYC; Ethical Culture Society School; Columbia College and Law School; Legislative Drafting Fund; Kuhn, Loeb; Brooklyn Heights society, 1921–25; ACLU; Sunnyside and Radburn developments; Croton-on-Hudson; zoning law; Public Administration Clearing House, 1932–36; Martha's Vineyard, 1921–71; Regional Planning Association of America; SSRC, 1935–42; UNESCO; US and European regional and city planning; New Deal housing programs: PWA and WPA; Chicago World's Fair, 1933; management associations; National Association of Housing Officials; National Resources Planning Board; Urban studies; Maxwell School, Syracuse University; Greenbelt towns; Spelman Fund; FHA; TVA; National Housing Agency, 1942–47; city government; National Municipal League; impressions of Roger Baldwin, Dr. Mary Calderone, Louis Brownlow, Henry Beetle Hough, Julian Huxley, Harold Ickes, Lewis Mumford, Eleanor and Franklin D. Roosevelt, Clarence Stein, Harlan F. Stone, Rexford Guy Tugwell, Henry L. Wright.
In process.

ASSOCIATION FOR THE AID OF CRIPPLED CHILDREN

Until its reorganization in 1948, the Association had provided a variety of services to handicapped children in metropolitan New York for fifty years. Interviews with members of the Association's board and staff focus on the transition from service agency to foundation made possible by the bequests of Milo Belding. In the last quarter century, the Association's grants have supported research in prenatal and perinatal problems, genetics, and embryology, as well as conferences on prematurity, the placenta, limb morphology, and teratology. Studies of learning disabilities, mental retardation, and accident prevention are detailed. The Association's international collaborative studies with the University of Aberdeen, the Karolinska Institute, and the University of Kyoto are described. Staff cooperation with the NIH and the background of President Kennedy's Panel on Mental Retardation are recalled.

Memoirs include personal recollections of Drs. Howard Rusk, John Lind, Dugald Baird, and Clement Reid; and of William McPeak and Laurance Rockefeller.

Participants and pages: Herbert Birch and Stephen Richardson, 97; Lewis Cuyler, 58; Charles Dollard, 30; Mrs. Richard Emmet, 45; Alice Fitz-Gerald, 78; Mrs. Ross McFarland, 31; Leonard Mayo, 71; Milton Senn, 46; Robert Slater, 67; Chester Swinyard, 52.

575 pp. *Permission required.* 1972.
Underwritten by the Association for the Aid of Crippled Children, New York City.

ASTIN, Allen Varley (1904–   ) Physicist.
EISENHOWER ADMINISTRATION

National Bureau of Standards, 1932–67; recollections of Secretary of Commerce Sinclair Weeks; Kelly Committee; moving of Bureau to Gaithersburg, Maryland; change to metric system.
57 pp. *Permission required.* 1967.

ASWELL, Edward C. (1900–1958) *See* McGraw-Hill.

ATCHLEY, Dana Winslow (1892–   ) Physician.

Early education at University of Chicago; Johns Hopkins Medical School; internship at P & S; impact of WWI; academic medicine at Johns Hopkins, 1921–23; P & S, 1924–56; developments in physiological medicine in association with Robert Loeb.

174 pp. *Open.* 1956. Papers.

ATKINSON, Joseph Hampton (1900–   ) *See* Aviation.

ATKINSON, Justin Brooks (1894–   ) *See* Journalism Lectures.

ATTWOOD, William (1919–   ) *See* Adlai E. Stevenson Project.

ATWOOD, John Leland (1904–   ) *See* Henry H. Arnold Project.

AUB, Joseph Charles (1890–   ) Physician.

Education, Harvard College and Medical School; internship, MGH; metabolic research, Russell Sage laboratories; WWI service; lead poisoning; calcium metabolism; cancer research, Huntington Memorial Hospital, 1929–43; impact of WWII on research; work at MGH, 1943–57; early use of radioisotopes; 1911 trip to Wilfred Grenfell Mission, Labrador; magnesium metabolism; radium poisoning; hormones and cell growth; liver regeneration; work in traumatic shock, WWII; growth studies of deer; American Cancer Society; Physiological Congress, 1929; Unitarian Service Committee mission, Czechoslovakia, 1946; WHO mission, India, 1953. Impressions of David Edsall, Fred Shattuck, Edwin Locke, Walter Cannon, George Wislocki, Eugene DuBois, Ira Nathanson, Robley Evans, Edward Churchill, William Salter, and Ivan Pavlov.

481 pp. *Permission required to cite or quote.* 1957. Papers.

AUDEMARS, Edmond. *See* Aviation.

REFER TO "NOTES ON USE" IN INTRODUCTION

AUNG, U H'tin (1909–   ) Burmese educator.

Early life; education, Burma and Europe; teaching experiences, University of Rangoon; Council of National Education; Thankin Movement; WWII experiences, 1942–45. 128 pp. *Permission required.* 1965.

AURAND, Evan Peter (1917–   ) Naval officer.
EISENHOWER ADMINISTRATION

Appointment as Naval aide to President Eisenhower, 1957; role as aide; use of helicopters; Nikita Khrushchev's visit and "Spirit of Camp David"; arrangements for Presidential travels to Bermuda, Europe, India, Latin America. 138 pp. *Permission required to cite or quote.* 1967.

AURAND, Henry S. (1894–   ) Army officer.
EISENHOWER ADMINISTRATION

Impressions of President and Mrs. Eisenhower. 34 pp. *Permission required to cite or quote.* 1968.

AVIATION

A broad survey of the development of aviation, beginning with accounts by associates of the Wright brothers and other pioneers in the US and abroad. Those interviewed include designers, engineers, pilots and executives, stunt flyers, and barnstormers; their recitations are informal and seasoned with anecdote. Veterans of WWI describe the development of aerial warfare in that conflict. Scores of recollections trace the rapid progress of aviation between the two World Wars: commercial aviation, air mail development, record flights, technological improvements, air races and polar flights, gliders, and lighter-than-air craft. Gen. William Mitchell's campaign for strengthening military aviation and Charles Lindbergh's solo flight to Paris provide focal points for many accounts of this period.

Eyewitness stories of episodes in WWII deal with exploits of the RAF, the Luftwaffe, and the US air forces, and range from the Battle of Britain to Hiroshima. Research and production problems and achievements are detailed from the outset to the jet era and the beginnings of rockets and missiles.

The material includes descriptions of the breaking of the sound barrier, stories of test pilots for supersonic planes, and accounts of aerial warfare in Korea.

Participants and pages: John Alison, 132; Orvil A. Anderson, 51; Leslie P. Arnold, 25; Joseph H. Atkinson, 71; Edmond Audemars, 8; Leon Bathiat and Raymond Saladin, 8; Hilary Beachey, 25; Lawrence D. Bell, 288; Otis Benson, 38; Harold M. Bixby, 50; Adrienne Bolland, 16; Albert Boyd, 53; Lord Brabazon of Tara, 39; Gregory J. Brandewiede, 66; Carl A. Brandt, 34; William B. Bridgeman, 57; James E. Briggs, 39; Sir Harry Brittain, 36; Georgia T. Brown, 27; Ross Browne, 115; Harry A. Bruno, 118 *(closed until May 1, 1985);*

Cyril C. Caldwell, 39; Felix Camerman, 7; Douglas Campbell, 30; Clarence Chamberlain, 11; Reed Chambers, 84; Ellen Church, 22; Jerrie Cobb, 8; Alan Cobham, 39; Jacqueline Cochran, 105; Frank T. Coffyn, 43; Franklin Rudolf Collbohm, 21; Sir Harold Roxbee Cox, 28; Lawrence C. Craigie, 53; Albert Scott Crossfield, 30; Didier Daurat, 18; James Dodson, 34; Charles Dollfuss, 31; James H. Doolittle, 28; Lord Douglas of Kirtleside, 28; Hugh L. Dryden, 40; Delos C. Emmons, 21; Francis Evans, 37; Maurice Farman, 17; Luis de Florez, 39; Benjamin D. Foulois, 81; Henry J. Friendly, 24;

Esther C. Goddard (Mrs. Robert H.), 85 *(closed until 5 years after death);* Harry F. Guggenheim, 64; Dennis Handover, 42; Beckwith Havens, 75; A. Heurtaux, 13; H. Mansfield Horner, 28; Ben Odell Howard, 67; Jerome Clarke Hunsaker, 112; Leslie Irvin, 37; James Jabara, 21; Jack Jefford, 37; Robert S. Johnson, 35; Charles Sherman Jones, 45; Alexander Kartveli, 43; Aron Krantz, 60; Emory Scott Land, 42; William Powell Lear, 49; Kenneth Littauer, 30; William R. Lovelace, II, 30;

John A. Macready, 69; Willy Messerschmitt, 14; Richard M. Mock, 54; Mathilde Moisant, 52; Muriel E. Morrissey, 20; James P. Murray, 36; Ruth Rowland Nichols, 45; Umberto Nobile, 64; Blanche Noyes, 68; Ruth Law Oliver, 33; Alan Campbell Orde, 50; Ray Petersen, 80; Leroy Ponton de Arce, 23; Ramsay Potts, 39; Thomas S. Power, 35; Leroy Prinz, 60; Max Pruss, 20; Elwood Quesada, 76; Robert Reeve, 63; Hanna Reitsch, 44; Holden C. Richardson, 29; Edward Vernon Rickenbacker, 19; James Sargent Russell, 51; Ryan Roundtable, 57;

Christian Franklin Schilt, 23; H. Shaw, 57; Cyrus Rowlett Smith, 48; Dean Smith, 77; Merle Smith, 33; Sir Thomas Octave Murdoch Sopwith, 31; John Paul Stapp, 28; Katherine Stinson, 47; Paul Tibbets, Jr., 38; Roscoe Turner, 38; George A. Vaughan, 39; Alfred Verville, 85; Gabriel Voisin, 8; Theodore Von Karman, 15; Charles Wald, 32; Otto P. Weyland, 71; Robert M. White, 27; Thomas D. White, 47; Noel Wien, 68; A. S. Wilcockson, 24; Harold B. Willis, 75; Gill Robb Wilson, 89; Charles Yeager, 34.

5,264 pp. *Permission of individual contributors required to cite or quote, except as otherwise noted. 1961. Underwritten by American Heritage Publishing Company,*

REFER TO "NOTES ON USE" IN INTRODUCTION

Inc. Also available at the USAF Academy and University of the Air, Maxwell Air Force Base. See also Air Force Academy, Henry H. Arnold Project, and Flying Tigers.

AYMAN, Sven. *See* Dag Hammarskjold Project.

AZCARATE Y FLOREZ, Pablo de (1890–   ) Diplomat.
LEAGUE OF NATIONS
Discussion of recruiting international civil servants, illustrated by his own experience from 1922 in League of Nations; problems of conflict between national and international loyalties; morale; building of Palace of Nations in Geneva; role of Secretary General as illustrated by Sir Eric Drummond and M. Joseph Avenol.
80 pp. *Permission required to cite or quote.* 1966.

Pablo de Azcarate, Edouard de Haller, and W. Van Asch Van Wijck, the three leaders of the Section on Minorities of the League of Nations during the 1920's and 30's recall how each came to the League and describe the Section: what it covered, how it operated, procedure, personnel, area of responsibility; committee of 3; relationship with other sections and with World Court; analysis of examples: Rumania, Czechoslovakia, Upper Silesia.
156 pp. *Permission required to cite or quote.* 1965.

BABCOCK, Margaret. *See* Hart Crane Project.

BACALL, Lauren (1924–   ) *See* Adlai E. Stevenson Project.

BACON, Edmund Norwood (1910–   ) *See* Independence Park.

BAEHR, George (1887–   ) *See* Mt. Sinai Hospital.

BAER, Abel. *See* Popular Arts.

BAILYN, Bernard (1922–   ) *See* American Historians.

BAINBRIDGE, Kenneth Tompkins (1904–   ) Physicist.

Education and early research at MIT, Princeton, and the Cavendish Laboratory at Cambridge, England; teaching and research at Harvard, 1934; creation of NDRC Radiation Laboratory at MIT, 1940; technical mission to England on radar development, 1941; Los Alamos, 1943; security problems, testing first atom bomb, 1945; use of the bomb; May-Johnson and MacMahon bills; Federation of Atomic Scientists; Joseph McCarthy investigations. Impressions of Karl Compton, Henry D. Smyth, Leo Szilard, Robert Oppenheimer.
150 pp. *Permission required.* 1960. Papers.

BAKER, Carl. *See* Health Science.

BAKER, Dorothy (1907–1968) Author.

Early life; beginnings as writer; reactions to writing and criticism; *Young Man With a Horn, Trio, Cassandra at the Wedding;* Robert Frost, Robert Penn Warren, Carson McCullers, F.O. Matthiessen, May Sarton.
146 pp. *Open.* 1962.

BAKER, James Chamberlain (1879–   ) *See* China Missionaries.

BAKER, Moses Nelson (1864–1955) *See* McGraw-Hill.

BAKER, Walter Ransom Gail (1892–1960) *See* Radio Pioneers.

BAKHMETEFF, Boris Alexander (1880–1951) Diplomat.

Early life in Russia; engineering studies in Switzerland and US, 1903–05; political life in Russia, 1903–14; European politics, 1914; Russia in WWI; War Supply Mission to US, 1915–16; Russian Revolution; Kerensky government; Ambassa-

REFER TO "NOTES ON USE" IN INTRODUCTION

dor to US, 1917–22; impressions of Woodrow Wilson administration, J.P. Morgan, Edward Stettinius, Sr., Dwight Morrow, John Spargo, Frederic Coudert, Nicholas Murray Butler; US citizenship and career.
568 pp. *Permission required.* 1950.

BALDWIN, Calvin Benham (1902–   ) Executive.

Henry A. Wallace and the Progressive Party.
37 pp. *Closed during lifetime.* 1951.

BALDWIN, Hanson. *See* Journalism Lectures.

BALDWIN, Joseph Clark (1897–1957) Congressman.

NY politics; national politics during WWII; Free French during WWII; Gen. Charles de Gaulle; Argentina and Palestine, 1947–48.
73 pp. *Permission required to cite or quote.* 1950. NYT (Part I).
Papers: 271 items (microfilm).

BALDWIN, Mildred. *See* James B. Duke Project.

BALDWIN, Roger Nash (1884–   ) Political reformer.

Teacher of sociology, Washington University, 1906–09; pioneering work in probation, social and political reform movements, St. Louis, 1906–17; pacifist organizations in NYC, conscientious objectors; Free Speech League, Theodore Schroeder; ACLU: formation and development, 1920–50, cooperation with other organizations, defense policies, publicity tactics, relations with New Deal; celebrated cases: Mooney-Billings, Scottsboro, Sacco-Vanzetti; contact with anarchists; IWW, 1910–20; William D. Haywood; Negro rights; Indian independence movement, India League; travel abroad and work for international agencies, 1924–54; visits to Russia, postwar Japan, Korea, and Germany.
666 pp. *Permission required to cite or quote.* 1954. NYT (Part I).

International League for the Rights of Man; UN, world tour, 1959; Margaret Sanger, Krishna Menon, Madame Pandit, Jawaharlal Nehru, Mrs. Franklin D. Roosevelt. 183 pp. *Permission required to cite or quote.* 1963. NYT (Part I). Papers.

Pedro Albizu Campos; visits in prison hospitals; defense by ACLU. 30 pp. *Permission required to cite or quote.* 1965. Papers.

OCCUPATION OF JAPAN

In Japan and Korea for ACLU during the occupation; impressions of MacArthur; differences between headquarters and the prefectures; the forming of a Japanese civil liberties organization; new Japanese constitution; the general strike; interview with the Emperor; women in public life; impressions from visit in 1960. 116 pp. *Permission required to cite or quote.* 1961. NYT (Part II).

BALINT, Michael

PSYCHOANALYTIC MOVEMENT

Early life; development of interest in psychoanalysis; predictions of future of psychoanalysis. 78 pp. *Permission required to cite or quote.* 1965.

BALL, George Wildman (1909–   ) *See* Adlai E. Stevenson Project.

BALL, Robert M. (1914–   ) *See* Social Security.

BALLANTINE, Joseph (1888–1973) Consular officer.

OCCUPATION OF JAPAN

Childhood in India; US consular service beginning at Tokyo, 1909; Dairen and Yokohama earthquakes; Japan Desk, State Department; London Naval Conference; Consul General, Canton and Mukden; Japanese government in Manchuria; adviser to Cordell Hull during Japanese conversations, 1941; Pearl Harbor investigations; Head, Far

Eastern Division; Director, Office of Far Eastern Affairs; post-war program for Far East; occupation policies; Owen Lattimore, Joseph Grew, Eugene Dooman, Douglas MacArthur.

271 pp. *Permission required to cite or quote.* 1961. NYT (Part I). Papers.

BALLENTINE, John Jennings (1896–1970) Naval officer.

Childhood and education; interest in naval air during WWI; flight training, Pensacola, Kelly Field; testing and development work, Dahlgren Naval Proving Grounds; Norden bombsight; Japanese naval aviation; air support, Operation Torch; command of *Bunker Hill;* Pacific operations: Rabaul, Tarawa, Kwajalein, Eniwetok; fleet liaison with Gen. MacArthur for Japanese surrender; Military Staff Committee, UN, 1947; Mediterranean, 1947–48; Commander, 6th Fleet. Impressions of Adms. Ernest King, H.K. Hewitt, Chester Nimitz, Richmond Turner and Gens. George Patton and Douglas MacArthur.

758 pp. *Permission required to cite or quote.* 1964. NYT (Part I).

BANE, Frank (1893–   ) Government official.
SOCIAL SECURITY

Executive director, American Public Welfare Association, 1931–35; consultant to FERA, 1932; Advisory Committee on Public Employment and Public Assistance; executive director, Social Security Board, 1935–38; Advisory Council to the Senate Finance Committee. Impressions of Harry Hopkins, Frances Perkins, John Winant, Arthur Altmeyer.

121 pp. *Open.* 1965.

Experiences in public welfare administration; Brookings Institution, 1931–35; Social Security Board, Council of National Defense; Office of Civilian Defense, 1941; director of field operations, OPA, 1941–42; National Housing Authority, 1942; executive director, Council of State Governments.

281 pp. *Permission required to cite or quote.* 1965. *Acquired from University of California, Berkeley.*

BANKS, Charles Louis (1914–   ) *See* Marine Corps.

BANNISTER, Harry Ray (1894–1967) *See* Radio Pioneers.

BARA, Walter (1919–1966) *See* McGraw-Hill.

BARAGWANATH, John Gordon (1888–1965) *See* Mining Engineers.

BARBER, Bernard (1918–   ) *See* Danforth Lectures.

BARCO, James William (1916–   ) Lawyer, ambassador.
EISENHOWER ADMINISTRATION
Family background, education in Michigan; Harvard Law School; Home Owners Loan Corporation, 1941–42; US Navy, WWII; wartime London, preparations for D-Day; US State Department posts, 1946 on; UN Good Offices, Commission for Indonesia, 1948; UN Conciliation Commission for Palestine, 1948–49; US mission to UN, 1949–61; various international problems and crises: Indonesian question, 1947–51; Middle East, Arab nationalism; Suez and Hungary, 1956; India; Congo; Cuba; US foreign relations; Un diplomacy; UN policies. Impressions of many international figures, including John Foster Dulles, Warren Austin, Philip Jessup, Jawaharlal Nehru, Achmed Sukarno, Nikita Khrushchev, Patrice Lumumba, Fidel Castro, Dag Hammarskjold.
1,061 pp. *Closed until January 1, 1984.* 1963.

BARDEEN, John (1908–   ) *See* Nobel Laureates.

BARE, Robert Osborne (1901–   ) *See* Marine Corps.

BARKAN, Alexander Elias (1909–   ) *See* Social Security.

REFER TO "NOTES ON USE" IN INTRODUCTION

BARKER, James Madison (1886–   ) Businessman.

Family background and childhood; education at MIT, first experiences in engineering; teaching at MIT, 1914–18; Manager, First National Bank, Buenos Aires, 1920–28; administrative experiences with Sears, Roebuck and Co., 1928–40, and with various business and educational institutions; Chairman of Board, Allstate Insurance, 1943–52; Overseas Consultants mission to Iran, 1948–49; Chief of World Bank mission to Turkey, 1949–50; philosophy of life and views on travel, modern education, government, foreign affairs; impressions of George F. Swain, Daniel G. Wing, Julius Rosenwald, Charles G. Dawes, Gen. Robert E. Wood.
380 pp. *Closed until 5 years after death.* 1952.

BARKIN, Solomon (1907–   ) Economist.

Economic and political studies at CCNY, 1920's; economist in various New Deal agencies; International Ladies' Garment Workers' Union; origins of the Textile Workers' Union of America and its role in the CIO.
141 pp. *Closed during lifetime.* 1960.

BARLOW, Howard (1892–1972) Orchestra conductor.
RADIO PIONEERS

Early life, education; NYC choral groups; early orchestral experiences; Neighborhood Playhouse; CBS: William S. Paley, public service programs, advertising; "Voice of Firestone"; planning and production problems in television. Recollections of Arthur Judson, Jerome Louckheim, Julius Sieback.
213 pp. *Open.* 1951.

BARNARD, Rollin (1922–   ).
EISENHOWER ADMINISTRATION

Director of Real Estate, US Post Office Department, 1953–55; Deputy Assistant Postmaster General, 1955; Assistant Postmaster General, 1959–61.
60 pp. *Permission required.* 1967.

BARNES, Joseph (1907–70) Newspaperman.

NY *Herald Tribune;* editor and co-owner, NY *Star;* IPR; Russia in the 1920's and '30's; mass media in American life. 300 pp. *Closed until February 28, 1975.* 1953.

BARNES, Patrick Henry (–1969) *See* Radio Pioneers.

BARNETT, Joseph M. *See* Radio Pioneers.

BARNETT, Ross. *See* Journalism Lectures.

BARR, David Preswick (1889–   ) Physician.

Early education at Cornell Medical School; internship at Bellevue; physiological medicine. 130 pp. *Permission required.* 1957.

BARSHOP, Irving. *See* Socialist Movement.

BARTHELMESS, Richard (1897–1963) *See* Popular Arts.

BARTLETT, David. *See* Weyerhaeuser Timber Company.

BARUCH, Bernard Mannes (1870–1965) *See* James B. Duke Project *and* Robert P. Patterson Project.

BARZUN, Jacques (1907–   ) Author, educator.

Childhood in Passy, 1910–20; *salons* and *soirees*; observations on French artists and artistic movements of the decade; poetry and painting; effect of WWI on artists; Apollinaire, Jean Cocteau.
In process.
See also Columbia Crisis of 1968.

BATEMAN, Alan Mara (1889–1971) *See* Mining Engineers.

REFER TO "NOTES ON USE" IN INTRODUCTION

BATHIAT, Leon. *See* Aviation.

BATTELL, William P. (1906–   ) *See* Marine Corps.

BATTLE, Samuel J. (1883–1966) Police officer.

Childhood and education; first Negro policeman in Manhattan; lieutenant and first Negro Parole Commissioner; race riots in Harlem; impressions of Eleanor Roosevelt, Mayors James Walker, Fiorello LaGuardia, and William O'Dwyer; other NYC political figures.
60 pp. *Permission required to cite or quote.* 1960. NYT (Part I).
Contributed by John K. Kelly of Newark, Delaware.

BAYNE-JONES, Stanhope (1888–1971) *See* Robert A. Taft Project.

BEACH, Edward Latimer (1918–   ) Naval officer.
EISENHOWER ADMINISTRATION

Early Navy days; WWII submarine service; Atomic Defense Section, Naval Operations; atomic submarine development; Adm. Hyman Rickover; Peace Ship; Naval Aide to Gens. Omar Bradley and Dwight D. Eisenhower; White House social aides; arrangement of presidential trips; ship launchings; NSC; the *Williamsburg;* Camp David; Secret Service; press conferences; Atoms for Peace; President Eisenhower at ease: family relaxation, hobbies; Eisenhower's relations with staff. Recollections of Sherman Adams, Robert Schulz, Lewis Strauss.
470 pp. *Permission required.* 1967.

BEACHEY, Hilary. *See* Aviation.

BEADLE, George Wells (1903–   ) *See* Nobel Laureates.

BEALE, Elizabeth. *See* Adlai E. Stevenson Project.

BEAN, Lillian. *See* Allan Nevins Project.

BEAN, Louis H. (1896–   ) Economist.

Early life as immigrant; statistics, Department of Agriculture; price and economic analysis, BAE; economic adviser, AAA Agricultural-Industrial Relations Section; fiscal analyst, Bureau of the Budget; economic adviser, Office of the Secretary of Agriculture; change of administration, 1953; long-range weather forecasting.
303 pp. *Permission required to cite or quote.* 1953. NYT (Part I). Papers.

BEANS, Fred D. (1906–   ) Marine Corps officer.

Enlisted service, education; duty in Nicaragua, Shanghai, Peking, Tientsin; Okinawa campaign; occupation of Yokosuka and Tsingtao; postwar problems in Division of Plans and Policies, 1946–48.
119 pp. *Permission required.* 1971.

BEARD, Robert L. (1896–1965) *See* McGraw-Hill.

BEARD, William Kelly, Jr. (1898–   ) *See* McGraw-Hill.

BECKER, Harry J. (1909–   ) *See* Social Security.

BECKER, J. Bill. *See* Eisenhower Administration.

BEDONI, Sidney. *See* Marine Corps.

BEEBE, Eugene. *See* Henry H. Arnold Project.

BEEBY, Clarence Edward (1902–   )
CARNEGIE CORPORATION
Carnegie Commonwealth Program in New Zealand; New Zealand Council for Educational Research, 1934–63; effect on New Zealand educational policy; travel grants, museum

REFER TO "NOTES ON USE" IN INTRODUCTION

development, public libraries, rural education, National Library Association, publications, adult education.
89 pp. *Permission required.* 1968.

BEHR, Karl Howell (1885–   ) *See* Theodore Roosevelt Association.

BEHRENS, Earl C. (1892–   ) Newspaperman.
EISENHOWER ADMINISTRATION

Political editor, San Francisco *Chronicle;* William F. Knowland Senate campaign; 1948 Presidential campaign. Recollections of Earl Warren, Richard M. Nixon.
44 pp. *Permission required.* 1967.

BEIRNE, Joseph Anthony (1911–   ) Labor leader.

Early experiences in Western Electric maintenance shop; communications workers in the Depression; origins of Communications Workers of America, role in CIO; unification of AFL and CIO.
66 pp. *Permission required.* 1957.

BELKNAP, Chauncey (1891–   ) *See* Robert P. Patterson Project.

BELL, Daniel (1919–   ) *See* Richard Hofstadter Project *and* Socialist Movement.

BELL, Daniel Wafena (1891–1971) Banker.

Department of the Treasury, 1911–46: foreign loans, 1919–20; Commissioner of Accounts and Deposits, 1931–35; acting director of the Bureau of the Budget, 1934–39; Under Secretary of the Treasury, 1940–46; President of the American Security & Trust Company; observations of Congress, the Depression, Federal Reserve System, NRA, New Deal, RFC, public works, WWI and WWII.
526 pp. *Closed until October 3, 1996.* 1954.

BELL, Jack L. (1904–   ) Newspaperman.
ROBERT A. TAFT PROJECT
Association with Senator Taft as AP representative.
22 pp. *Permission required to cite or quote.* 1969.
See also Eisenhower Administration.

BELL, Lawrence Dale (1894–1956) Corporation executive.
AVIATION
Speeches from management dinners, Bell Aerospace Co.;
broadcast from world-record helicopter flight, Texas to
Niagara Falls, 1952; Larry Bell Library dedication, Men-
tone, Indiana, 1955; first contact with airplane; exhibition
flying; developing various types of planes; barnstorming;
Bell Aircraft from 1935: developing the company, new
techniques, new planes, work for military; world records;
developing the helicopter; first supersonic flight. Impressions of Glenn Martin, Lincoln Beachey, Gens. Henry H.
Arnold and William S. Knudsen and others.
288 pp. *Open.* 1955.

BELLAMY, Ralph (1904–   ) *See* Popular Arts.

BENALLY, John. *See* Marine Corps.

BENDER, Morris P. *See* Mt. Sinai Hospital.

BENEDICT, Stephen (1927–   ) Consultant.
EISENHOWER ADMINISTRATION
1952 pre-convention campaign for Eisenhower; campaign
train; speech writing; transition between administrations,
1952; White House staff and activities. Recollections of Gabriel Hauge, C. D. Jackson, Richard M. Nixon, George Marshall, Joseph McCarthy, Harry Dexter White.
137 pp. *Closed during lifetime.* 1968.

BENEDUM, Darwin (1902–   ) *See* Benedum and the Oil
Industry.

REFER TO "NOTES ON USE" IN INTRODUCTION

BENEDUM, James Claxton (1909–   ) *See* Benedum and the Oil Industry.

BENEDUM, Michael Late (1869–1959) Oil executive.
BENEDUM AND THE OIL INDUSTRY

Firsthand account of early days of oil development: wildcatting, buying leases and royalty rights, experiences drilling and opening fields in Pennsylvania, West Virginia, Illinois; later larger operations in Texas and Louisiana; expansion, financial arrangements; building gas pipelines and marketing natural gas; transportation and storage problems; geology and geophysics; Mexican undertakings with E. L. Doheny; impressions of John Archbold, Joseph Trees.
144 pp. *Open.* 1951.

BENEDUM, Paul (1902–   ) Oil executive.
BENEDUM AND THE OIL INDUSTRY

Ohio State University; early interest in petroleum industry; experiences as geologist in Texas and Louisiana oilfields for M. L. Benedum during 1920's and '30's: oilbearing formations, leasing, financing, drilling, pipelines; Air Corps during WWII, development of aviation gasoline facilities worldwide; history and description of Benedum holdings; role and influence of M. L. Benedum.
87 pp. *Open.* 1951.

BENEDUM, Pearl. *See* Benedum and the Oil Industry.

BENEDUM, Sophie. *See* Benedum and the Oil Industry.

BENEDUM AND THE OIL INDUSTRY

A record of the oil industry from 1890 to 1950 as shown in the development of the Benedum oil interests and the experiences of Michael Late Benedum (1869–1959) and his associates, notably Joseph Clifton Trees (1869–1943). The material consists of interviews with people having special knowledge of leasing, financing, geology, oil and gas production, legal and tax problems. The memoirs contain several accounts of Benedum and Trees as wildcatters, going into virgin territory and finding new sources of oil and gas in the US (Illinois, 1905, Caddo, Louisiana, 1908, Central Texas, 1918, Big Lake and Yates fields in West Texas, 1923–26); problems of oil exploration outside the US (Mexico, 1911–16, Colombia, 1915, Rumania, 1918–19, the Philippines, 1920, and China, 1936); development of companies and coporate holdings including Transcontinental Oil Co. (1919), Plymouth Oil Co. (1923), Hiawatha Oil and Gas Co. (1926), and Bentex Oil Corp. (1936); storage, transportation, marketing, and refining; conservation and proration practices leading to Interstate Oil Compact Commission, 1933; US income tax claim against M. L. Benedum and Foster B. Parriott for $79,000,000, 1925, Supreme Court decision in their favor, 1937; extensive biographical material on M. L. Benedum, including early life and political activities.

Incidental material of interest includes: impressions of Woodrow Wilson at Princeton (McClintock memoir), E. L. Doheny, Senator Joseph Guffey, John Archbold (M. L. Benedum memoir), John W. Davis (Johnson memoir); Texas General Land Office (Giles memoir) and Slick Research Foundation (Slick memoir).

Participants and pages: John Charles Adams, 32; William W. Arnold, 15; Darwin Benedum, 6; James Claxton Benedum, 16; Michael Late Benedum, 144; Paul Benedum, 87; Sophie and Pearl Benedum, 30; Charles E. Beyer, 38; Al A. Buchanan, 14; Clem S. Clarke, 17; A. B. Dally, Jr., 36; Margaret E. Davis, 71; John W. Dieringer, 13;

Bascom Giles, 18; William Morris Griffith, 22; Walter Simms Hallanan, 63; Houston Harte, 37; Harry B. Hickman, 26; David Dean Johnson, 42; Caswell S. Jones, Thomas J. Newlin and Alex U. McCandless, 18; William J. Jones, 22; Winchester Kelso, 13; W. B. Lane and Roy Gardner, 44; Charles A. McClintock, 11;

Will E. Odom, 16; Alexander P. Olivey, 43; Foster B. Parriott, 30; Andrew Donaldson Robb, 13; Ovid Daniel Robinson, 71; Frank B. Shepard, 17; Tom Slick, 38; Ernest A. Stiller, 14; Milton E. Witherspoon, 8.

1,085 pp. *Open.* 1951.
Underwritten by a gift of Michael Late Benedum.

BENITEZ DE CASTRO, Cecilio. *See* Argentina in the 1930's.

REFER TO "NOTES ON USE" IN INTRODUCTION

BENJAMIN, Curtis G. (1901–) Publisher.
McGRAW-HILL

College representative of McGraw-Hill, 1928; book publishing policies of the company; growth of college and technical book and visual education departments; development of export markets; evolution of corporate organization and operation.
78 pp. *Permission required.* 1953.

BENJAMIN, Robert S. (1909–) *See* Adlai E. Stevenson Project.

BENNET, William Stiles (1870–1962) Lawyer, congressman.

NYC politics, 1898–1945; NY politics, 1901–18; national politics, Grover Cleveland to Franklin D. Roosevelt; NY election, 1910.
216 pp. *Permission required to cite or quote.* 1951. NYT (Part I).

BENNETT, Charles Edward (1910–) *See* Eisenhower Administration.

BENNETT, John. *See* Socialist Movement.

BENSON, Ezra Taft (1899–) Cabinet member.
EISENHOWER ADMINISTRATION

Informing the public on farm issues; population and surplus food problems.
12 pp. *Permission required to cite or quote.* 1968.

BENSON, Otis (1902–) *See* Aviation.

BENTLEY, Richard (1894–) *See* Adlai E. Stevenson Project.

BENTON, William (1900–) Senator, publisher.

Family background, schooling in Minnesota, Montana;

Carleton College, Yale University; National Cash Register Co.; advertising agencies, Lord & Thomas, Batten Company, Benton & Bowles, 1929–36; new techniques of consumer research, General Foods accounts; vice president, University of Chicago, 1937–45; America First; government research at University of Chicago, WWII; Assistant Secretary of State, 1945–47; Senator from Connecticut, 1949–53: resolution to expel Senator Joseph McCarthy, 1951; Smith-Mundt Bill; creation of Commission for Economic Development; vignettes of Chester Bowles, Robert E. Wood, Charles Lindbergh, Nelson Rockefeller, Anna Rosenberg, James Byrnes, Will Clayton, Arthur Vandenburg, Robert A. Taft, and many others.

224 pp. *Open except for specified pages.* 1968. Papers. *See also* Adlai E. Stevenson Project.

BERDING, Andrew H. (1902–   ) Government official.
EISENHOWER ADMINISTRATION

Deputy Director USIA, 1953–57; Assistant Secretary of State for Public Affairs, 1957–61.
38 pp. *Open.* 1967.

BERELSON, Bernard R. (1912–   ) Educator.
CARNEGIE CORPORATION

Carnegie grants for library studies, graduate education, behavioral science; Educational Testing Service; Ford Foundation and Carnegie Corporation.
119 pp. *Permission required.* 1967.

BERGER, Lawrence. *See* Columbia Crisis of 1968.

BERKELEY, James Phillips (1907–   ) Marine Corps officer.

China duty, Peking, 1932–34; formation of Fleet Marine Force, prewar communications training, procedures, and equipment; WWII communications personnel procurement; Iwo Jima, occupation of Japan; duty in office of Secretary of the Navy, Joint Army-Navy Secretariat; Adviser, Argentina: Naval War College and Marine Corps;

REFER TO "NOTES ON USE" IN INTRODUCTION

Student and Instructor, Armed Forces Staff College, Naval War College; Chief of Staff, 1st Marine Division, Korea, 1954–55; Assistant Chief of Staff, G–1, HQMC, 1955–58, personnel; subsequent commands. Major USMC events, decisions, personalities.
481 pp. *Open.* 1969.

BERKNER, Lloyd Viel (1905–1967) Physicist.

Organization and results of IGY, 1957–58.
60 pp. *Permission required to cite or quote.* 1959. NYT (Part I).

BERLE, Adolf Augustus (1895–1971) Lawyer.

Education; early law career; Justice Louis Brandeis's nomination to Supreme Court; Versailles Peace Conference; service in the Dominican Republic; early teaching career; *The Modern Corporation and Private Property;* impressions of Harlan Stone, Nicholas Murray Butler, and others; Henry Street Settlement; Raymond Moley, Rexford Tugwell, Franklin D. Roosevelt and the prenomination period of the New Deal Brain Trust.
190 pp. *Permission required.* 1970. Papers.

Depression; First Hundred Days after Roosevelt's inauguration, Bank Holiday; Charles W. Taussig.
36 pp. *Permission required.* 1969.
Contributed by James E. Sargent, Clemson, South Carolina.
See also Journalism Lectures.

BERNAYS, Edward L. (1891–   ) Public relations counselor.

Psychological and legal ramifications of public relations; societal techniques; symbolism and propaganda; "engineering of consent"; social consciousness-raising and consumerism; Gallup polls; corporations and research; segmental approach; industrial and labor relations; politicians and pollsters; reminiscences of the Sigmund Freud family;

39

the Franklin D. Roosevelt family; Senator Joseph McCarthy; opera and ballet personalities; impressions of many public figures.
403 pp. *Closed during lifetime.* 1971.

BERNSTEIN, Bernice. Lawyer.

SOCIAL SECURITY

University of Wisconsin, 1926–32: interest in unemployment insurance, Wisconsin legislation on stabilization of unemployment, influence of Senator Robert LaFollette; NIRA, Social Security Board, Social Security Administration: legal problems and procedures, preparation of Draft Act; use of reserve funds, tax offset, merit ratings, old age insurance program; federal-state relationships; roles of Social Security Board and US Employment Service; 1939 amendments to Social Security Act; effect of WWII; War Manpower Commission; 1947, regional attorney for Federal Security Agency; specific legal problems and cases. Impressions of Thomas Eliot, Jack Tate, John Winant, Arthur Altmeyer.
125 pp. *Open.* 1965.

BERNSTEIN, Louis (1878–1962) *See* Popular Arts.

BERNSTIEN, Oscar. *See* New York Political Studies.

BERRY, Frank Brown (1892–   ) Physician.

Family background; boyhood; Harvard College and Medical School, 1910–17; respiratory experiments under Walter Boothby, WWI: US Army Medical Corps, France, 1918–19; training in surgery and internal medicine; thoracic surgery; WWII: 9th Evacuation Hospital, North Africa and Italy; treatment of chest wounds, blood supplies, penicillin; consultant surgeon, 7th Army, France and Germany, 1943–45; postwar German medical facilities; Bellevue Hospital, 1946–54.
In process.
Contributed by Dr. William Ward Heroy, Huntington, N. Y.

BERRY, Watson. *See* Journalism Lectures.

BETHEL, Ion Maywood (1900–   ) Marine Corps officer.

Texas A & M, 1925; WWI; China, 1927–29; CCC, 1935–37; WWII, supply officer, Island Command, Peleliu; Procurement Section, Philadelphia, 1945–50, and HQMC, 1950–52; USMC Quartermaster General, 1957–58; USMC supply and procurement procedures, personalities.
115 pp. *Open.* 1969.

BEYER, Charles E. *See* Benedum and the Oil Industry.

BIEMILLER, Andrew John (1906–   ) *See* Social Security.

BIGELOW, Karl Worth (1898–   ) Educator.
CARNEGIE CORPORATION
Carnegie grants for African educational programs; TC; Afro-Anglo-American Program in teacher education; ICA; Teachers for East Africa; AID; Peace Corps; Overseas Liaison Committee.
138 pp. *Permission required.* 1967.

BILLEY, Wilfred. *See* Marine Corps.

BILLINGTON, Ray Allen (1903–   ) *See* American Historians *and* Allan Nevins Project.

BINGHAM, Barry (1906–   ) Editor.
ADLAI E. STEVENSON PROJECT.
Campaigns of 1952 and 1956; Far East trip; impressions of Jawaharlal Nehru, Dwight Eisenhower, John F. Kennedy, Estes Kefauver.
117 pp. *Permission required.* 1969.

BINKERD, Robert Studebaker (1882–   ) Businessman, civic worker.

Municipal Voters League of Buffalo; Citizens Union of

NYC; NY State politics, 1904–18; NYC politics, 1910–32; national politics during Wilson administration; WWI, railroads; WWII, OPA.
107 pp. *Open.* 1949.

BIOGRAPHICAL PROJECTS

See Henry H. Arnold, Benedum and the Oil Industry, Hart Crane, James B. Duke, Thomas A. Edison, James Lawrence Fly, John Robert Gregg, Dag Hammarskjold, Richard Hofstadter, Herbert H. Lehman, Allan Nevins, Robert P. Patterson, Joseph M. Proskauer, Adlai E. Stevenson, Robert A. Taft.

BIRCH, Herbert. (1918–1973) *See* Association for the Aid of Crippled Children.

BIRD, Hobart Stanley (1873–1960) Journalist, lawyer.

William McKinley administration; Puerto Rico, 1898–1904; election of 1924; railroad finance, 1925; NY State finances, 1932.
55 pp. *Permission required to cite or quote.* 1949. NYT (Part I).

BISHOP, Isabel (Mrs. Harold G. Wolff) (1902–   ) Artist.

Early life and training; the life of an artist; philosophy of art; painting techniques; the creative process; commentary on some of her own work (illustrated); process of producing an effective painting through etchings, drawings; abstract art.
107 pp. *Permission required to cite or quote.* 1956. NYT (Part II).

BISHOP, Jack. *See* Weyerhaeuser Timber Company.

BISHOP, Walter. *See* Popular Arts.

REFER TO "NOTES ON USE" IN INTRODUCTION

BISSELL, Richard Mervin, Jr. (1909–   ) Economist.
EISENHOWER ADMINISTRATION

Guatemala, Bay of Pigs; U-2 project; Harold Stassen.
48 pp. *Permission required to cite or quote.* 1967.

BIXBY, Harold McMillan (1890–1965) *See* Aviation.

BLACK, Algernon David (1900–   ) Philosopher.

NYC early life; Ethical Culture schools; Harvard; Ethical
Culture movement, 1923, service as its Leader; Citizens'
Committee on Harlem; NY State and National Committees
Against Discrimination in Housing; work camps; Encamp-
ment for Citizenship; ACLU; Civilian Complaint Review
Board-NYC Police Department.
In process. Papers.

BLACK, Douglas M. (1895–   ) Publisher.
EISENHOWER ADMINISTRATION

The publication of *Crusade in Europe;* Eisenhower as
president of Columbia University.
53 pp. *Closed during lifetime.* 1967.

BLACK, Eugene Robert (1898–   ) Banker.
WORLD BANK

Experiences as American Executive Director, later President, of World Bank: decisions on foreign loan defaults,
bond issues and corollary legislation, domestic and foreign
bond marketing, National Advisory Council, technical assistance services, mediation of disputes on Indus River development and Suez Canal seizure.
62 pp. *Open.* 1961.

BLACK, Richard Blackburn (1902–   ) Naval officer, ex-
plorer.

Education in North Dakota and on NYU's floating university, 1926–27; mining, rescue, and recovery work; Adm.

Richard Byrd and second Antarctic expedition, 1933–34; Hawaii, 1936; Antarctic Service Expedition, 1939; Hawaii and Pearl Harbor, 1941; Antarctic Support Forces, 1954–56; Adm. Byrd's staff, 1956–57; Office of Naval Research.
89 pp. *Permission required to cite or quote.* 1962. NYT (Part I).

BLACK, Mrs. Robert L. *See* Robert A. Taft Project.

BLACKBURN, James Edward, Jr. (1902–) *See* McGraw-Hill.

BLACKMER, Sidney (1898–) *See* Popular Arts.

BLAIR, Paxton (1892–) Lawyer.

Assistant Corporation Counsel in Fiorello LaGuardia administration; NYC politics, Welfare Department and education.
25 pp. *Open.* 1949.

BLAIR, William McCormick, Jr. (1916–) Ambassador.
ADLAI E. STEVENSON PROJECT

Governor Stevenson's administration in Illinois; the Presidential campaigns of 1952, 1956, 1960.
94 pp. *Permission required.* 1969.

BLAKE, Robert (1894–) Marine Corps officer.

WW I; German occupation; antibanditry activities, Nicaragua; Nicaraguan Electoral Mission, 1928–30; Spanish language studies, Spain, 1931–32; ONI, 1937–40; Naval War College; 5th Marines, 1941–42; Solomon Islands, 1942–43; 3rd Marine Division, Bougainville and Guam; Island Command, Guam, 1944–45; Occupation Forces, Truk and Central Caroline Islands, 1945–46; USMC Postwar Personnel Reorganization Board and USMC Inspector General, 1946–49.
117 pp. *Permission required to cite or quote.* 1968.

REFER TO "NOTES ON USE" IN INTRODUCTION

BLANKENHORN, Heber (1884–1956) Labor researcher.

NY *Sun;* NY *Call;* leaflet warfare; steel strike, 1919; NRA; Robert LaFollette Civil Liberties Committee.
564 pp. *Permission required to cite or quote.* 1955.

BLATCHFORD, Paul. *See* Marine Corps.

BLEDSOE, Samuel B. (1898–   ) Agriculturist.

Childhood and education; newspaper work in Memphis, 1921–23, and Washington, D.C., 1928–35; AAA Information Section, 1935–40; assistant to Vice President Henry Wallace, 1941; assistant to Secretary of Agriculture Wickard: preparing for war; commodity production and price ceilings; Farm Bureau Federation and the Farmers' Union; political influence of the Department of Agriculture; Pearl Harbor, reorganization and prices; control of food production and agricultural manpower; WPB; congressional relations; relations of the FSA with labor and the political left; production and supply of farm machinery; control of the WFA; departmental reorganization, November, 1942; Herbert W. Parisius and the Food Production Administration; Gardner Jackson; Claude Wickard as War Food Administrator, 1941–43; work with NY *Times, US News,* National Cotton Council, NAM, 1943–53.
689 pp. *Permission required to cite or quote.* 1954. NYT (Part I). Papers.

BLISS, C. Presby (1900–   ) *See* McGraw-Hill.

BLIVEN, Bruce Ormsby (1889–   ) Editor.

Youth and education; early experiences in journalism with NY *Globe;* editor, *New Republic;* Henry A. Wallace and the Progressive Party; Twentieth Century Fund.
60 pp. *Permission required.* 1964.

BLOCH, Felix (1905–   ) *See* Nobel Laureates.

45

BLOCK, Herbert (1909–   ) *See* Journalism Lectures.

BLYER, Bob. *See* Flying Tigers.

BOAS, Franziska.

Reminiscences of her father, Franz Boas (1858–1942). 76 pp. *Permission required to cite or quote.* 1972. *Contributed by John R. Cole, New York.*

BOATWRIGHT, Mody. *See* American Cultural Leaders.

BOBROW, Davis. *See* International Negotiations.

BOESCHENSTEIN, Harold (1896–1972) *See* Eisenhower Administration.

BOGER, Robert Forrester (1900–1968) *See* McGraw-Hill.

BOHLEN, Charles Eustis (1904–   ) *See* Eisenhower Administration.

BOHRER, Joseph. *See* Adlai E. Stevenson Project.

BOLLAND, Adrienne. *See* Aviation.

BOND, Nelson L. (1903–   ) *See* McGraw-Hill.

BONILLA, Lucio. Labor leader.

ARGENTINA IN THE 1930's

Textile industry in Argentina, 1920–46: formation of Workers' Textile Union, 1930, new products, wages, unemployment, benefits achieved by union pressure, political influences, factional divisions; General Confederation of Workers (CGT) during 1940's; rise of Juan Peron and role of unions in 1943 revolution; relations with Department of Labor.
103 pp. *Open.* 1971.

REFER TO "NOTES ON USE" IN INTRODUCTION

BONN, Louis A. *See* Popular Arts.

BOOHER, Edward E. (1911–   ) *See* McGraw-Hill.

BOOK-OF-THE-MONTH CLUB

The founding and development of the Book-of-the-Month Club from 1926 to 1955. The material consists of interviews with the founders, members of the Selection Committee, executive and technical personnel. In the most detailed of these memoirs, Harry Scherman, founder and board chairman, describes his own background, gives the origins of the idea of selling current books by mail to subscribers, tells of the first judges and later additions to the Selection Committee, discusses problems of editorial policy and the preferences of various judges, and recalls many of the selections and their reception. Mr. Scherman and other participants also deal with: the reader system for culling books submitted by publishers, attempts of outsiders to influence selection, relationships with publishers, membership and sales through the years, characteristics of subscribers, the book dividend system, the use of premiums, the preparation and testing of advertisements, distribution of art reproductions and musical recordings, book design and calligraphy, the Literary Guild and other book clubs, opposition of the book sellers, book manufacture, corporate structure of the company, problems of servicing subscribers, personnel and employee relations. Students of the literary scene in these years will find the Canby, Fadiman, Fisher, Highet, Loveman, Marquand, Scherman and Wood memoirs of particular interest.

Participants and pages: Henry Seidel Canby, 45; Harry Dale, 22; Clifton Fadiman, 45; Helen R. Feil, 16; Dorothty Canfield Fisher, 129; George Gallup, 32; Robert K. Haas, 31; Gilbert Highet, 18; Gordon Hyle, 24; Edwina Kohlman, 18; Amy Loveman, 17; Warren Lynch, 28; John Marquand, 30; Oscar Ogg, 25; Axel Rosin, 45; Maxwell Sackheim, 17; Harry Scherman, 371; Ralph Thompson, 28; Lester Troob, 26; Edith Walker, 40; Meredith Wood, 117.

1,124 pp. *Open.* 1955.
Underwritten by a gift of the Book-of-the-Month Club, Inc.

47

BOOLE, Ella Alexander (Mrs. William H.) (1858–1952) Church and temperance worker.

Development, political activities and personnel of WCTU; Prohibition.
28 pp. *Open.* 1950.

BOONE, Richard Allen (1917–   ) *See* Popular Arts.

BORIE, Lysbeth Boyd. *See* Independence Park.

BORTON, Hugh (1903–   ) State Department official.

Training in Japanese studies; US State Department, 1942–48; US-Japan relations during WWII and Occupation; Gen. Douglas MacArthur.
52 pp. *Permission required to cite or quote.* 1956.

BOSCH, John. *See* Farm Holiday Association.

BOSCH, Richard. *See* Farm Holiday Association.

BOSLER, Gustave A. *See* Radio Pioneers.

BOURKE, Thomas Eugene (1896–   ) *See* Marine Corps.

BOWERS, Claude Gernade (1878–1958) Ambassador, historian.

Boyhood in Indiana; Senate in the Progressive era; NY *Evening World;* W. R. Hearst; *The Tragic Era* and other books; Democratic Conventions, 1924 and 1928; Ambassador to Spain during Civil War, and to Chile during WWII.
149 pp. *Permission required to cite or quote.*
NYT (Part I).

BOWERS, Faubion. *See* Occupation of Japan.

REFER TO "NOTES ON USE" IN INTRODUCTION

BOWIE, Robert Richardson (1909–   ) Lawyer, educator.
EISENHOWER ADMINISTRATION
Policy Planning Board; NSC; foreign policy; Project Solarium; impressions of Dwight D. Eisenhower, John Foster Dulles.
51 pp. *Permission required to cite or quote.* 1967. *See also* Robert P. Patterson Project.

BOWLES, Chester (1901–   ) Diplomat, government official.

Education at Choate and Yale; advertising, 1925; Benton & Bowles; radio advertising, product research and pricing; Defense Council; America First movement; Connecticut rationing administrator; Price Administrator; relations with Congress, Cabinet, and government officials; OPA; stabilization, postwar period; campaign for Democratic gubernatorial nomination, Connecticut, 1946; ADA; UNESCO, UNICEF, UNRRA, 1946–47; Governor, Connecticut, 1948–50; appointment of William Benton as Senator from Connecticut; 1950 campaign; Ambassador to India, 1951–53; Senate campaign, 1958; posts and relationships, Kennedy administration; Ambassador to India, 1963. Observations on national and international political figures, especially Franklin D. Roosevelt, Eleanor Roosevelt, Harry Truman, John F. Kennedy, James Byrnes, Donald Nelson, Jawaharlal Nehru, Adlai E. Stevenson.
866 pp. *Closed during lifetime.* 1963.

BOWLES, Dorothy Stebbins (Mrs. Chester)

Description of the political events in the life of Chester Bowles, especially in Connecticut; John Bailey, William Benton.
89 pp. *Closed during lifetime of Chester Bowles.* 1963.

BOWMAN, Karl M. (1888–   ) Psychiatrist.

Medical education and early practice; psychiatric treat-

49

ment for soldiers, 1917–19; Jungian and Freudian influences; Boston Psychopathic Hospital, Harvard Medical School, Bellevue Hospital; American Psychiatric Association: president, 1944–45, use of shock treatment, internal politics; chemical and organic aspects of mental disease; relation of law to mental disorders: *Research on Alcoholism, Sexual Deviation, Narcotics;* Leopold-Loeb trial; Langley Porter Clinic, 1941–56. Recollections of teachers, students, and colleagues.

102 pp. *Permission required.* 1968.
Contributed by Alden B. Mills, Sacramento.

BOWMAN, Waldo G. (1900–   ) *See* McGraw-Hill.

BOWSER, Alpha Lyons (1910–   ) Marine Corps officer.

Naval Academy, 1928–32; artillery schooling, staff and command assignments; WWII: Bougainville, Guam, and Iwo Jima operations, artillery techniques and innovations, preinvasion planning; Head, Records Branch, HQMC, 1945–46; USMC Schools, Quantico, 1946–49; naval gunfire officer, Fleet Marine Force, Pacific, 1949–50; Operations officer, 1st Marine Division, 1950–51; planning for division deployment to Korea, Inchon landing, Chosin reservoir operations; SHAPE HQ, Paris, 1952–54; National War College; staff, Amphibious Force, Pacific Fleet, 1955–56; Recruit Training Command, San Diego, 1956–58; personnel policies; CG, Fleet Marine Force, Atlantic, 1965–67; USMC doctrine, training, contingency planning, personalities.

393 pp. *Permission required to cite or quote.* 1970.

BOYD, Albert (1906–   ) *See* Aviation.

BOYD, Ralph. *See* Weyerhaeuser Timber Company.

BOZELL, Harold Veatch (1886–   ) *See* McGraw-Hill.

BRABAZON OF TARA, Lord (1884–1964) *See* Aviation.

REFER TO "NOTES ON USE" IN INTRODUCTION

BRACKETT, Charles (1892–   ) *See* Popular Arts.

BRADEMAS, John (1927–   ) *See* Adlai E. Stevenson Project.

BRADEN, Anne (Mrs. Carl) (1924–   ) Journalist, civil rights activist.

Girlhood, education, Alabama; reporter, Birmingham, Louisville; postwar race relations in the South, especially in Louisville; the Bradens' arrest for sedition, 1954; Southern Educational Conference Fund, 1957–66.
In process.

BRADEN, Spruille (1894–   ) Diplomat, mining engineer.

Childhood and education; development of copper mining in Chile; business enterprises in NY and Latin America; experiences as chairman of the NY State Crime Commission; detailed description of career with the government, with special emphasis on the Chaco Peace Conference, 1935–39; embassies to Colombia, 1939–42, Cuba, 1942, and Argentina, 1945, and role as Assistant Secretary of State for Latin American Affairs, 1945–47; impressions of Cordell Hull, Sumner Welles, and Carlos Saavedra Lamas.
3,188 pp. *Permission required.* 1956. Papers.

BRADLEY, Carter. *See* Social Security.

BRADLEY, Michael Joseph (1897–   ) *See* Independence Park.

BRADLEY, Omar Nelson (1893–   ) Army officer.
EISENHOWER ADMINISTRATION
Recollections of Dwight D. Eisenhower: West Point, Africa, Normandy.
23 pp. *Permission required to cite or quote.* 1965.

BRAGDON, Everett L. *See* Radio Pioneers.

BRAITHWAITE, William Stanley Beaumont (1878–1962) Author.

Work on the Boston *Transcript;* reminiscences of literary friends, including E. A. Robinson, Amy Lowell, Robert Frost, and Sara Teasdale; experiences in publishing and teaching.
233 pp. *Open.* 1956.

BRANCH, Hilarion Noel (1880–1966) Lawyer.

Boyhood, British West Indies; teaching in Mexico, 1900–10; Mexican Embassy, Washington; oil industry in Mexico, 1920's and 30's. Impressions of William Gibbs McAdoo, Edward L. Doheny, Dwight Morrow.
182 pp. *Permission required to cite or quote.* 1966. NYT (Part I).

BRANDEWIEDE, Gregory J. (1899–) *See* Aviation.

BRANDT, Carl Amandus (1906–) *See* Aviation.

BRANDT, Harry (1897–) *See* Popular Arts.

BRANDT, Karl (1899–) *See* Eisenhower Administration.

BRANNAN, Charles Franklin (1903–) Secretary of Agriculture.

Education; early law practice; first experiences in politics; work with the government during the New Deal and WWII, with emphasis on his association with the RA and FSA; Secretary of Agriculture, 1948–53.
183 pp. *Closed during lifetime.* 1953.

BRANTON, Wiley Austin (1923–) *See* Eisenhower Administration.

BRITTAIN, Walter Houser (1902–) *See* Nobel Laureates.

REFER TO "NOTES ON USE" IN INTRODUCTION

BRAY, Howard.

SOCIAL SECURITY

Work for Senator Clinton Anderson in late 1950's and '60's; Medicare legislation; health insurance role of private insurance companies, Blue Cross, and federal government.
112 pp. *Closed during lifetime.* 1966.

BRECHER, Edward. *See* James Lawrence Fly Project.

BRECKINRIDGE, Henry (1886–1960) Lawyer.

Family background; Princeton; Harvard Law School; law clerk in Baltimore; practice in Lexington, Ky.; election of 1912; appointment as Assistant Secretary of War; the Army (generals, red tape, Board of Review); Woodrow Wilson and the New Freedom; Mexico; WWI in Europe; mission to Europe; *Lusitania;* preparedness and the administration; congressional relations; Supreme Court justices; Army justice and discipline; soldiers in alien lands; growth of aviation; the New Deal.
327 pp. *Permission required to cite or quote.* 1953. NYT (Part I). Papers.

BREITENBACH, Harry P. *See* Radio Pioneers.

BREWER, Vivion (Mrs. Joe) *See* Eisenhower Administration.

BRICE, William O. (1898–1972) *See* Marine Corps.

BRICKER, John W. (1893–   ) Senator.

EISENHOWER ADMINISTRATION

Republican Conventions of 1944 and 1952; Eisenhower administration; Bricker amendment.
40 pp. *Closed during lifetime.* 1968.

BRIDGEMAN, William B. *See* Aviation.

BRIDGES, Hal. *See* Allan Nevins Project.

BRIGGS, Ellis O. (1899–   ) Writer, ambassador.

EISENHOWER ADMINISTRATION

Duties of an ambassador; relations with State Department and John Foster Dulles; ambassador to Czechoslovakia, 1949; Oatis spy trial; ambassador to Korea (1952), Peru (1955), Brazil (1956); American business interests in Latin America; ambassador to Greece, 1959–61; Eisenhower's visit to Greece.
139 pp. *Closed until January 1, 1978.* 1972.

BRIGGS, James Elbert (1906–   ) *See* Aviation.

BRINDLE, James (with Martin Cohen) *See* Social Security.

BRISCOE, Robert. *See* Journalism Lectures.

BRITTAIN, Sir Harry E. (1873–   ) *See* Aviation.

BRITTON, Mason (1890–   ) *See* McGraw-Hill.

BRODE, Wallace Reed (1900–   ) *See* Eisenhower Administration.

BROOKE, Bryan. *See* Mount Sinai Hospital.

BROOKLYN POLITICS, 1930–50. *See* New York Political Studies.

BROOKS, Jack. *See* Alaskan Pioneers.

BROPHY, John (1883–1963) Labor union official.

Family background and childhood; miners' organizations in England and US before 1900; life of a typical miner; organizational work with UMW, Western Pennsylvania and Michigan, 1899–1917; struggles of UMW, 1899–1940; John L. Lewis; visits to England and Russia, 1927; UMW and AFL, 1918–35; emergence of new CIO, 1935–41; posts and activities with CIO, 1935–41; relations of CIO and AFL, 1935–55; national director, Industrial Union Councils, 1940–47; wartime labor relations boards, 1941–45; Philip Murray's Industrial Council Plan; opening conference, WFTU and ILO, 1945; ICFTU, 1949; comments on labor's view of socialism, the New Deal, Communists and the labor movement, the Department of Labor, future of the labor movement. Impressions of labor figures: William B. Wilson, Samuel Gompers, William Z. Foster, Philip Murray, Sidney Hillman, William Green, Walter Reuther, Lee Pressman, Frances Perkins, Maurice Tobin.

1,036 pp. *Permission required to cite or quote.* 1955. NYT (Part I).

BROSIO, Manlio. *See* International Negotiations.

BROWDER, Earl (1891–   ) Communist leader.

Childhood in Kansas; Populist Party; social and economic characteristics of Kansas; socialism; Office Workers Union, AFL, union activities, 1914; WWI; anti-war group; Tom Mooney; Russian Revolution, 1917; Communist Party, 1919; IWW vs. AFL; International Trade Union Congress, Russia, 1921; 3rd Congress Communist International; LaFollette movement; Chinese Revolution, 1927; Pan-Pacific Trade Union Secretariat, 1928; Communist magazines; development of CIO, 1930's; Scottsboro case; Negro rights; 1936 presidential campaign; leftist organizations, 1930's; United Front and 7th Congress Communist International, 1935; Spanish Civil War and International Brigade; Stalin-Hitler Pact, 1939; WWII; postwar changes in Communist Party; discussion of ideology; impressions of Communist leaders.

525 pp. *Permission required.* 1964. Papers.
Also available at Syracuse University.

BROWN, Emerson Lee (1901–   ) *See* McGraw-Hill.

BROWN, Georgia T. *See* Aviation.

55

BROWN, James Douglas (1898–   ) Economist.
SOCIAL SECURITY

Chairman of Advisory Council, Subcommittee of Senate Finance Committee; Social Security Board, 1937–38; advisory councils, 1947–48, 1957–58, 1963–64; efforts toward old age insurance legislation; impressions of Edwin Witte, Barbara Armstrong, Murray Latimer.
105 pp. *Open.* 1965.

BROWN, John Paulding. *See* Adlai E. Stevenson Project.

BROWN, Katharine Kennedy. *See* Robert A. Taft Project.

BROWN, Sevellon Ledyard (1886–1956) Editor, publisher.

Early years on Washington newspapers and with the UP; President William H. Taft and the press; NY *Herald* Washington bureau during WWI; career with the Providence *Journal* and *Evening Bulletin;* origins of the AP Managing Editors' Association and the American Press Institute; comments on American journalism.
99 pp. *Permission required to cite or quote.* 1956. NYT (Part I).

BROWN, Wilburt S. (1900–1968) Marine Corps officer.

Education in Massachusetts; Marine Corps training, WWI; Naval Academy, 1920; Quantico, Marine Corps, 1922; Officers School and commission; Sea School; experiences in Pacific Theater: artillery, quartermaster, executive officer 8th Battalion; Pearl Harbor, Commander 15th Marine Regiment; CG, Force troops, Fleet Marine Force, Pacific.
314 pp. *Open.* 1967.

BROWN, William Wilbur (1889–   ) *See* Radio Pioneers.

BROWNE, Nat. *See* Alaskan Pioneers.

REFER TO "NOTES ON USE" IN INTRODUCTION

BROWNE, Ross (–1963) Flyer.

AVIATION

With Louis Bleriot in France, 1908; Wilbur Wright and the first circular flight; first flight across the English Channel; aviation meet in Belmont Park; touring with "International Aviators"; aviation pictures.
115 pp. *Permission required to cite or quote.* 1960.

BROWNELL, Herbert (1904–   ) Lawyer, politician.

EISENHOWER ADMINISTRATION

1952 pre-convention and election campaigns; Republican Party; selection of the Cabinet; other appointments; Justice Department and Attorney General's Office; immigration; integration; Emmett Till case; Brown case; Tidelands case; Bricker amendment; Julius and Ethel Rosenberg; Joseph R. McCarthy; Adam Clayton Powell; Civil Rights Act of 1957; Little Rock crisis; presidential incapacity legislation; national security; labor racketeering prosecution; anti-trust law enforcement; impressions of Dwight Eisenhower.
347 pp. *Permission required to cite or quote.* 1967.

BROWNELL, Samuel Miller (1900–   ) Educator.

EISENHOWER ADMINISTRATION

Service on US delegation to UNESCO, 1954; Conference of Ministers of Education of the Americas, 1956; International Conference on Education, 1960.
83 pp. *Permission required to cite or quote.* 1967.

BROWNING, Gordon (1889–   ) Governor.

Early years and family background in Tennessee; education, law training; early experience in law and politics; WWI; Congressman, description of Washington political scene in the 1920's and 30's; Senate campaign, 1934; Governor of Tennessee, 1937–39, TVA, state finances; WWII; Governor, 1949–53. Anecdotes of many political figures: Huey Long, Edward H. Crump, Kenneth McKellar, Estes Kefauver.

144 pp. *Open.* 1965.
Contributed by Joseph H. Riggs and the Memphis Public Library.

BRUCHEY, Stuart (1917–   ) *See* American Historians.

BRUERE, Henry (1882–1958) Civic worker, financier.

NYC politics, 1904–17; Bureau of Municipal Research from its founding; US-Mexico relations, 1916; banking, 1926–1933; national politics under Franklin D. Roosevelt.
170 pp. *Permission required to cite or quote.* 1949. NYT (Part I).

BRUNDAGE, Percival Flack (1892–   ) Consultant.
EISENHOWER ADMINISTRATION

The Budget Bureau during the Eisenhower Administration; consultations with departments and with President Eisenhower.
52 pp. *Permission required to cite or quote.* 1967.

BRUNO, Harry A. (1893–   ) Public relations counsel.
AVIATION

First experiences in glider aviation, 1910; School of Military Aeronautics, University of Toronto; Aeromarine Airways, 1919–23; aviation public relations, 1923; flight safety; Airplane Owners and Pilots Association; women's contribution to world aviation; impressions of Bert Acosta, Wiley Post.
118 pp. *Closed until May 1, 1985.* 1960.

BRYAN, W. Ray. *See* Health Science.

BRYANT, William Cullen II. *See* Allan Nevins Project.

BRYSON, Lyman Lloyd (1888–1959) Educator.
RADIO PIONEERS

Family background and education; journalism instructor,

University of Michigan; Army, 1917; American Red Cross; lecturer, University of California, 1925; director, San Diego Museum; TC; radio commentator from 1927; educational broadcasts for CBS; networks and local stations; radio and fiscal matters; views on broadcasting; impressions of academic and broadcasting personalities.
254 pp. *Open.* 1951.

BUCHANAN, A. A. *See* Benedum and the Oil Industry.

BUCHANAN, Clarence E. *See* James B. Duke Project.

BUCHANAN, Wiley Thomas, Jr. (1914–   ) *See* Eisenhower Administration.

BUCHANAN, William Walter (1914–   ) *See* Marine Corps.

BUCHER, E. R. *See* James B. Duke Project.

BUCK, Paul Herman (1899–   ) Author, university dean.
CARNEGIE CORPORATION
Discussion of grants received from Carnegie Corporation and programs carried out in educational fields at Harvard University.
87 pp. *Permission required.* 1967.

BUCK, Solon Justus (1884–1962) Historian, archivist.

AHA: policies, financial problems, administration, members and officers; AHR and Annual Reports.
44 pp. *Permission required to cite or quote.* 1955.
NYT (Part I).

BUCKNER, Elmer La Mar (1922–   ) *See* Eisenhower Administration.

BUHROW, Herbert (1914–   ) *See* McGraw-Hill.

BULLOCK, Earl R. (1912–   ) *See* Weyerhaeuser Timber Company.

BUNDY, Harvey Hollister (1888–1963) Lawyer.

Childhood and education; legal experience in Boston; government service in the Departments of State and War. Impressions of Henry L. Stimson, Herbert Hoover, Gen. George Marshall, and many other national figures.
313 pp. *Permission required to cite or quote.*
NYT (Part I). Papers.

BUNKER, Arthur Hugh (1895–1964) *See* Mining Engineers.

BUNZL, Mrs. Walter (1907–1968) Research assistant to Mayor LaGuardia.

NYC politics and the Citizens Union; Fiorello LaGuardia.
24 pp. *Permission required to cite or quote.* 1949. NYT (Part I). Papers.

BURCKHARDT, Frederick H. (1912–   ) Educator.
CARNEGIE CORPORATION

Carnegie grants to Bennington College; ACLS, SSRC, and Council on Higher Education in the American Republics; Carnegie personnel and administration.
84 pp. *Permission required.* 1968.

BURDEN, William Armistead Moale (1906–   ) Diplomat.
EISENHOWER ADMINISTRATION

National Aeronautics and Space Council; State Department; Department of Defense; Belgium; Congo crisis.
81 pp. *Closed during lifetime.* 1968.

BURGER, Joseph Charles (1902–   ) Marine Corps officer.

Early training and assignments; China duty, 1927, 1935–37;

development of amphibious warfare doctrine in early 1930's; operations planning in South Pacific, 1st Marine Amphibious Corps, 1942–43; Military Secretary to Gen. Alexander Vandegrift, 1944–46; CO, Basic School, 1949–50; Chief of Staff, Fleet Marine Force, Pacific, 1950–51, Korean War; Director of Information, Director of Reserve, HQMC, 1954–56; CG, Recruit Depot, Parris Island, 1956, Ribbon Creek affair; CG, Camp Lejeune and 2d Marine Division, 1956–59; Marine operations in Lebanon; CG, Fleet Marine Force, Atlantic, 1959–61. USMC operational planning, developments, personalities.
357 pp. *Permission required.* 1969.

BURGESS, Carter L. (1916–   ) Corporation executive.
EISENHOWER ADMINISTRATION

Gen. Walter B. Smith, WWII; Wriston Report; studies on White House organization; Assistant Secretary of Defense for Manpower, 1954–57; impressions of the Eisenhower administration.
40 pp. *Open.* 1967.

BURGESS, Warren Randolph (1889–   ) Government official.
CARNEGIE CORPORATION

Trustee of the Carnegie Corporation; vignettes of fellow trustees and discussions of policies.
50 pp. *Permission required.* 1967.

BURKE, Agnes. Educator.

Childhood, Winona, Minnesota; Normal School, Miss Wheelock Kindergarten Training School, TC; experiences as tutor, reading consultant, teacher.
50 pp. *Open.* 1969.

BURKE, Arleigh Andrew (1901–   ) Naval officer. *See* Eisenhower Administration.

BURKE, James Vincent, Jr. (1911–   ) *See* Eisenhower Administration.

BURKE, John G. (1902–   ) *See* McGraw-Hill.

BURLINGHAM, Charles Culp (1858–1959) Lawyer.

Legal and political recollections of NYC; impressions of prominent jurists.
45 pp. *Permission required to cite or quote.* 1949.
NYT (Part I). Papers.

BURNEY, Leroy E. (1906–   ) *See* Health Science.

BURNS, Arthur Edward (1908–   ) Economist.
EISENHOWER ADMINISTRATION

Technical Cooperation Administration; Foreign Operations Administration, 1953–57; Consultant, Joint Federal State Action Committee, White House staff, 1957–60; economic policies of the Eisenhower Administration.
45 pp. *Permission required to cite or quote.* 1967.

BURNS, Eveline Mabel (1900–   ) Economist.
SOCIAL SECURITY

Board of the Consumer's League of New York; grant to study unemployment security in England and Germany; staff member, Committee on Economic Security, 1934; committee on social security, National Resources Planning Board, 1939; studies of social security programs; impressions of Mary W. Dewson, Edwin Witte, Wilbur Cohen, Arthur Altmeyer, John Winant.
180 pp. *Open.* 1965.

BURNS, James Henry (1885–   ) *See* Henry H. Arnold Project.

BURT, Katharine Newlin (Mrs. Struthers) *See* Jackson Hole Preserve.

REFER TO "NOTES ON USE" IN INTRODUCTION

BUSE, Henry W., Jr. (1912–   ) Marine Corps officer.

Education, Naval Academy, 1930–34; USS *Oklahoma*, 1935–36; prewar duty at Quantico, Pearl Harbor, Fort Benning; WWII: Guadalcanal, Cape Gloucester operations; Fleet Marine Force, Pacific, 1947–49; 1st Marine Division, Korea, 1952–53; Fleet Marine Force, Pacific, 1956–57; Fleet Marine Force, Atlantic, 1957–58; USMC Liaison Officer to Vice Chief of Naval Operations, 1958–61; CG, 3d Marine Division, 1962–63; Chief of Staff, HQMC, 1967–68; Fleet Marine Force, Pacific, 1968–70.
In process.

BUSH, Prescott (1895–1972) Banker, Senator.
                    EISENHOWER ADMINISTRATION
Yale; WWI; early business experience; investment banking; W. A. Harriman & Co., 1926–31, Brown Brothers Harriman, from 1931, role of private banking; early political activities, Republican Party in Connecticut; Senator, 1952–62: committees, legislation, Randall Commission on tariff and trade; campaign of 1956, development of Republican platform; impressions of President Eisenhower, John Foster Dulles, Senators Robert A. Taft and Joseph McCarthy; Averell Harriman, Robert Roosa.
454 pp. *Permission required to cite or quote.* 1966.

BUSH, Vannevar (1890–   ) Administrator, engineer.
                    CARNEGIE CORPORATION
Discussion of Carnegie Institution of Washington and Carnegie Corporation of New York, 1939–55.
58 pp. *Permission required.* 1967.

BUTLER, Richard Austen (1902–   ) Statesman.

Recollections of Sir Winston Churchill, his speeches.
9 pp. *Open.* 1971.
Contributed by Benjamin D. Wood, New York.

BUTLER, Richard C. *See* Eisenhower Administration.

BUTZ, Earl Lauer (1909–   ) Government official.

EISENHOWER ADMINISTRATION

Assistant Secretary of Agriculture, 1954–57; programs of the Department of Agriculture, and relations with Congress and other departments; impressions of Ezra Taft Benson and President Eisenhower.
51 pp. *Open.* 1968.

BUXMAN, William (1884–1954) *See* McGraw-Hill.

BYRNES, John W. (1913–   ) *See* Social Security.

CABELL, Charles Pearre (1903–1971) *See* Air Force Academy *and* Henry H. Arnold Project.

CABONA, Andres (1899–   ) Labor leader.

ARGENTINA IN THE 1930's

Joined union of wicker workers, 1917; official in various labor organizations, 1922–55; development of unions, 1930's: percentage of workers organized, political tendencies and influences, personalities; relations of labor movement with different administrations; formation and internal organization of General Confederation of Workers; effects of unemployment and Depression, 1930's and '40's; workers in petroleum industry; factionalism.
116 pp. *Open.* 1970.

CAESAR, Irving (1895–   ) *See* Popular Arts.

CAGNEY, James (1904–   ) *See* Popular Arts.

CAHILL, Holger (1893–1960) Writer, art director.

Early life in North Dakota, wanderings and odd jobs; arrival in NYC, newspaper work, Greenwich Village; NY art world in the 1920's; folk art; Americana; collecting; Mrs. John D. Rockefeller, Jr.; politics in art; the Depression; relief of artists; Federal Arts Project; NY World's Fair, art,

especially abstract expressionism, since 1943. Memoir includes brief interviews with Dorothy Canning Miller (Mrs. Cahill) and Clair Laning.
622 pp. *Permission required.* 1957.

CAKE, Ralph Harlan (1891–   ) Executive.
EISENHOWER ADMINISTRATION

Experience in law and finance in Oregon; Republican National Committee, 1940; conventions of 1940, 1944, 1948; detailed description of National Committee meeting and convention of 1952; campaign; citizens' groups; impressions of Gen. Eisenhower, Sherman Adams, Robert Taft, and other political figures; Panama Canal Company.
78 pp. *Permission required to cite or quote.* 1969.

CALDWELL, Cyril C. *See* Aviation.

CALDWELL, Orestes Hampton (1888–1967) *See* Radio Pioneers.

CALLAHAM, John (1911–   ) *See* McGraw-Hill.

CALVIN, Melvin (1911–   ) *See* Nobel Laureates.

CAMERMAN, Felix. *See* Aviation.

CAMPBELL, Douglas (1896–   ) *See* Aviation.

CAMPBELL, Hugh B. *See* Weyerhaeuser Timber Company.

CAMPBELL, James Winchester (1903–   ) Foundation executive.
CARNEGIE CORPORATION

Associations with the Carnegie Corporation in 1925 and 1928–29; sale of US Steel bonds; accountant for Corporation, 1933; impressions of the Treasurer's office and other parts of the Corporation, fiscal matters; Assistant Treasurer, 1953; Treasurer, 1961; the role of the treasurer in a

foundation. Impressions of various foundation personalities.
151 pp. *Permission required.* 1967.

CANBY, Henry Seidel (1878–1961) *See* Book-of-the-Month Club.

CANE, Melville Henry (1879–   ) Lawyer, poet.

Columbia University, 1900; legal practice specializing in copyright and publishing matters; recollections of Sinclair Lewis, John Erskine, Thomas Wolfe, Harry Houdini; commentary on writing poetry.
83 pp. *Permission required to cite or quote.* 1956. NYT (Part I).

CANFIELD, Cass (1897–   ) Publisher.

Early youth, education, NY and abroad; Harvard; graduate study at Oxford, 1920; walked Burma Road, 1920; Harper & Bros. president from 1932; crossing on *Hindenburg,* 1936; interview with Leon Trotsky, 1940; BEW; OWI, 1944; International Planned Parenthood Federation; history of Harper's and comprehensive discussion of publishing; anecdotes about many notable literary and political figures including Edith Wharton, Julian and Aldous Huxley, Edna St. Vincent Millay, Franklin and Eleanor Roosevelt, Adlai Stevenson, Sumner Welles, and Jacqueline Kennedy.
417 pp. *Permission required to cite or quote.* 1966. NYT (Part II).

CANNON, Charles A. *See* James B. Duke Project.

CANNON, John D. *See* Columbia Crisis of 1968.

CAPERS, Roberta. Specialist in the fine arts.
CARNEGIE CORPORATION

Arts adviser for Carnegie Corporation, 1926–34: studies in Europe, 1925–26, College arts sets, arts fellowships; Met-

ropolitan Museum; American Federation of Arts; museum programs; chairman of Arts Department, Tulane College. Impressions of Frederick Keppel, Morse Cartwright, Robert Lester, and other Corporation officials.
124 pp. *Permission required.* 1967.

CAPPA, Joseph D. *See* Radio Pioneers.

CAPRA, Frank (1897–   ) *See* Popular Arts.

CARALEY, Demetrios. *See* New York Political Studies.

CARDON, Philip Vincent (1889–1965) Agriculturist.

Childhood and education; Nephi, Utah, Agricultural Station, 1909–14; cotton investigations and dry-land agriculture, 1914–18; Montana State Agricultural College and Experiment Stations, 1918–21; Utah State Agricultural College, *Utah Farmer*, Utah Agricultural Experiment Station, 1921–34; subsistence homesteads, land-use planning, 1934–35; Bureau of Plant Industry, 1935–42; Agricultural Research Administration, 1942–44; FAO; Department of Agriculture Graduate School, 1946–52.
806 pp. *Permission required to cite or quote.* 1952.
NYT (Part I).

CAREY, James Barron (1911–   ) Labor executive.

Early experiences in the Philco plant in Philadelphia; formative years of the United Electrical, Radio and Machine Workers; CIO; labor and New Deal; Communist Party and the labor movement; Secretary of the CIO; formation of WFTU; London and San Francisco labor conferences, 1945; merger of AFL and CIO.
352 pp. *Closed during lifetime.* 1958.

CARLIN, Phillips (1894–1971) *See* Radio Pioneers.

CARLISLE, Henry (–1964) *See* Mining Engineers.

CARLTON, Winslow. *See* Social Security.

CARMAN, Harry James (1884–1964) Educator.

Board of Higher Education, NYC, 1938–61: practices and policy, budgets, relationships with city and state administrations, problems of tenure, day and evening sessions; Russell case; Rapp-Coudert Committee and Strayer committee; impressions of Mayors Fiorello LaGuardia, William O'Dwyer, and Robert F. Wagner.
221 pp. *Permission required.* 1961.

CARMODY, John Michael (1881–1963) Administrator.

Family background and description of life in northern Pennsylvania and upstate NY at the turn of the century; education and early work experiences as a steel inspector; later as an executive in the garment industry and coal mining industry; editor-in-chief successively of *Coal Age* and *Factory & Industrial Management* for the McGraw-Hill Publishing Company; detailed account of service in government: Civil Works Administration, FERA, National Defense Mediation Board, NLRB, REA, President's Power Policy Committee, the Cabinet-rank position as head of the Federal Works Agency (encompassing PWA, WPA, USHA, Bureau of Public Roads, Bureau of Public Buildings, Fine Arts Commission, and Lanham Act Defense Housing Program), US Maritime Commission, Maritime War Emergency Board, and Federal Interdepartmental Safety Council.
763 pp. *Permission required to cite or quote.* 1954.

CARNEGIE CORPORATION

This project traces the first 58 years of Andrew Carnegie's central philanthropic organization. Officers, staff members, and grant recipients discuss its work in adult education, area studies, art education, cognitive research, education testing, library science, music education, national security, social science research, teacher education, and

REFER TO "NOTES ON USE" IN INTRODUCTION

other areas. The Corporation's relations with other Carnegie institutions over the years are delineated in many memoirs. Others detail its own administrative history, as well as its relations with other major foundations and with the federal government. Still others trace the work of independent agencies which originally received all or part of their funds from the foundation. In general, the design was to provide comprehensive and candid information about the foundation, its work, and those who have served its end, "to promote the advancement and diffusion of knowledge and understanding."

The material is rich in personal recollections of grantees and members of the Corporation's board and staff. Prominent among them are James R. Angell, James Bertram, Nicholas Murray Butler, Oliver C. Carmichael, Robert Franks, Walter Jessup, Nicholas Kelley, Frederick Paul Keppel, Clyde Kluckhohn, Thomas W. Lamont, William S. Learned, Russell C. Leffingwell, Frederic A. Mosher, Arthur Page, Henry Pritchett, Elihu. and Elihu Root, Jr., Beardsley Ruml, James E. Russell, William F. Russell, Whitney H. Shepardson, Irvin Stewart, and Samuel A. Stouffer. There is a comprehensive index.

Participants and pages: Florence Anderson, 656; Geoffrey Andrew, 64; Clarence Beeby, 89; Bernard Berelson, 119; Karl Bigelow, 138; Paul Buck, 87; Frederick H. Burckhardt, 84; W. Randolph Burgess, 50; Vannevar Bush, 58; James W. Campbell, 151; Roberta Capers, 124; Morse Cartwright, 242; Henry Chauncey, 88; Eric Clarke, 76; James B. Conant, 88; Lawrence Cremin, 107; Cornelis deKiewiet, 117; Rene d'Harnoncourt, 65; Harold W. Dodds, 70; Charles Dollard, 329; Katherine Ford, 61; William T. R. Fox, 97; John W. Gardner, 221;

Morris Hadley, 84; Samuel S. Hall, Jr., 115; Caryl P. Haskins, 251; Edward Pendleton Herring, 129; Alger Hiss, 67; Alice Hoctor, 48; Kenneth Holland, 35; John C. Honey, 82; Robert Hoppock, 49; Everett C. Hughes, 43; Frederick Jackson, 305; Guion G. Johnson, 67; Guy B. Johnson, 64; Joseph Johnson, 50; Devereux C. Josephs, 150; Francis Keppel, 61; Eric Larrabee, 89; Robert M. Lester, 872; R. McAllister Lloyd, 67; Trevor Lloyd, 45; Dorothy R. Loemker, 73;

Thomas R. McConnell, 86; Constance McCue, 60; Earl McGrath, 107; Margaret Mahoney, 86; Ernst G. Malherbe, 68; William Marvel, 278; Lloyd Morrisett, 214; Lois Murkland, 24; Gunnar Myrdal, 122; Isabelle C. Neilson, 42; Frederick Osborn, 140; G. Raleigh Parkin, 152; Talcott Parsons, 41; James Perkins, 64; Alan Pifer, 273; Alan Pifer and Eli Evans, 149; David Riesman, 84; John Russell, 290; Frederick Sheffield, 61; Arthur Singer, 138; Harold Spivacke, 76; Stephen Stackpole, 398; Ralph Tyler, 139; Robert E. Ward, 81; Robertson D. Ward, 49; Bethuel Webster, 25;

Robert J. Wert, 200; Benjamin D. Wood, 123; John E. F. Wood, 52; Henry Wriston, 219; Donald Young, 180.

9,948 pp. *Permission required. 1966–70. Underwritten by the Carnegie Corporation of New York.*

CARNEY, Robert Bostwick (1895–   ) Naval officer.

Family background, Naval Academy, 1916; first cruises, assignments; WWI convoying; navigation instructor, Naval Academy, 1923–24; Interior Control Board manual, 1928; Orange Plan and naval preparedness, 1940; Adm. Arthur Bristol, organization of Support Force Operation; North Atlantic convoy duty; Chief of Staff, Adm. William Halsey, South Pacific theater: strategy, operations, logistics, personalities, problems; theater of war approach, Adm. Chester Nimitz, Gen. Douglas MacArthur; 3d Fleet operations, Central Pacific; Leyte Gulf and China Sea, 1945; British participation; Japan's defeat and surrender; Deputy Chief of Naval Operations for Logistics, 1946–50; computers; War College, problems of command and staff training, postwar Navy; unification of services, 1947; impressions of many military figures.

768 pp. *Closed until July 1, 1989. 1964.*

CARNOVSKY, Morris (1897–   ) *See* Popular Arts.

CARPENTER, Charles I. (1906–   ) *See* Air Force Academy.

CARPENTER, Mrs. John. *See* Adlai E. Stevenson Project.

CARR, William George (1901–   ) Educator.

UN Conference, San Francisco; UNESCO; various international teachers' associations; NEA.

31 pp. *Permission required to cite or quote. 1961.*

CARSON, Mrs. Joseph. *See* Independence Park.

REFER TO "NOTES ON USE" IN INTRODUCTION

CARSTENSON, Blue.

SOCIAL SECURITY

Technical director for education for aging at HEW, 1959; chairman of the technical directors for the White House Conference on Aging; staff member of the Democratic National Committee; organizing senior citizens; efforts toward medical legislation; impressions of Ivan Nestingen, Abraham Ribicoff.
227 pp. *Open.* 1966. Papers.

CARTER, Hodding (1907–1972) *See* Journalism Lectures.

CARTWRIGHT, Morse Adams (1890–   ) Educational administrator.

CARNEGIE CORPORATION

Assistant to Frederick Keppel at the Carnegie Corporation, 1924–26; developing a program; policies; trustees and staff; studies at the Rockefeller Foundation; adult education; American Association for Adult Education; executive director, Des Moines Experiment; leisure programs; the Association's relationship with the Carnegie Corporation; TC; comments on grants through the years. Impressions of Frederick Keppel, Walter Jessup, Devereux Josephs, and other Corporation officials.
242 pp. *Permission required.* 1967.

CASSAVETES, John (1929–   ) *See* Popular Arts.

CASTLE, Benjamin. *See* Henry H. Arnold.

CASTRO, Fidel (1927–   ) Revolutionary leader.

Recordings of several speeches in Spanish, followed by a series of tape-recorded interviews in English (with the aid of an interpreter). The interviews cover a range of subjects on Cuba: agricultural policy, especially the sugar industry, land use, and people's farms; economy in general and foreign trade, future potentialities; revolutionary philosophy, how the Communist revolution worked in different regions, political prisoners and indemnification; local government organizations; questions of leadership, nature and use of power; education, creative arts, voluntary exiles and counterrevolutionaries; relations with the US: Vietnam, Dominican Republic; missile crisis; US press; relations with Russia.

381 pp. *Permission required.* 1965.
Contributed by Lee Lockwood, Boston, Massachusetts.

CASWELL, Hollis (1901–   ) Educator.

Family, education; experiences as graduate student at TC; consultant to southern state departments of education, General Education Board; school surveys, curricula, national associations; return to TC, 1937–62: head of department of curriculum and teaching, 1937–47, director, division of instruction, 1938–50, President, 1954–62; relations with Fund for Advancement of Education and Carnegie Corporation; teaching as a profession, teachers' unions, trustees, administration; travel; consultant to *World Book Encyclopedia;* retirement. Vignettes of James and William Russell, Professor George Strayer, James B. Conant and many others in education.

205 pp. *Permission required to cite or quote.* 1969. NYT (Part II).

CATES, Clifton Bledsoe (1893–1970) Marine Corps officer.

Education; WWI; aide to Commandant Marine Corps and CG, Department of the Pacific, 1920–23; China, 1929–32; War Plans Division, 1935–37; Shanghai, 1937–39, Sino-Japanese War; Army War College: wartime training program; President, USMC Equipment Board and Commandant, USMC Schools, 1947; USMC Commandant, 1948–51, unification fight; Korea; USO.

254 pp. *Open.* 1967.

CATES, Louis Shattuck (1881–1959) *See* Mining Engineers.

REFER TO "NOTES ON USE" IN INTRODUCTION

CATLEDGE, Turner (1901–   ) *See* American Cultural Leaders.

CAVANAUGH, Robert William (1914–   ) *See* World Bank.

CELLER, Emmanuel (1888–   ) *See* Herbert H. Lehman Project.

CERF, Bennett Alfred (1898–1971) Publisher.

Childhood and education in NYC; Columbia College: *Spectator, Jester;* journalism; Wall Street; Boni & Liveright; purchase of Modern Library; partnership with Donald Klopfer; travels and meetings with European authors; marriage to Sylvia Sidney; trip to Russia; building up Random House: contacts with authors, editors, other publishers; marriage to Phyllis Fraser; WWII publishing; *Try and Stop Me* and later books; magazine columns, radio programs, lecture tours; paperbacks, reprints, Bantam books; "What's My Line?"; role of an editor in a publishing house; dictionary and its promotion; purchase of other publishing houses: Singer, Knopf; stock issue, going public, 1959; purchase by RCA, 1965; educational developments, teaching machines; juvenile lists; spurt of growth in all publishing after WWII; purchase of Pantheon; foreign contacts; Peabody Awards Committee; director of MGM; Miss America pageant; Famous Writers School; many anecdotes about well known personalities in literary and entertainment fields.

1,029 pp. *Permission required.* 1968.

CHADBOURNE, William Merriam (1879–1964) *See* Theodore Roosevelt Association.

CHAMBERLAIN, Clarence. *See* Aviation.

CHAMBERLAIN, Owen (1920–   ) *See* Nobel Laureates.

CHAMBERLAIN, Thomas Gassner (1892–   ) Lawyer.

Law career; experiences with William H. Taft, 1919–20, Herbert Hoover campaign in California, 1920; Pro-League Republicans' campaign for James M. Cox; Finance Committee of the Republican Party.
181 pp. *Closed until 5 years after death.* 1951.

CHAMBERLAIN, Waldo (1905–   ) Historian.

UN Conference, San Francisco, 1945; Preparatory Commission, London, 1945; Secretariat, NY, 1945–48.
112 pp. *Permission required to cite or quote.* 1952.
NYT (Part II).

CHAMBERS, Reed. *See* Aviation.

CHANDLER, George Fletcher (1872–1964) Surgeon, penologist.

Early life, medical research; organization of NY State Police Force, 1919–1926; Governors Charles S. Whitman and Alfred E. Smith; Lackawanna steel strike; NY State Police School; Auburn prison riots.
113 pp. *Open.* 1950.

CHANG, Fa-k'uei. *See* Chinese Oral History.

CHAPIN, Emerson. *See* International Negotiations.

CHAPMAN, Alger Baldwin (1904–   ) Lawyer.

NY Republican politics, 1930–49.
76 pp. *Closed during lifetime.* 1949.
See also New York Political Studies.

CHARLTON, Lillian. *See* McGraw-Hill.

CHASINS, Abram (1903–   ) *See* Radio Pioneers.

REFER TO "NOTES ON USE" IN INTRODUCTION

Columbia University

CHATELAIN, Nicolas (1913–   ) Journalist.

Experiences as US correspondent for *Le Figaro;* comments upon coverage of the US by the press of Europe; Presidential press conferences; trip to Russia; comparison of US and European journalism.
55 pp. *Open.* 1961.

CHAUNCEY, Henry (1905–   ) *See* Carnegie Corporation.

CHEN, K. P. *See* Chinese Oral History.

CHEN, Li-fu. *See* Chinese Oral History.

CHEN, Theodore. *See* International Negotiations.

CHENNAULT, Anna. *See* Flying Tigers.

CHERNE, Leo (1912–   ) Economist, political analyst.

Childhood and education, NYC; New York Law School; Depressions and rise of leftist movements; Research Institute of America; figures and policies of Dwight D. Eisenhower Administration; 1960 presidential campaign; International Rescue Committee in Germany, Hungary, Vietnam; US policy toward Vietnam; Cuba under Fidel Castro. Impressions of Senator Joseph McCarthy, President Ngo Dinh Diem, Gen. Douglas MacArthur, Dr. Tom Dooley.
590 pp. *Closed during lifetime.* 1961.

CHEVALIER, Willard Townshend (1886–1961) Editor, publisher.

McGRAW-HILL

Early training and occupations; joined *Engineering News-Record* as associate editor; 1922; formation of McGraw-Hill

75

Publishing Company; evolution of various trade magazines; administration and policies of McGraw-Hill; impressions of James H. McGraw.
129 pp. *Permission required.* 1953.

CHIDLAW, Benjamin W. (1900–) *See* Air Force Academy.

CHILDREN'S TELEVISION WORKSHOP

This series of interviews traces the development of the Children's Television Workshop and the creation of "Sesame Street" in the words of some of those principally responsible. They recall 1966 discussions of how television might be made to serve pre-school children, preliminary studies, the roles of the Carnegie Corporation, of Harold Howe II as US Commissioner of Education, and of the Ford Foundation in advancing the concept and helping to finance it, the founding of the Workshop and its staffing, and the emergence of the Sesame Street format, as well as the changing relationship of the Workshop with National Educational Television, from which it became independent.

Participants and pages: David Connell, 33; Joan Cooney, 24; Robert Davidson, 36; Barbara Finberg, 11; Louis Hausman, 21; Edward Meade, 14; Lloyd Morrisett, 12; John White, 13.

134 pp. *Closed until Jan. 1, 1974.* 1972.
Contributed by Richard M. Polsky, New York.

CHILDS, Marquis William (1903–) Journalist.

Education and early work on the St. Louis *Post-Dispatch;* impressions of Chicago and St. Louis journalists; coverage of the 1936 presidential campaign; impressions of members of the Supreme Court: Robert H. Jackson, Harlan Stone, and Felix Frankfurter.
132 pp. *Permission required to cite or quote.* 1958.
NYT (Part I).
See also Adlai E. Stevenson Project.

REFER TO "NOTES ON USE" IN INTRODUCTION

CHILDS, Richard Spencer (1882–   ) Businessman, civic worker.

Growth of the city manager plan of government; short ballot movement; Citizens Union.
48 pp. *Open.* 1950.

CHINA MISSIONARIES

The Oral History Program at Claremont Graduate School, Claremont, California launched a project to assess the influence of the China missionary movement, 1900–50. Christian workers of various denominations give their recollections of conditions and experiences in China; they include educators, medical administrators, teachers, ministers, authors, and translators. The accounts deal with local conditions in urban and rural China and interaction between American residents and Chinese communities.

Participants and pages: Netta Powell Allen, 83; James Chamberlain Baker, 26; Earl Cranston, 130; Rowland McLean Cross, 200 (*certain pages closed*); Helen Dizney, 23; Leslie and Mary Fairfield, 75; Edward Pearce Hayes, 23; Clarence H. Holleman, 95; Lyda Suydam Houston, 79; Lydia Johnson, 38; Francis Price Jones, 69; Lucile Williams Jones, 47; Alice Clara Reed, 122; Roderick Scott, 113; Marjorie Rankin Steurt, 33; George Thomas Tootell, 34; William Hill Topping, 25; Martha Wiley, 106; Pearl Fosnot Winans, 47.

1,368 pp. *Open.* 1969–71.
Underwritten by the Henry Luce Foundation of New York.

CHINESE ORAL HISTORY

In 1958 Professors Franklin L. Ho and C. Martin Wilbur formulated a project within the East Asian Institute of Columbia University to record the oral recollections of prominent Chinese leaders of the Republican era, 1911–49. In the ensuing decade eighteen outstanding figures have devoted hundreds of hours to compiling oral records of their careers. These have been transcribed, translated, researched, and edited to produce memoirs for use by scholars interested in this half-century of Chinese history. Many are accompanied by private papers. The memoirs represent the lives of men who played major roles in Republican China in such capacities as Acting President, Vice President, Ambassador to the UN, Ambassador to the US and other countries, Minister of Foreign Affairs, Commander-in-Chief in the National Revolutionary Army, mayors of the capitals in WWII, governors of provinces divided by the Sino-Japanese War and by civil war, philosopher and spokesman for the Literary Revolution, financier, industrialist, educator, founders of a new political party opposed to and outlawed by both the Chinese Communist Party and the Kuomintang, and activists in the Third Force.

Many attended American universities and returned to China bringing modern attitudes to the still traditional society. Their detailed reminiscences help clarify hitherto confused areas of scholarly inquiry: the historian, sociologist, literary historian, economist, and political scientist will find a wealth of material for research.

Participants and pages: Chen, K.P., 167, *closed;* Ho, Franklin L., 450; Hu, Shih, 295; Huang, Fu, 489; Kung, H.H., 147; Li, Han-hun, 239, *certain pages closed;* Li, Huang, 1030, *closed;* Li, Shu-hua, 243, *certain pages closed;* Li, Tsung-jen, no running pagination (4 vols. 54 chapters), *permission required;* Liu, J. Heng, 8, *closed;* Tsiang, Tingfu F., 250, *closed;* Tso, Shun-sheng, 489; Wu, K.C., 391.

4,198 pp. *Open, except as noted. Descriptions of individual memoirs available on request.*
In process: Chang, Fa-k'uei; Chen, Li-fu; Choy, Jun-ke; Koo, V.K. Wellington; Yee, Chiang.

CHING, Cyrus Stuart (1876–1967) Industrial relations expert.

Labor relations in US, 1914–65; supervisor of industrial relations, US Rubber Co., 1919–47: centralizing personnel policies, factory councils, arbitration, industrial and craft unions; boyhood and education, Prince Edward Island; career with Boston Elevated Railway, 1901–19: air brakes, rapid transit unions, Storrow arbitration board, state receivership; a mediator's qualifications; American Management Association; NAM; US Chamber of Commerce; NLRB; NIRA industrial codes; organization of rubber industry by International Rubber Workers; Bethlehem Steel strike, 1939; 1941 National Defense Mediation Board cases: Allis-Chalmers, North American Aviation, Federal Shipbuilding, Air Associates, mineworkers; closed shop; WLB, 1942–43: Little Steel formula, auto industry; Federal Mediation and Conciliation Service, 1947–52: steel and auto industries, longshoremen, Taft-Hartley Act, General Electric; AEC Labor Relations Panel, 1953–67; Commerce Department Business Advisory Council; 1966 elections; AFL-CIO merger; Wage Stabilization Board, 1950; UMW; effectiveness of wage-price controls. Anecdotes of leaders in industry, labor, and government. Memoir includes a joint interview with Ralph T. Seward, executive secretary of National Defense Mediation Board.

805 pp. *Permission required to cite or quote.* 1967. NYT (Part II).

Acquired from Cornell Program in Oral History, Cornell University.

CHORLEY, Kenneth (1893–   ) Conservationist.
JACKSON HOLE PRESERVE

Conservationist activities of John D. Rockefeller, Jr.; the beginning of Jackson Hole Preserve; Robert E. Miller and the buying of land; cattlemen; the Forest Service versus the Park Service; political opposition; the Monument; the hotels; famous guests at Jackson Hole; notes for official reports; impressions of John D. Rockefeller, Jr. and his family.
160 pp. *Permission required.* 1966.

CHOY, Jun-ke. *See* Chinese Oral History.

CHURCH, Ellen. *See* Aviation.

CHURCHILL, Edward Delos (1895–1972) Surgeon.

Family history and boyhood; education, Northwestern University and Harvard Medical School; clinical training, Faulkner and MGH, 1919–24; techniques of surgery, anesthesiology, and blood transfusion, 1920's; anecdotes of Boston medical profession, 1920–40; observations in European clinics and laboratories, 1926–27; Boston City Hospital, 1929–52; relationship of Harvard teaching hospitals and University; cancer research; Huntington and Vincent Hospitals; medical planning, WWII; Surgical Consultant, North African and Mediterranean Theaters, 1943–46; battle wound management; shock research; debate on plasma use; postwar Veterans Administration; chairman, advisory committee to Secretary of War Robert P. Patterson, 1946; impressions of colleagues in medicine, education, and government, especially Cecil Drinker, David Edsall, Harvey Cushing, Elliott Cutler, James B. Conant, Henry Beecher, Edwin Cohn, Sidney Burwell, Evarts Graham, Howard Snyder, Michael DeBakey, and Henry L. Stimson.

691 pp. *Permission required to cite or quote.* 1957.
Notes, correspondence, supplementary documents interfiled with pages of memoir.

CITIZENS BUDGET COMMISSION. *See* New York Political Studies.

CIVIL RIGHTS IN ALABAMA

Leaders and participants in the movement at Tuscaloosa, Alabama in 1964 describe clashes with local law enforcement personnel, culminating in the tear gassing of the First Baptist Church. Included are the transcripts of two mass meetings and interviews with residents expressing widely varying attitudes towards the movement.

Participants and pages: Rev. Willie Herzfeld, 39; James Jacquith, 50; George LeMaistre, 31; Jay Murphy, 20; T. Y. Rogers, 60; Robert Shelton, 59.

259 pp. *Open.* 1964.
Contributed by Harvey Burg, New York.

CIVIL WAR CENTENNIAL

Civil War scholars at the final Centennial meeting in Springfield, Illinois discuss sources, problems in historiography, and research experiences in the field.

REFER TO "NOTES ON USE" IN INTRODUCTION

Participants and pages: Harold M. Hyman, 15; E. B. Long, 53; Bell I. Wiley, 44; T. Harry Williams, 31.

143 pp. *Permission required to cite or quote.* 1965.

CLAGUE, Ewan (1896–   ) Economist.

Education; work at Brookings Institution; New Deal legislation; social security; relationship of Bureau of Labor Statistics to other Federal agencies; Department of Labor under Franklin D. Roosevelt, Harry S. Truman, and Dwight D. Eisenhower; Frances Perkins and subsequent Secretaries of Labor; John Winant, Arthur Altmeyer, Isador Lubin, John Steelman, and others.

468 pp. *Permission required.* 1958.

SOCIAL SECURITY

Student days at University of Wisconsin and relations with John R. Commons; work with Bureau of Employment Security, Social Security Board and development of unemployment insurance; impressions of Frank Bane, John Winant; appointment as Commissioner of Labor Statistics.

152 pp. *Open.* 1966.

CLAPP, Norton (1906–   ) *See* Weyerhaeuser Timber Company.

CLARK, Grenville (1882–1967) *See* Robert P. Patterson Project.

CLARK, Harold Florian (1899–   ) Educator.

Early education; London School of Economics, 1926–27; teaching, Indiana University, 1923–25, TC, 1928 on; Sloan project in applied economics; work abroad: India, Southeast Asia, South America; consultant to Special Assistant for USAF Academy; political activities; impressions of educators, especially John Dewey and William H. Kilpatrick.

306 pp. *Open.* 1963.

CLARK, Joseph James (1893–1971) Naval officer.

Early life in Indian Territory; Oklahoma A&M; Naval Academy; WWI convoys and patrols; Turkey; destroyer duty; teaching at Naval Academy; naval aviation; Adm. William Moffett and Gen. William Mitchell; Naval Air Stations; stunt and test flying; relationships with members of Congress; Inspector of Naval Aircraft; early Pacific operations; North African landings; "Fighting Lady," 1943; detailed descriptions of Pacific operations; Task Group Commander, Assistant Chief of Naval Operations for Air; the "Revolt of the Admirals," Korea; Command of 7th Fleet, 1952. Impressions of many military, naval, and political figures, especially Adms. John H. Towers, Ernest King, Chester Nimitz, Arthur Radford, Marc Mitscher, and Raymond Spruance, and Secretaries of the Navy John L. Sullivan and James V. Forrestal.

840 pp. *Permission required.* 1962. Papers.

CLARK, Mark Wayne (1896–   ) Army officer.
EISENHOWER ADMINISTRATION

Association with Dwight D. Eisenhower at West Point and during WWII; US involvement in Korea; military tactics, negotiations to end Korean War; Eisenhower as President-elect.

91 pp. *Permission required.* 1970.

CLARK, Maud. *See* McGraw-Hill.

CLARK, Thomas E. (1869–1962).

RADIO PIONEERS

Chicago World's Fair, 1893; Edison General Electric in Schenectady; experiments with wireless; automatic radio train control; police car radios.

38 pp. *Open.* 1951.

CLARKE, Clem S. (1897–   ) *See* Benedum and the Oil Industry.

CLARKE, Eric. *See* Carnegie Corporation.

REFER TO "NOTES ON USE" IN INTRODUCTION

CLARKE, Gilmore David (1892–   ) Landscape architect.

Training at Cornell; early work on Bronx River Parkway; WWI; Westchester County park system; planning parks, parkways, and expressways, 1930's through 1950's; housing projects, including Metropolitan Life Insurance Company; city planning in Portland, Oregon, and Nashville, Tennessee; National Commission of Fine Arts, 1932–50; NYC traffic control report; NY World's Fair, 1939; College of Architecture, Cornell, 1935–50; planning for NY State Power Authority, Naval Academy, Military Academy; UN headquarters; consulting services to universities and colleges.

372 pp. *Permission required.* 1959. Papers and pamphlets.

CLAY, Lucius DuBignon (1897–   ) Army officer.

Alexander Stephen Clay: political career, US Senate, 1897–1915; Europe, 1919; Marietta, Georgia politics, the Negro vote during early 1900's; West Point, 1914–21, 1924–28; military training, instructorship; beginning of ROTC; assignment to Panama, mapping the terrain; Rivers and Harbors Division; Depression in Pittsburgh; effect of New Deal, WPA policies on Rivers and Harbors; Franklin D. Roosevelt, Harry Hopkins; Los Angeles Flood Control project; Europe during early 1930's; TVA controversy; Harold Ickes; flood control bill in early 1930's; Douglas MacArthur; duty in the Philippines; building Denison Dam, Texas; Sam Rayburn.

1,101 pp. *Closed pending publication.* 1971.
EISENHOWER ADMINISTRATION

Career relations with Gen. and President Eisenhower; drafting Eisenhower for President in 1952; selection and evaluation of the Cabinet members.

113 pp. *Open.* 1967.

CLAY, Lucius DuBignon, Jr. (1919–   ) Air Force officer.

Reminiscences of his father, Gen. Lucius D. Clay, particularly Panama experiences, 1928–29, and interest in commu-

nity projects; own career in Army Aerospace, Chief of Staff, Programming and Resources, 1967–68.
25 pp. *Closed pending publication.* 1969.
Contributed by Jean E. Smith, Toronto, Canada.

CLAYTON, William Lockhart (1880–1966) Cotton executive, government official.

Childhood and education in Mississippi; Jerome Hill and the cotton business; Anderson, Clayton and Co.; Congressional investigations; New Deal agricultural policy; Liberty League; John W. Davis, Jesse Jones, Nelson Rockefeller, Henry Wallace, Edward Stettinius, James Byrnes, George Marshall, the Marshall Plan.
235 pp. *Open.* 1962.
See also Marshall Plan.

CLEMENT, Thomas. *See* Socialist Movement.

CLOUD, George Harlon (1904–   ) *See* Marine Corps.

CLUTE, R. V. *See* Weyerhaeuser Timber Company.

CLUTTERBUCK, Haroldo Rodolfo Guido (1907–   ) Corporation executive.

ARGENTINA IN THE 1930'S

Association with Torcuato di Tella and his industrial enterprises from 1929; manufacture of machinery for baking, petroleum industry, refrigeration; development of Argentine technology, adaptation and licensing of foreign products; work force; incentive premium, growth of unions, strikes; financial problems, effects of Depression and WW II; Peronism; introduction of assembly line, door to door salesmanship.
61 pp. *Open.* 1971.

COASH, Carl (1905–   ) *See* McGraw-Hill.

COATNEY, George Robert (1902–   ) *See* Health Science.

REFER TO "NOTES ON USE" IN INTRODUCTION

COBB, Candler (1887–1955) Lawyer.

Childhood and education at Harvard and Oxford; assistant in office of US District Attorney; commercial attaché to London Embassy, repayment of WW I debts, techniques of diplomatic service; Andrew Mellon, George Harvey, William H. Taft; law practice in London, 1932–40.
175 pp. *Permission required to cite or quote.* 1951. NYT (Part I).

COBB, Cully Alton (1884–   ) Editor.

Detailed account of the AAA Cotton Section, 1933–37: establishment of program and work with state extension directors, sources of support and opposition, public and press relations, dispute over landlord-tenant relations; Meyers Report. Recollections of W. B. Camp, Jerome Frank, Chester C. Davis, Gen. Stephen D. Lee, Walter F. George, Henry A. Wallace.
130 pp. *Permission required to cite or quote.* 1966. Papers. *Acquired from Regional Oral History Office, University of California, Berkeley.*

COBB, Jerrie. *See* Aviation.

COBHAM, Alan. *See* Aviation.

COCHRAN, Jacqueline (Mrs. Floyd B. Odlum).
AVIATION

Pilots license, 1932; the Australian race; instrument flying; aviation medicine; ferry flights during WWII; women pilots in the Air Force; use of jet planes; world records; FAI; visits to Russia; Northeast Airlines. Recollections of Howard Hughes, Amelia Earhart.
105 pp. *Open.* 1960.

COCKE, Norman Atwater (1884–   ) Lawyer.
JAMES B. DUKE PROJECT

Educational background; founding of Duke Power Co.,

85

1912; anti-trust case, American Tobacco Co., 1911–12; impressions of James B. Duke as a businessman; planning the Duke Endowment; building and operating Duke University; trustee of the Duke Endowment, 1924; President, Duke Power Co., 1953; description of the Duke home in Charlottesville.
204 pp. *Permission required.* 1964.

COFFYN, Frank T. (–1960) *See* Aviation.

COGGESHALL, L.T. *See* Health Science.

COHEN, Henry. *See* New York Political Studies.

COHEN, Martin (with James Brindle) *See* Social Security.

COHEN, Wilbur Joseph (1913–) *See* Social Security.

COHN, Marcus. *See* James Lawrence Fly Project.

COLAHAN, Thomas S. *See* Columbia Crisis of 1968.

COLEMAN, Henry. *See* Columbia Crisis of 1968.

COLLADO, Emilio Gabriel (1910–) *See* Marshall Plan.

COLLBOHM, Franklin Rudolf (1907–) *See* Aviation.

COLLINS, Joseph (1866–1950) Neurologist, writer.

NY medicine and psychiatry, 1888–1912; publishers and authors, 1912–30; Sir William Osler; Henry James; James Joyce. 62 pp. *Permission required to cite or quote.* 1949. NYT (Part I). Papers: 5 Henry James letters; 36 other letters; 23 clippings.

COLP, Ralph. *See* Mt. Sinai Hospital.

COLUMBIA CRISIS OF 1968

In this series of interviews, almost all conducted on campus in May, 1968, participants and observers of every hue— student activists (conservative, independent, and radical), junior and senior faculty, administrators, supporting staff, and parents—describe and discuss the many phases of the crisis that resulted in the occupation of five Columbia buildings by students April 23 and 24, the suspension of classes, fruitless negotiations, police intervention on April 30, a campuswide strike, a lesser eruption May 21–22, and the eventual restructuring of the University. Factors behind the crisis are examined and weighed in tones ranging from analytical detachment to passionate concern. A researcher for the Archibald Cox Fact Finding Commission read a small fraction of this material, with the explicit permission of the contributor in each instance. The project was conducted independently by the Oral History Office.

Participants and pages: Jacques Barzun, 17; Lawrence Berger, 43; Bureau of Applied Social Research Study, 46; John D. Cannon, 86; Thomas S. Colahan, 49; Henry S. Coleman, 46; Columbia Concerned Parents meeting, 72; Cathleen Cook, 45; William Cumming, 58; Herbert A. Deane, 34; William T. de Bary, 29; Jay Facciolo, 59; Mark Flanigan, 95; Robert Fogelson, 44; Joel Frader, 48; James Goldman, 24; James Grossman, 38; Marvin Harris, 50; Richard Hofstadter, 30; Terence Hopkins, 74;

International Journalism Students, 41; Jeffrey Kaplow, 59; Peter Kenen, 73; Grayson Kirk, 40; Polykarp Kusch, 33; Robert Masters, 47; Seymour Melman, 37; Walter Metzger, 33; Barbara and David Nasaw, 97; Alexander B. Platt, 41; Project Planners Meeting, 57; Orest Ranum, 49; David Rothman, 68; Frank Safran, 156; Howard Schless, 10; James P. Shenton, 8; Bruce Smith, 74; Lionel Trilling, 78; David B. Truman, 83; Paul Vilardi, 90; Immanuel Wallerstein, 265.

2,426 pp. *Permission required.* 1968. *Supporting papers. Underwritten by the Edward W. Hazen Foundation, New Haven, Connecticut.*

COLUMBIA TELEVISION LECTURES

Lectures on current world issues by Columbia scholars.

Participants and pages: L. Gray Cowan, 29; Marvin Harris, 74; Robert Jastrow, 32; J. E. Kimmy, 33; James W. Morley, 49.

217 pp. *Open.* 1962–63.

COLUMBIANA

From time to time the Oral History Research Office has interviewed persons who have made significant contributions to the development of Columbia University, or observed various phases of its development over the years. A few were asked specifically for their recollections of President Nicholas Murray Butler and his administration (1902–1945); these are listed below. In addition, a number of individual memoirs in this catalogue provide information of special interest on the University and on President Butler. *See* Harry James Carman, Luther Evans, Frank Fackenthal, William Fondiller, George B. Ford, Frank H. Hankins, Polykarp Kusch, Allan Nevins, Edmund A. Prentis, Isidor Rabi, Lindsay Rogers, Constance M. Winchell.

Participants and pages: Virginia Gildersleeve, 8; Philip M. Hayden, 11; Carlton J. H. Hayes, 23; Isadore Mudge, 50; E. Berthol Sayre, 16; Eugene Sheffer, 55; James T. Shotwell, 23.

186 pp. *Open.* 1955–71.

COLVIN, Fred Herbert (1867–1965) *See* McGraw-Hill.

COMBS, George Hamilton, Jr. (1899–   ) Lawyer, congressman, news analyst.

Kansas City: Thomas J. Pendergast machine; Congress, 1927–29; election of 1932; NYC politics and Tammany Hall, 1932–50; NY election of 1950; Estes Kefauver investigation. 191 pp. *Closed during lifetime.* 1951.
See also New York Political studies.

COMDEN, Betty (1919–   ) (with Adolph Green) *See* Popular Arts.

COMMAGER, Henry Steele (1902–   ) *See* American Historians.

COMMINS, Dorothy Berliner (Mrs. Saxe)

Editorial career of Saxe Commins at Liveright and Ran-

dom House; Modern Library. Impressions of Mr. Commins' relationship with authors, especially Eugene O'Neill and William Faulkner.
181 pp. *Closed during lifetime.* 1962.

CONANT, Frederick Warren (1892–   ) *See* Henry H. Arnold Project.

CONANT, James Bryant (1893–   ) *See* Carnegie Corporation.

CONDON, John Pomeroy (1911–   ) *See* Marine Corps.

CONGER, Clement (1912–   ) *See* Eisenhower Administration.

CONKLIN, Chester (1888–1971) *See* Popular Arts.

CONNELL, David. *See* Children's Television Workshop.

CONNELLY, Marc (1890–   ) *See* Popular Arts.

CONNORTON, John V. *See* New York Political Studies.

CONOLLY, Richard L. (1892–1962) Naval officer.

Early education and training at Annapolis; junior naval officer experiences aboard destroyers and battleships; WWI; Washington, Geneva, and London Conferences; naval training schools, 1920's and 1930's; Pearl Harbor; wartime experiences in the Pacific; Joint Chiefs of Staff in Washington; invasion of North Africa; assault on Sicily; Operation Avalanche (assault on Salerno); cooperation with the British; Guam, Saipan, and the Philippines; Paris Peace Conference, 1946; Commander US Fleet in Eastern Atlantic and Mediterranean; 6th Fleet; struggle over unification of the armed forces; President US Naval War College.
411 pp. *Open.* 1959.

COOK, Cathleen. *See* Columbia Crisis of 1968.

COOK, Charles D. (1924–   ) Lawyer.
EISENHOWER ADMINISTRATION

Education and training in Michigan; US Navy, 1943–47: V–12 program, Saipan; Columbia University: Law School, School of International Affairs; US Mission to UN, 1950–62: UN civil service, the Secretary Generalship, UN diplomacy, relations with US State Department, Uniting for Peace resolution, admission of new members, voting, various crises; Henry Cabot Lodge, John Foster Dulles, Adlai Stevenson, Dwight Eisenhower, Krishna Menon.
658 pp. *Closed until 1979.* 1964.

COOK, Howard Alexander (1915–   ) *See* Eisenhower Administration.

COOLEY, Albert Dustin (1900–   ) *See* Marine Corps.

COOLIDGE, Charles Allerton (1894–   ) Lawyer.
EISENHOWER ADMINISTRATION

Special Assistant to the Secretary of Defense, 1955–58; reorganization of the Defense Department and disarmament policy under President Eisenhower.
35 pp. *Permission required.* 1967.

COONEY, Joan Ganz. *See* Children's Television Workshop.

COOPER, Jackie (1922–   ) *See* Popular Arts.

COOPER, William G., Jr. *See* Eisenhower Administration.

COPE, Sidney Raymond (1907–   ) *See* World Bank.

CORBIN, Hazel (1895–   ) Nurse.

Description of her work for better maternity care through

Maternity Center Association (1918–65): prenatal care, maternity institutes, training public health nurses, certification program for nurse-midwives, teaching aids; health legislation and federal agencies; WHO.
78 pp. *Permission required.* 1970.
Underwritten by friends of Miss Corbin; contributed by Ruth Watson Lubic, New York City.

CORCORAN, Thomas. *See* Flying Tigers.

CORCORAN, Thomas Gardiner (1900–   ) *See* James Lawrence Fly Project.

CORCUNDALE, Thomas. *See* Flying Tigers.

CORDIER, Andrew Wellington (1901–   ) UN official, educator.

Executive assistant to UN Secretary-General, 1946; comprehensive discussion of UN: as a propaganda arena, role of small nations, administration and duties of officers, rules of procedure, staffing, effect of press, General Assembly, Security Council, early development of Secretariat; impressions of Russian leaders: Nikita Khrushchev, Andrei Gromyko, and deputies; comparison of Trygve Lie, Dag Hammarskjold, and U Thant; discussion of Hammarskjold's personality with anecdotal illustrations; plane crash in Ndola. Detailed description of UN handling of Korean prisoner problem, Congo, Suez, Hungary, and Lebanon crises.
532 pp. *Permission required.* 1964.
See also Dag Hammarskjold Project.

CORI, Carl Ferdinand (1896–   ) *See* Nobel Laureates.

CORNELL, Katharine (1898–   ) *See* Popular Arts.

CORSO, Gregory Nunzio (1930–   ) *See* Poets on their Poetry.

CORT, William Walter (1887–1971) Parasitologist.

Education, Colorado College, University of Illinois; Professor, Johns Hopkins School of Hygiene and Public Health, 1919–53; work on hookworm and other parasites in southern US, China, Puerto Rico, Panama, Trinidad, and Egypt; recollections of biologists.
31 pp. *Open.* 1966.

CORWIN, Norman (1910–   ) Writer, director, producer.
RADIO PIONEERS
Early days in radio; WQXR; "Twenty-six by Corwin" radio program on WCBS; reaction of radio industry, advertising agencies, and the public to *Red Channels.*
100 pp. *Closed during lifetime.*
See also James Lawrence Fly Project.

CORYELL, Charles DuBois (1912–1971) Chemist.

Education in California and Germany; political philosophy; Manhattan Project, Chicago and Oak Ridge; security restrictions and problems; relationships with Army and DuPont Company; tension among scientists; emotional and scientific impact of bomb and its use; attempts to inform and influence public opinion and Congress; Smyth report; Europe and Israel sojourn; Robert Oppenheimer case; impressions of many prominent atomic scientists.
441 pp. *Open.* 1960.

COSIO VILLEGAS, Daniel (1898–   ) Lawyer, educator.

Family background, education; interior of Mexico, 1905–06; Mexican Revolution, 1914; National Student Federation; University of Mexico; Mexican politicians and intellectuals during the 1920's; Law School; teaching at the University of Mexico and formation of its School of Economics; founding of publishing house, *Fondo de Cultura Economica,* 1933; Financial Counselor, Mexican Embassy

in Washington, 1936; chargé d'affaires, Lisbon; Spanish Civil War. The memoir is in Spanish.
297 pp. *Permission required to cite or quote.* 1963.

COSTELLO, Jerry. *See* Flying Tigers.

COSTIKYAN, Edward (1924–   ) Politician.

Part I: Childhood and education, NYC: Horace Mann, Columbia, 1949; Army Infantry: Okinawa and Korea, 1943–45; NYC politics: New Democratic Club, 1951–66; NY County Democratic leader, 1964; Robert Wagner as Mayor; Wagner-Carmine DeSapio feud; relationships with Reform leaders and other political figures, including anecdotes of Adlai Stevenson, Eleanor Roosevelt, Herbert Lehman, James Farley, Averell Harriman, Robert F. Kennedy.Detailed analysis and description of NYC mayoralty campaign and election, 1965.
677 pp. *Permission required.* 1966.

Part II: NY State Democratic Party politics, 1966–70; breakdown of district leader-captain relationships; Constitutional Convention; national Democratic politics: 1968 preconvention, convention, and campaign; Robert Kennedy, Eugene McCarthy, and others.
76 pp. *Permission required.* 1970.

COTT, Ted (1917–   ) Radio and television executive.

Radio interest during high school and college; WNYC and Mayor Fiorello LaGuardia; early radio techniques and programming; Radio Code; independent stations and networks; FCC; sponsorship, spot announcements; television pioneering; political broadcasting; educational television; National Talent Associates; Nikita Khrushchev interview on "Open End"; censorship; pay television.
297 pp. *Closed during lifetime.* 1961.
See also Journalism Lectures.

COTTON, Thomas (–1964) *See* Flying Tigers.

COTTONE, Benedict Peter (1909–   ) *See* James Lawrence Fly Project.

COUCH, William Terry (1901–   ) Publisher.
SOUTHERN INTELLECTUAL LEADERS

Childhood and education, rural Virginia;University of North Carolina; University of North Carolina Press, Associate Director, 1926–32 and Director, 1932–45; freedom of the press in the South; problems of tenant farmers and the FSA; Southern Policy Committee; Southern Conference for Human Welfare; Federal Writers Project, Regional Director, 1937–39; *These Are Our Lives;* University of Chicago Press, Director, 1945–50; *Collier's Encyclopedia,* editor-in-chief, 1952–59; *Oxford Junior Encyclopedia,* editor, 1959–63; William Volker Foundation; impressions of the Nashville Agrarians, Henry G. Alsberg, Clarence Carson, Harry Woodburn Chase, Jonathan Daniels, Frank P. Graham, Robert M. Hutchins, Herman C. Nixon, Howard W. Odom, and others.

571 pp. *Closed pending publication of a study.* 1970. Papers.

COUDERT, Frederic Rene (1871–1955) Lawyer.

Recollections of his father; early political impressions, notably the "Cross of Gold" speech; Spanish-American War; Insular cases; NY politics, John P. Mitchel; legal adviser to British Government regarding legal controversies involving US, especially British blockade and problems of international maritime law, 1915–20; impressions of Woodrow Wilson, Sir Cecil Spring-Rice, Robert Lansing, Alexis Carrel, Benjamin Cardozo, Cornelius Clifford, Boris Bakhmeteff, Henri Bergson, Simon Flexner; Columbia University and Nicholas Murray Butler.

170 pp. *Permission required to cite or quote.* 1950. NYT (Part I). Papers.

COUGHLIN, Edward. *See* Federated Department Stores.

COURNAND, Andre F. (1895–   ) *See* Nobel Laureates.

REFER TO "NOTES ON USE" IN INTRODUCTION

COUSINS, Norman (1912–   ) *See* Journalism Lectures.

COWAN, Charles S. *See* Forest History Society.

COWAN, L. Gray. *See* Columbia Television Lectures.

COWAN, Louis G. (1909–   ) Communications executive.
RADIO PIONEERS
Early interest in communications; University of Chicago; radio work in Chicago in the 1930's; various early productions, including "Quiz Kids"; work during WWII: Director, Voice of America and OWI NYC office; programs for War Department, including "Command Performance," "Chaplain Jim"; Louis G. Cowan radio and television productions, 1946–55; transition from radio to television; Negroes in broadcast industry; use of broadcasting and television in Adlai Stevenson 1952 Presidential campaign; Peabody and other broadcast awards; CBS network role.
225 pp. *Permission required to cite or quote.* 1967.

COWAN, Thomas H. (1884–   ) Radio station executive.
RADIO PIONEERS
Family background; pioneer work in radio, WJZ, Newark, 1921; milestones in the history of WNYC from 1924; work with various NYC mayors. Impressions of Thomas A. Edison and various radio figures.
119 pp. *Open.* 1951.

COWELL, Henry (1897–1965) Composer.

Early compositions; tone clusters, influence on other composers; travel and study in Europe and US; teaching; OWI; folk music; Oriental music; music publishing; lectures; Columbia, New School; anecdotes of notable musicians, especially Charles Ives.
142 pp. *Open.* 1963.

COWLES, William Sheffield. *See* Theodore Roosevelt Association.

95

COWLEY, William Harold (1899–　) Educator.

Brooklyn childhood and education; American Steel and Wire Company; YMCA work, night school, Mt. Hermon, Clark School; Dartmouth, 1920–24; Western Electric Company; graduate work, Chicago, 1925–27; Board of Vocational Guidance and Placement, 1927; Ohio State University, Bureau of Educational Research, 1929–38; editing *Journal of Higher Education*; residential housing study, administering NYA, state educational conferences, bibliographic work; Carnegie Corporation; student personnel work; American Council on Education; President, Hamilton College, 1938–44; admissions and curriculum studies; Washington, 1942, role of education in war effort; Air Force programs at Hamilton; Professor of Higher Education, Stanford, from 1945; work with graduate students, fundamental concepts. Impressions of noted educators, includingW. W. Charters, Robert Hutchins, Frederick Keppel, J. L. Morrill, James B. Conant, Harold Dodds.
768 pp. *Permission required.* 1962. Papers.

COX, Sir Harold Roxbee (1902–　) *See* Aviation.

COX, Joseph Aloysius (1896–　) Judge.

Early life, WWI; CCNY; teaching; Fordham Law School; NYC politics; attorney for Public Administrator; law practice; detailed description of notable cases, including Ida Wood, Mabel Greer, Collyer brothers, heir chasing, undue influence; State Supreme Court, 1952; Judicial Conference; Apellate Division; Surrogate of NY County, 1956.
407 pp. *Closed during lifetime.* 1962.

COX, O. T. *See* Marine Corps.

CRABB, Jarred V. (1902–　) Air Force officer.

Peacetime Air Corps training and morale; Kelly and Selfridge Fields; bomb sight maintenance; 14th Reconnaissance Squadron, Gander, 1941; communications training,

1941–42; South Pacific Theater, 1943–46: 5th Air Force and 5th Bomber Command; bombing tactics; Philippines, 1948–49; FEAF staff, 1949–52; Korea air operations; Air Defense Command, 1952–54; recollections of WWII colleagues, especially Gen. George C. Kenny, Douglas MacArthur, Ennis C. Whitehead, and Thomas D. White. 150 pp. *Open.* 1970.

CRAIG, Edward Arthur (1896–   ) Marine Corps officer.

Early assignments, Haiti, Santo Domingo, Philippines, Shanghai, Peking; Aide to the USMC Commandant, 1926–29; antibanditry activities, Nicaragua, 1929–31, Nicaraguan Electoral Mission, 1932; fleet landing exercises, development of amphibious warfare doctrine and techniques, San Diego, 1931–37; Staff, Aviation Battle Force, Pacific Fleet, 1939–41; WWII: Bougainville, Guam, Iwo Jima; interwar assignments; occupation of North China, 1947; CG, 1st Marine Brigade, 1947–50; Korea: Pusan perimeter, Inchon landing; Director, USMCR, 1951. 199 pp. *Open.* 1968.

CRAIG, Robert (1920–   ) *See* McGraw-Hill.

CRAIGIE, Laurence C. (1902–   ) *See* Air Force Academy *and* Aviation.

CRANE, Burton (–1963) *See* Occupation of Japan.

CRANE, Esther. *See* Occupation of Japan.

HART CRANE PROJECT

Impressions of Hart Crane and the literary scene in Ohio and NYC during the 1920's.

Participants and pages: Mrs. Margaret Babcock, 50; Waldo Frank, 53; Fredrica Crane Lewis, 17; Samuel Loveman, 46; Allen Tate, 35 (*closed during lifetime*).

201 pp. *Permission required.* 1963.
Contributed by John E. Unterecker, New York.

CRANSTON, Earl (1895–1970) *See* China Missionaries.

CRARY, Albert P. (1911–   ) Geophysicist, oceanographer.

Seismic and geologic explorations, oceanography and geophysics; oil exploration in Colombia and Venezuela; early loran and sofar; Maurice Ewing; air acoustics and balloons; Alamogordo; Arctic and Antarctic glaciology; IGY.
87 pp. *Permission required to cite or quote.* 1962.
NYT (Part I).

CRAWFORD, Edward. *See* Alaskan Pioneers.

CRAWFORD, Kenneth Gale (1902–   ) Journalist.
EISENHOWER ADMINISTRATION
Eisenhower's relations with the press as General and President; impressions of Eisenhower administration.
26 pp. *Permission required to cite or quote.* 1967.

CREMIN, Lawrence Arthur (1925–   ) Educator.
CARNEGIE CORPORATION
Contacts with the Carnegie Corporation; TC; *The Transformation of the School;* National Academy of Education, 1964–65; Behavioral Science Center, Stanford University, 1963; Carnegie grant for a history of American education, 1964; Institute of Philosophy and Politics of Education, 1964. Impressions of Lloyd Morrissett, James B. Conant, and others.
107 pp. *Permission required.* 1968.

CRENA DE IONGH, Daniel. *See* World Bank.

CROHN, Burrill Bernard (1884–   ) *See* Mt. Sinai Hospital.

CROMWELL, John (1888–   ) *See* Popular Arts.

REFER TO "NOTES ON USE" IN INTRODUCTION

CROSS, Robert Dougherty (1924–   ) *See* American Historians.

CROSS, Rowland McLean (1888–   ) *See* China Missionaries.

CROSSFIELD, Albert Scott (1921–   ) *See* Aviation.

CROSSMAN, John. *See* McGraw-Hill.

CROWDER, Walter (1907–   ) *See* McGraw-Hill.

CROWELL, Paul (1891–1970) *See* New York Political Studies.

CROWTHER, Bosley (1905–   ) *See* Popular Arts.

CRUGER, Bertram D. (1893–1952) Secretary to John Purroy Mitchel.

The Mitchel administration, NYC.
33 pp. *Open.* 1950.

CRUIKSHANK, Nelson Hale (1902–   ) Labor economist.
SOCIAL SECURITY
War Manpower Commission; AFL office for Social Security, 1944; Advisory Committee to the Senate Finance Committee, 1949; chairman, labor staff coordinating committee on Medicare, 1959–60; Commission on Church and Economic Life; staff executive officer, AFL Committee on Social Security; AFL-CIO efforts toward national health insurance: 1956 disability bill and Medicare bill and its precursors, 1957–65; AMA opposition to Medicare, support of Medicare by National Council of Churches and National Council of Senior Citizens; drafting AFL-CIO constitution. Impressions of Andrew Biemiller, Wilbur Cohen, John F. Kennedy, George Meany, Walter Reuther, Abraham Ribicoff.
506 pp. *Open except for specified pages.* 1967.

The Oral History Collection

CUMBERLAND, William Wilson (1890–1955) Economist.

Early life; research in Mexico on economic conditions, 1917; Paris Peace Conference with John Foster Dulles: economic decisions, personalities; economic adviser to State Department: post WWI economic conditions in US and Europe; mandated territories; economies of Peru, Haiti, Nicaragua; stock market and US economy; NRA, 1933; consultant, UN conference, 1945.
286 pp. *Permission required to cite or quote.* 1951.
NYT (Part I).

CUMMING, William. *See* Columbia Crisis of 1968.

CUMMINGS, Martin. *See* Health Science.

CUPP, Roderick B. *See* Radio Pioneers.

CURRAN, Joseph (1906–   ) Labor union executive.

Early life; National Maritime Union, president, 1931; influence of Communist party in unions; vice president, AFL-CIO.
193 pp. *Closed during lifetime.* 1964.

CURTIS, Albert B. (1903–   ) Chief fire warden.
WEYERHAEUSER TIMBER COMPANY

Work with Fire Protection Association, Idaho, from 1918; early years in fire protection, Weyerhaeuser Co.; Cattle Grazers Association, 1935; air control. Impressions of J. P. Weyerhaeuser, Theodore Fohl.
103 pp. *Permission required.* 1956.

CURTIS, Donald (1896–   ) Marine Corps officer.

Family background, education; WWI, balloon training; Office of the Judge Advocate General of the Navy; Shanghai, 1930–31; experiences in prisoner of war camps, libera-

tion, 1942–45; Military Secretary to Gen. Alexander Vande-grift, 1946–48.
117 pp. *Open.* 1970.

CURTIS, James Freeman (1878–1952) Lawyer.

Childhood; education at Harvard; early law practice; Assistant Attorney General, Assistant District Attorney, Massachusetts, 1906–09; Assistant Secretary of the Treasury, Customs Bureau, 1909–13; establishment of Federal Reserve System, 1914–19; Liberty Loan; private legal practice in NY, 1919–51; impressions of Franklin MacVeagh, Boies Penrose, William Howard Taft, T. E. Lawrence, and Efrem Zimbalist; personal experiences in financial speculation, travels; avocations; philosophy of life.
334 pp. *Permission required to cite or quote.* 1951. NYT (Part I).

CURTIS, Thomas B. (1911–   ) *See* Eisenhower Administration.

CUSHMAN, Thomas Jackson (1895–   ) *See* Marine Corps.

CUSTER, Benjamin Scott (1905–   ) Naval officer.

Family background, childhood; Naval Academy; early cruises; Pensacola, flight training; flying boat squadron, Alaska; teaching at Annapolis; Caribbean Sea Frontier, Adm. John Hoover; executive officer, *Croatan;* Adm. John Vest; command of the *Norton Sound;* WWII: Atlantic and Pacific theaters; atomic bomb; Flight Safety Board, Pay Board; Naval Attaché to Canada; Northwest cruise to Hudson's Bay; Floyd Bennett Field; Strauss Commission; Princeton. Impressions of contemporaries in the Navy and of government officials; discussion of strategy and battle plans, World Wars I and II.
1,022 pp. *Permission required.* 1965.

DA COSTA, Morton. *See* Popular Arts.

DALE, Harry (–1962) *See* Book-of-the-Month Club.

DALLY, A. B., Jr. *See* Benedum and The Oil Industry.

DALY, Charles Ulick (1927–   ) *See* Social Security.

DALY, Edward (1898–   ) *See* Thomas A. Edison Project.

DANAHER, John Anthony (1899–   ) Judge.
EISENHOWER ADMISTRATION
Early career; Republican Party and National Committee; Director, Division of Special Activities, 1952 campaign. 58 pp. *Permission required.* 1968.

DANDISON, Basil Gray (1900–   ) *See* McGraw-Hill.

DANFORTH FOUNDATION LECTURES

Lectures on relationships between religion, the social sciences, and education.

Participants and pages: Bernard Barber, 40; Will Herberg, 60; Robert Lekachman, 48; Eugen Rosenstock-Huessy, 87.

235 pp. *Permission required.* 1961–62.

DANGERFIELD, George (1904–   ) *See* American Historians.

DANIEL, E. Clifton, Jr. (1912–   ) *See* Journalism Lectures.

DANIELIAN, Noobar R. (1906–   ) *See* Eisenhower Administration.

DANIELS, Alfred Harvey (1912–   ) *See* Federated Department Stores.

DANIELS, Jonathan Worth (1902–   ) Journalist.
SOUTHERN INTELLECTUAL LEADERS

Childhood in North Carolina; education, University of North Carolina; writer for *Fortune;* editor, *The News and Observer;* politics and race relations in North Carolina; *A Southerner Discovers the South;* Assistant Director, US Office of Civilian Defense; Administrative Assistant, later Press Secretary, to President Franklin D. Roosevelt; racial problems during WWII; senatorial campaign of Frank Porter Graham, 1950; Democratic Party since 1945. Impressions of Josephus Daniels, Henry Luce, Eleanor Roosevelt, Harry S. Truman, Thomas Wolfe, and leading southern journalists.
176 pp. *Closed pending publication of a study.* 1972.
See also Adlai E. Stevenson Project.

DANUSSI, Luis (1913–   ) Labor leader.
ARGENTINA IN THE 1930'S

Political climate in Argentina, especially during 1920's and 30's; early experiences in union: contribution of intellectuals, reaction to violence, student agitation; Spanish Civil War and labor movement; printers' union, 1939: history and organization, new techniques, working conditions, strikes; Peronism and its effect on labor.
87 pp. *Open.* 1971.

DARBY, Harry (1895–   ) Senator.
EISENHOWER ADMINISTRATION

Republican Party and politics; pre-convention moves to encourage Eisenhower to run in 1952; impressions of Robert A. Taft.
73 pp. *Permission required.* 1967.

DAURAT, Didier. *See* Aviation.

DAVENPORT, Frederick Morgan (1866–1956) Politician.

Childhood and education; NY State legislature; Theodore Roosevelt; Bull Moose Party; NY State Republican politics;

US House of Representatives; National Institute of Political Affairs.
101 pp. *Open.* 1952.

DAVES, Delmer Lawrence (1904–   ) *See* Popular Arts.

DAVID, Alvin. *See* Social Security.

DAVIDSON, Howard Calhoun. *See* Air Force Academy.

DAVIDSON, Robert. *See* Children's Television Workshop.

DAVIE, Eugenie Mary (Mrs. Preston) (1895–   ) *See* Robert A. Taft Project.

DAVIS, Chester Charles (1887–   ) Agriculturist.

Newspaper work in South Dakota and Montana; Commissioner of Agriculture and Labor in Montana, 1921–23; Illinois Agricultural Association; AAA; Federal Reserve System; WFA, 1943.
537 pp. *Permission required to cite or quote.* 1953. NYT (Part I).

DAVIS, Clarence Alba. Lawyer.
                    Eisenhower Adminstration
Education; early political career in Nebraska; Under Secretary of Interior, 1954–60; fisheries, water conservation, electric power.
106 pp. *Permission required.* 1967.

DAVIS, Doreen. *See* Flying Tigers.

DAVIS, Elmer Holmes (1890–1958) Writer.

The Henry Ford Peace Ship, 1915.
34 pp. *Permission required to cite or quote.* 1955. NYT (Part I).

REFER TO "NOTES ON USE" IN INTRODUCTION

DAVIS, John William (1873–1955) Lawyer.

Early life and law practice in Clarksburg, W. Va.; Solicitor General of the US; 1924 campaign for President; comments on the Supreme Court, President, Cabinet and Washington, D.C.; ambassador to Great Britain; exchange and treatment of prisoners in WWI; law practice.
172 pp. *Permission required to cite or quote.* 1954. NYT (Part I).

DAVIS, Kenneth S. (1912–   ) *See* Adlai E. Stevenson Project.

DAVIS, Malcolm Waters (1889–   ) Internationalist.

Early life, education, training in journalism; Springfield *Republican*, 1911–13; relief work and USIS, Russia, 1917–19; October Revolution; NY *Evening Post*; Council on Foreign Relations; Yale University Press; Carnegie Endowment for International Peace, League of Nations, 1931–39; impressions of Nicholas Murray Butler; Germany and National Socialism; International Red Cross, 1939–40, European leaders, WWII; OSS, 1941–45; San Francisco UN Conference, 1945.
435 pp. *Open.* 1950. Papers.
See also United Nations Conference.

DAVIS, Margaret E. (1892–   ) *See* Benedum and the Oil Industry.

DAVIS, Michael Marks (1879–1971) *See* Social Security.

DAVIS, William Hammatt (1879–1964) Labor mediator.

Work as Deputy Administrator and Compliance Director of NRA ; NY State Mediation Board; work as Chairman of National Defense Mediation Board and WLB; impressions of James Byrnes, John L. Lewis, Herbert Lehman, George Meany, Robert Wagner, and Robert Taft.

205 pp. *Permission required to cite or quote.* 1958. NYT
(Part I). Papers.

DAVISON, Frederick Trubee (1896–   ) Lawyer, public
official.

Family background and early life; Groton; Yale and the
Yale Unit; Columbia Law School; NY politics, 1920–26;
Crime Commission, 1926; Assistant Secretary of War for
Air, 1926–32; American Museum of Natural History; elec-
tion of 1940; Air Force and WWII.
280 pp. *Closed until 10 years after death.* 1951.
See also Theodore Roosevelt Association.

DAVISON, Wilbert Cornell (1892–   ) Physician.
JAMES B. DUKE PROJECT
Family background, childhood, education; Princeton,
1909–13, Rhodes scholar, Oxford, 1913; WWI: volunteer in
France and Yugoslavia, 1914; Johns Hopkins Medical
School, 1914; First Army Unit, Europe, 1918; Dean, Duke
Medical School: construction of School and hospital, open-
ing of School in 1930, furnishing library, selection of staff;
trustee of Duke Endowment, 1960. Impressions of Doris
Duke and numerous academic figures.
153 pp. *Permission required.* 1963.

DAWSON, Marion Lindsay (1905–   ) *See* Marine Corps.

DAY, Karl Schmolsmire (1896–1973) *See* Marine Corps.

DAY, James Edward (1914–   ) *See* Adlai E. Stevenson Project.

DEAKIN, Harold Osborne (1913–   ) Marine Corps officer.

Education; USMC training, 1934–39; WWII: Salerno, Cape
Gloucester, Peleliu, and Okinawa; Planning Officer, US
Navy Group, American Aid Mission to Greece, 1947–49,
Greek Civil War; special assistant to Secretary of State,

1954–56; Personnel Department, HQMC, 1956–57. 101 pp. *Permission required to cite or quote.* 1968.

DEAN, Gordon Evans (1905–1958) Lawyer.

Education at Duke University; journalism; legal education at University of Southern California; teaching law at Duke and early practice; Criminal Division of Department of Justice; work with Homer Cummings, Frank Murphy, Robert H. Jackson and Thurman Arnold. 146 pp. *Permission required to cite or quote.* 1954. NYT (Part I).

DEANE, Herbert A. *See* Columbia Crisis of 1968.

DEARING, Warren Palmer (1905–   ) *See* Health Science.

DE BARY, William Theodore. *See* Columbia Crisis of 1968.

DE FOREST, Lee (1873–1961) *See* Radio Pioneers.

DeKIEWIET, Cornelis Willem (1902–   ) Historian.

CARNEGIE CORPORATION

Carnegie Corporation program for education in developing African nations; British participation. Impressions of Alan Pifer, Stephen Stackpole, Whitney Shepardson, Charles Dollard, and John Gardner. 117 pp. *Permission required.* 1968.

DE LA CHAPELLE, Clarence E. (1897–   ) Physician.

Education and medical training; NYU and Bellevue Hospital Medical College as teacher and administrator, 1924–62; teaching pathology, Medical Examiner system, police work; consultant practice; aviation and aerospace medicine; unusual patients; postgraduate medical education; medical training during WWII and postwar; women in medicine; research and clinical investigation; Heart Associations, socialized medicine and AMA.

461 pp. *Permission required.* 1962.
See also New York Political Studies.

DELACORTE, Alfred. *See* Popular Arts.

DELANO, William Adams (1874–1960) Architect.

Education at Yale and Columbia School of Architecture; early practical work; study abroad; notable buildings and clients; Washington experiences; Board of Design for NY World's Fair, 1936; LaGuardia and Idlewild airports; West Point; charitable work.
94 pp. *Permission required to cite or quote.* 1950.
NYT (Part I).

DELONG, Edmund (1900–   ) Journalist.

Crime reporting on the NY *Sun*; Hall-Mills murder case; Philip Musica and his F. Donald Coster impersonation; Lindbergh kidnapping and the trial of Bruno Richard Hauptmann.
198 pp. *Permission required to cite or quote.* 1962.
NYT (Part I).

DEL RIO, Jorge. Lawyer.

ARGENTINA IN THE 1930'S

Campaign to end monopolies and lower rates in electric power and petroleum industries; investigations; Peronist movement, 1946.
41 pp. *Open.* 1971.

DEL VALLE, Pedro (1893–   ) Marine Corps officer.

Tours of duty in Santo Domingo, Haiti, Nicaragua; Cuba, 1933; Italy, 1935–36; concepts of amphibious assaults; WWII: Guadalcanal, Okinawa, Shuri Castle, Guam; Marine aviation.
245 pp. *Permission required to cite or quote.* 1966.

DEMAREST, William (1892–   ) *See* Popular Arts.

REFER TO "NOTES ON USE" IN INTRODUCTION

DE MILLE, Cecil Blount (1881–1959) *See* Popular Arts.

DEMUTH, Richard Holzman (1910–   ) International official.

WORLD BANK

Prior experience and appointment to World Bank; relationship between directors and staff; Meyer and McCloy presidencies; creation of Development Advisory Service and Economic Development Institute; negative pledge clause; survey missions; political loans; development banks; project loans; balance of payment loans; lines of credit.
91 pp. *Permission required to cite or quote.* 1961.

DENHAM, Reginald. *See* Popular Arts.

DENNIS, Lawrence (1893–   ) Writer, banker.

Childhood; education, Exeter and Harvard; military experiences; diplomatic service to 1927: Haiti, Rumania, Honduras, Nicaragua; banking experiences with Seligmans; theories of government; isolationism; *The Coming American Fascism; Appeal to Reason;* impressions of Adolf Hitler, Benito Mussolini, Hermann Goering, Joseph Goebbels; WWII; Vietnam; trial for sedition.
90 pp. *Permission required to cite or quote.* 1967.

DENNY, Charles Ruthven (1912–   ) *See* James Lawrence Fly Project.

DENNY, Reginald Leigh (1891–1967) *See* Popular Arts.

DEVEREUX, James Patrick Sinnott (1903–   ) Marine Corps officer.

Family background; duty in Nicaragua, 1926–29; China, 1930–32; WWII: defense of Wake Island, prisoner of war, liberation; experiences as a member of Congress from 1951.
208 pp. *Permission required.* 1970.

D'EWART, Wesley Abner (1889–   ) Government official.
EISENHOWER ADMINISTRATION

Experiences as Assistant Secretary of the Interior: water
policy and development, national parks, public lands, Indian affairs.
136 pp. *Permission required to cite or quote.* 1967.

DEWEY, Godfrey (1887–   ) Educator and author.

Simplified spelling movement in US and Britain, 1876–1971.
38 pp. *Open.* 1971. Papers.
Contributed by Benjamin D. Wood, New York.

DEWEY, John (1859–1952) Philosopher.

Ninetieth birthday interview and tribute.
8 pp. *Open.* 1949.
Contributed by Oliver Reiser, Pittsburgh.

DEWEY, Thomas Edmund (1902–1971) Lawyer, governor.

Family background, childhood in Michigan, music; legal
education, University of Michigan and Columbia; early legal experience; Chief Assistant US Attorney, 1931–33;
George Z. Medalie; political experience, 9th and 10th Assembly Districts, NYC; US Attorney; Young Republican
Club; Fiorello LaGuardia; 1932 campaign, NY State; income tax and Samuel Seabury investigation; labor gangster
cases; private practice, 1934; special prosecutor, 1935; rack-
ets investigation and "Lucky" Luciano; NY County District Attorney, 1937: procedural changes, blue ribbon juries, Hines Case; campaigns 1938, 1939, 1940; USO
campaign, 1942.
659 pp. *Permission required.* 1959.
EISENHOWER ADMINISTRATION

Recollections of the Eisenhower administration.
43 pp. *Permission required.* 1970.

DE WILDE, John C. (with Gerald Alter) *See* World Bank.

REFER TO "NOTES ON USE" IN INTRODUCTION

D'HARNONCOURT, Rene (1901–1968) Museum director.
CARNEGIE CORPORATION
Relations of Carnegie Corporation and American Federation of Art.
65 pp. *Permission required.* 1968.

DIAMOND, Sigmund (1920–   ) *See* American Historians.

DIAMOND, William. *See* World Bank.

DICK, Jane (Mrs. Edison) (1906–   )
ADLAI E. STEVENSON PROJECT
Recollections of Adlai Stevenson during 1920's and 30's; Ellen Borden Stevenson; Stevenson's religious beliefs; views on capital punishment; Stevenson's gubernatorial campaign and nomination for President; 1952 campaign; Stevenson as UN Ambassador; reaction to Cuba missile crisis.
102 pp. *Permission required.* 1969.

DICKER, Edward T. *See* Eisenhower Administration.

DICKERMAN, Marion (1890–   ) Educator.

WWI; friendship with Franklin and Eleanor Roosevelt; Todhunter School; Valkill Industries; Alfred E. Smith; opposition to Tammany Hall; Democratic conventions, 1924–32; reminiscences of Hyde Park, Campobello, Warm Springs; Eleanor Roosevelt: childhood, interest in women's suffrage and West Virginia mine workers, travels in Tennessee, Kentucky, Illinois; 74th Congress, 1935–36; visiting royalty; international conferences; death of President Roosevelt; of Mrs. Roosevelt; recollections of Roosevelt children, Louis Howe, Sumner Welles, Marguerite LeHand, Harry Hopkins, and many others.
345 pp. *Permission required.* 1971.

DICKEY, James (1923–   ) *See* Poets on their Poetry.

DICKINSON, Edwin Walter (1891–   ) Artist.

Family background, childhood and early education; studies with William Chase and Charles W. Hawthorne; experiences as an art student; views on art and experiences as a professional painter; illustrated discussion of a number of his paintings.
227 pp. *Permission required to cite or quote.* 1958. NYT (Part II).

DICKMAN, Frank. *See* McGraw-Hill.

DICKSTEIN, Samuel (1885–1954) Lawyer, congressman.

Early 20th-century NY politics; House Un-American Activities Committee; Dickstein Nationality Act and immigration.
74 pp. *Permission required to cite or quote.* 1950. NYT (Part I).

DIEHL, Walter Stuart (1893–   ) Naval officer.

Pensacola; MIT, 1917; work in aerodynamics, aeronautics, 1918–46; designing and testing Navy planes, World Wars I and II; Taylor Model Basin.
93 pp. *Permission required.* 1965.

DIERINGER, John W. (1899–   ) *See* Benedum and the Oil Industry.

DILLON, Clarence Douglas (1909–   ) Government official, financier.

EISENHOWER ADMINISTRATION

Ambassador to France, 1953–57; Suez crisis, Indochina; Deputy Under Secretary, later Under Secretary of State, 1957–61: international economic policy, Secretaries John Foster Dulles and Christian Herter, Latin American policy, Inter-American Bank, Treasury Secretaries George Humphrey and Robert B. Anderson, U-2 incident, NSC,

AID, foreign assistance, Congo, 1960 gold crisis, EDC; evaluation of Eisenhower administration; administrative transition, 1961; appointment as Treasury Secretary, 1961. 94 pp. *Permission required; certain pages closed.* 1972.

DIXON, J. Curtis (1894–   ) Educator.

Family background, early schooling; Mercer and Columbia Universities; WWI; career as teacher, principal, businessman, school superintendent in Richland, Georgia; State Supervisor of School Administration and Finance; county schools survey; State agent for Negro schools; graduate work, TC; General Education Board; Rosenwald Fund; rural education conferences; Jeanes teachers; Vice Chancellor, University of Georgia, 1940–42; Vice President, Mercer University, 1942–46; Southern Education Foundation, 1945–65: moving headquarters to Atlanta, staff, financing, programs, travel, charter; analysis of Negro educational institutions; training for principals; effect of 1954 desegregation decision.
513 pp. *Permission required to cite or quote.* 1967. *Underwritten by the Rockefeller Foundation.*

DIXON, Sherwood (1896–   ) *See* Adlai E. Stevenson Project.

DIZNEY, Helen (1894–   ) *See* China Missionaries.

DMYTRYK, Edward (1908–   ) *See* Popular Arts.

DOAN, Richard K. *See* Radio Pioneers.

DOBZHANSKY, Theodosius (1900–   ) Geneticist.

Part I: Childhood and education in Russia; early interest in genetics; experiences during revolutionary and postrevolutionary years; training in genetics in Russia; Rockefeller fellowship to work in US, 1928; California Institute of Technology, 1930–40; professor of zoology, Columbia University, 1940. Detailed descriptions of work with T. H. Morgan, A. H. Sturtevant, and C. B. Bridges.

Part II: Problems of artificial selection; racism; Zoology Department, Columbia University, 1940–62; research in California, Mexico, Brazil; Latin American scientists; travels to New Guinea, Australia, Egypt, India, Indonesia. Impressions of noted scientists, particularly in the field of genetics.
637 pp. *Permission required.* 1962.

DOCHEZ, Alphonse Raymond (1882–1964) Physician.

Undergraduate work at Johns Hopkins; work at Rockefeller Institute, 1907–19 (pneumococcus and hemolytic streptococcus); work in 1920's on scarlet fever and early experiments on common cold; reflections on P&S during the 1920's and 1930's; WWII: OSRD.
165 pp. *Open.* 1955. Papers: Bibliography and 3 papers.

DODDS, Harold (1889–   ) University president.

Princeton University during his Presidency, 1933–57; Peruvian-Chilean dispute and Tacna-Arica Plebiscite Commission, 1925–26; President's Commission on Universal Military Training, 1947.
292 pp. *Permission required.* 1966.
See also Carnegie Corporation.

DODGE, Cleveland E. (1888–   ) *See* Mining Engineers.

DODGE, Homer Levi (1887–   ) *See* American Association of Physics Teachers.

DODSON, James. *See* Aviation.

DOHERTY, William Charles (1902–   ) Union official.

National Letter Carriers' Union during the late 1930's;

efforts of the Union to improve wages and working conditions through legislation; autobiographical details.
57 pp. *Open.* 1956.

DOISY, Edward Adelbert (1893–) *See* Nobel Laureates.

DOLAN, Charles. *See* Air Force Academy.

DOLAN, Henry P. *See* New York Political Studies.

DOLBERG, Glen. *See* Radio Pioneers.

D'OLIVE, Charles. *See* Air Force Academy.

DOLLARD, Charles (1907–) Foundation executive.
CARNEGIE CORPORATION

Career with Carnegie Corporation; assistant to president, 1938–45; executive associate, 1945–47; Vice President, 1947–48; President, 1948–54; grants in social sciences; Commonwealth program; discussion of policies, program, and personnel. Impressions of Frederick Keppel, Devereux Josephs, John Gardner, Florence Anderson, and others.
329 pp. *Permission required.* 1966.
See also Association for the Aid of Crippled Children.

DOLLFUSS, Charles. *See* Aviation.

DOMENECH, Jose. Labor leader.
ARGENTINA IN THE 1930'S

Detailed account of experiences as union leader, 1909–43: early work on railroads, local union official, founding of railway union, 1922; national labor official, 1926–43; Argentine representative to Latin American labor groups; political activity.
192 pp. *Open except for specified pages.* 1970.

DONAHUE, Richard. *See* Social Security.

DONALD, David (1920–) *See* American Historians.

DONOVAN, Hedley Williams (1914–) Publishing executive.

AMERICAN CULTURAL LEADERS

Boyhood, Minneapolis; University of Minnesota and Oxford University, 1930–36; experiences as *Washington Post* reporter, 1937–42; *Fortune* writer and editor, 1945–51; editorial procedures and management structure, *Time, Inc.*, 1951–67.
184 pp. *Closed pending publication of a study.* 1967.

DONOVAN, Robert John (1912–) Journalist.

EISENHOWER ADMINISTRATION

Washington Bureau Chief, NY *Herald Tribune*, 1957–63; *Eisenhower: The Inside Story;* impressions of Eisenhower and his administration.
51 pp. *Permission required.* 1968.

DOOLITTLE, James Harold (1896–) *See* Air Force Academy *and* Aviation.

DORR, Goldthwaite Higginson (1876–) Lawyer.

Harvard, European travel; early law practice; assistant US Attorney; War Department, 1917–19; renegotiating war contracts, conversion to peace; law practice, NY; travels in Middle East, 1931; WWII, special assistant to Secretary of War; Hoover Commission on Law Observance, 1930–31; Cotton Textile Code and early days of NRA, 1932–33; Cabinet Committee to prepare joint plan with British for solution to Palestine problem, 1947; International Refugees and Displaced Persons Bills, 1947; IRO, 1948; problems of European migration, Migration Conference, 1950; representative of Defense Department at Council of Foreign Ministers meeting in Paris, 1949; travels; Joseph McCarthy era. Impressions of Presidents Theodore Roosevelt, Wil-

liam H. Taft, Herbert Hoover, Franklin D. Roosevelt, Harry Truman; of Henry L. Stimson, Robert P. Patterson, Benedict Crowell, Hugh Johnson, and many other political figures.
647 pp. *Permission required.* 1962. Papers.

DOUGLAS, Donald Wills (1892–   ) Aircraft executive.
HENRY H. ARNOLD PROJECT

Family background; Naval Academy, MIT; aeronautical design; chief engineer, Martin Co., Los Angeles, 1915–16, Cleveland, 1917–20; chief, aeronautical engineering, US Signal Corps, 1916–17; Davis-Douglas Co., 1920; Douglas Co., 1921–28; Douglas Aircraft Co., 1928 to present. Comments on early aviation, planes, engines, changes in the aircraft industry, relations with government and military agencies; early designs, DC 1–3, B–19; recollections of Gen. H. H. Arnold, Glenn Martin, Harry Chandler, Howard Hughes, and other pioneers in aviation.
137 pp. *Permission required.* 1959.

DOUGLAS, James Henderson, Jr. (1899–   ) *See* Eisenhower Administration.

DOUGLAS, Lewis Williams (1894–   ) Diplomat.

Family history; reminiscences of his public career.
In process.
See also Eisenhower Administration *and* Marshall Plan.

DOUGLAS, Melvyn (1901–   ) *See* Popular Arts.

DOUGLAS, Paul Howard (1892–   ) *See* Herbert H. Lehman Project.

DOUGLAS OF KIRTLESIDE, Lord (William Sholto Douglas) (1893–   ) *See* Aviation.

DOUHTIT, George. *See* Eisenhower Administration.

DOWLING, Eddie (1894–   ) Actor, producer, director.

Family background; childhood and education, Rhode Island; early vaudeville career; 1919–20 *Follies;* Actors' strike, 1919; early plays: *Sally, Irene, and Mary; Honeymoon Lane; Sidewalks of New York;* Chrysler-Ziegfeld Radio Follies; NYC Democratic politics: William F. Kenny's Tiger Room; national and state campaigns, 1926–40, organization and finances; Banking Crisis; 1932 Federal Theater Project; organizer and first president, USO Camp Shows, WWII; Tennessee Williams, *The Glass Menagerie;* Eugene O'Neill, *The Iceman Cometh;* comments on many people in the theater, Hollywood, business, finance and politics, including L. B. Mayer, Marcus Loew, Sarah Bernhardt, Boris Said, George Jean Nathan, Alfred E. Smith, J. J. Raskob, Tim Mara, Henry Morgenthau, Frank Hague, Joseph P. Kennedy, Michael Curley.
838 pp. *Open.* 1963.

DRAPER, Warren Fales (1883–   ) *See* Health Science.

DRAPER, William H. *See* Eisenhower Administration.

DRESSLER, David (1907–   ) Social worker, writer.

Childhood and education; training as a social worker; service on Parole Board in NY; law enforcement in NYC; impressions of Thomas Dewey, Fiorello LaGuardia, Herbert Lehman, Louis Valentine.
185 pp. *Permission required to cite or quote.* 1961. NYT (Part I).

DRUMMOND, Roscoe (1902–   ) Columnist.
EISENHOWER ADMINISTRATION

Christian Science Monitor Washington Bureau, 1940–53; NY *Herald Tribune,* 1953–55; foreign policy under Eisenhower; John Foster Dulles, Richard Nixon.
32 pp. *Permission required to cite or quote.* 1967.

REFER TO "NOTES ON USE" IN INTRODUCTION

DRURY, Newton Bishop (1889–   ) Conservationist.

Secretary to University of California president Benjamin Ide Wheeler; Drury Brothers Advertising Agency; Save-the-Redwoods League; creation of California State Park system; National Park Service, 1940–51; Jackson Hole acquisition and other controversies; administration of California State Park system, 1951–59; first World Conference on National Parks; establishment of Redwood National Park; comments on campaigns, California legislators, state and federal officials, conservation leaders, and lobbying.

700 pp. *Permission required to cite or quote.* 1972. *Acquired from the Regional Oral History Office, University of California, Berkeley.*
See also Horace Marden Albright.

DRYDEN, Hugh Latimer (1898–1965) *See* Aviation.

DUARTE, Hector (1914–   ) Labor leader.

ARGENTINA IN THE 1930'S

Student political activity; railway worker, 1936–50: working conditions, training, promotion, foreign management; local and national organization of union: membership qualifications, degree of autonomy, social benefits, medical care, strikes, retirement provisions; relations with government.

40 pp. *Open.* 1970.

DU BOIS, William Edward Burghardt (1868–1963) Author, educator.

Family background, childhood and education; Fisk University; Harvard and graduate work in Germany; teaching at Wilberforce University; sociological studies for Wharton School; teaching and annual conferences at Atlanta University; Niagara Movement; Booker T. Washington.

191 pp. *Permission required to cite or quote.* 1960. NYT (Part I).

DUBOS, Rene Jules (1901–   ) Bacteriologist.

Part I: Development of his work in bacteriology to 1943, and, more particularly, his thinking about his work; childhood and early training; polysaccharide of pneumococcus; Oswald T. Avery; tyrocidine, streptomycin and gramicidin; Harvard University and the war years.

Part II: Development of his work in bacteriology since 1945 and in particular his concern with the physiological, biochemical, and metabolic aspects of tuberculosis research; writing of *Louis Pasteur, The White Plague, The Biochemical Determinants of Disease,* and *Bacterial and Mycotic Infections in Man;* scientific papers; Rockefeller Institute. 1,541 pp. *Closed until 5 years after death.* 1957.

DUER, Caroline King (1865–1956) Poet, writer.

NY society; hospital work in World Wars I and II; personal recollections of Henry James, Edith Wharton, and other writers.
76 pp. *Open.* 1950. Papers: letters from France during WWI (microfilm).

DUFFUS, Robert Luther (1888–1972) Author, journalist.

Youth and education; San Francisco journalism, 1911–19; NY *Globe* and *Herald,* 1919–24; free-lance writing, 1924–37; editorial board NY *Times,* 1937–51.
134 pp. *Permission required to cite or quote.* 1951. NYT (Part I).

DUGGER, Ronnie. *See* American Cultural Leaders.

JAMES B. DUKE PROJECT

Through a series of interviews, the origins and subsequent activities of the Duke Endowment are set forth, with particular focus upon the personality and career of the founder. Associates of James B. Duke (1857–1925) and persons active in his manifold interests provide personal reminiscences, anecdotes, and comments on the Duke family, the career of Duke, the development of the Duke Power Company and various other business ventures designed to advance the Piedmont region of North Carolina, his early interest in southern education, in particular Trinity College (now Duke University), and developments since his death. A number of the memoirs also contain firsthand material on life in the Piedmont in the early years of the century and the economic and social changes brought by industrialization, which followed hard upon the provision of dependable power. Others discuss the establishment of Duke University, with much material on the faculty and presidents during the Trinity College era. Recent efforts of the Endowment in education, religion and hospital work in the South are considered.

Participants and pages: Mildred Baldwin, 49; Bernard Baruch, 51; Clarence E. Buchanan, 31; E. R. Bucher, 35; Charles A. Cannon, 45; Norman Cocke, 204; Wilbert C. Davison, 153; Mary Few, 285; John Fox, 68; Bennette Geer, 94; Mary Glassen, 33; Edward S. Hansen, 176; Philip B. Heartt, 62; Christy Hibberd, 13; Leon E. Hickman, 7; Tom F. Hill, 18; Roy A. Hunt, 39; Thomas D. Jolly, 34; Marvin Kimbrell, 24; Carl Lee, 93; Mrs. E. C. Marshall, 54; Grier Martin, 73; Robert Mayer, 69; Mr. and Mrs. E. R. Merrick, 70;

Thomas L. Perkins, 126; Rufus P. Perry, 75; Richard Pfaehler, 20; John L. Plyler, 78; Grady Rankin, 41; Watson S. Rankin, 87; Charles S. Reed, 38; William Robinson, 20; Frank W. Rounds, Jr., 5; Mary Semans, 150; Hersey Spence, 78; Kenneth C. Towe, 168; C. T. Wanzer, 54; Edward Williams, 42; Mrs. John Williams, 64; Bunyan Snipes Womble, 81.

2,907 pp. *Permission required.* 1966. *Underwritten by the Duke Endowment.*

DULANY, George William, Jr. (1877–   ) *See* Forest History Society.

DULLES, Allen W. (1893–1969) *See* Journalism Lectures.

DULLES, Eleanor Lansing (1895–   ) Economist.
EISENHOWER ADMINISTRATION

Family background; childhood in NY State; Bryn Mawr; refugee work, Paris, 1917–19; graduate training, industrial management; factory employment manager; London School of Economics, 1921–22; Radcliffe and Harvard; European study and travel; teaching, Bryn Mawr, 1932–36; University of Pennsylvania; Social Security Board; BEW, 1942; State Department, 1942–62: UNRRA, Morgenthau Plan, displaced persons, Bretton Woods Conference, security investigations, occupation of Austria and treaty negotiations, currency reform and monetary conversion. Impressions of Robert Lansing, John Foster Dulles, Allen Dulles, and many others.

973 pp. *Permission required.* 1967.

DULLES, John Foster (1888–1959) *See* New York Political Studies.

DUMONT, Donald A. (1911–   ) *See* Eisenhower Administration.

DUNCAN, Donald (1896–   ) Naval officer.

Education, Michigan and Naval Academy; WWI; naval aviation, Pensacola, 1920; experience in ordnance, communication; Fleet Aviation Officer, 1930–31; training aviation unit, Naval Academy; Plans Division, Bureau of Aeronautics, 1933; carrier duty, air tactics, group tactics; development of auxiliary carriers: the *Long Island;* WWII: Adm. Ernest King's staff, Tokyo raid, commanding *Essex,* War Plans Officer for Adm. King, detailed description of Joint Chiefs of Staff and Combined Chiefs of Staff, Harry Hopkins, Quebec and Yalta conferences, Pacific carrier task groups; postwar chief of staff to Commander-in-Chief, Pacific; atom bomb tests; reorganization; Deputy Chief for Air, 1947; National Advisory Committee for Aeronautics; missiles; Naval air bases; 2nd Task Fleet; Korean War; Vice Chief of Naval Operations, 1951–56.

981 pp. *Closed until 5 years after death.* 1964.

DUNN, Leslie Clarence (1893–   ) Geneticist.

Training in the biological sciences in the US from 1905;

history of genetics in the US, Great Britain, Germany, and Russia; developmental genetics, interdisciplinary symposia, "Growth Symposia"; influence of genetics on pathological and biochemical researches; impressions of Soviet science and scientists: trip to Russia, 1927, Genetics Congress meeting at Columbia, 1932; plant breeding in Russia; demise of Gorki Institute of Medico-Genetics and of some Soviet scientists during 1938 crisis; Lysenko school versus the Mendelist-Morganist-Weissmanist school; American-Soviet Science Society; scientific debates in Russia, 1936, 1938–39, 1948. The Jackson Laboratory; experimental studies of wild mice; cytogenetics; population genetics and evolution; work in population genetics in Sweden; Institute for the Study of Human Variation; genetics studies in Japan; bacterial genetics; Nevis Biological Station; radiation and genetics; scientists and government; Columbia's Department of Zoology; chronological summary of developments in genetics. Impressions of William Castle, Thomas H. Morgan, William Bateson, Richard Goldschmidt, Alexander Serebrovskii, Nikolai Vavilov, Theodosius Dobzhansky, H. J. Muller, Trofim Lysenko, and others.
1,086 pp. *Permission required.* 1960.

DUNN, Loula Friend. *See* Social Security.

DUNNING, John R. (1907–   ) *See* Journalism Lectures.

DURDEN, Dennis. *See* Federated Department Stores.

DURDIN, Frank Tillman (1907–   ) *See* International Negotiations.

DURMENT, T. S. *See* Weyerhaeuser Timber Company.

DURR, Charles. *See* Thomas A. Edison Project.

DURR, Clifford Judkins (1899–   ) *See* James Lawrence Fly Project.

DURR, Virginia Foster (Mrs. Clifford) Civil rights worker.

Anti-poll tax movement; women's rights; unionization of Southern labor, 1930's; New Deal; Southern Conference for Human Welfare; National Committee to Abolish the Poll Tax; poll tax bills, US Congress; racial attitudes of Southern white liberals, 1930–50; recollections of Eleanor and Franklin Roosevelt, John L. Lewis, Joseph Gelders, Clark Foreman, Vito Marcantonio, and others.
96 pp. *Permission required.* 1970.
Contributed by Stephen Lawson, New York.

DURSTINE, Roy Sarles (1886–1962) Advertising man.

Election of 1912; William Howard Taft; Bruce Barton; advertising, 1912–49.
49 pp. *Open.* 1949.

DuVIGNEAUD, Vincent (1901–) *See* Nobel Laureates.

DYER, Edward Colston (1907–) Marine Corps officer.

Early ground and aviation training; Bureau of Aeronautics, 1934–36; postgraduate studies in air communications, 1936–39; naval air observer, England and Middle East, 1941; Officer in Charge, Air Communications Systems, Division of Aviation, HQMC, 1941–44; development of Marine air defense concepts; duty in Pacific, 1944–45; Special Helicopter Board, HQMC, 1945–46; CO, Marine Experimental Helicopter Squadron 1, 1947–49; Operations Officer, 1st Marine Aircraft Wing, Korea, 1950–51; National War College; CG, 1st Marine Air-Ground Task Force, 1954–56.
293 pp. *Open.* 1968.

DYER, Rolla Eugene (1886–) *See* Health Science.

EAKER, Ira C. (1896–) Manufacturing executive.
HENRY H. ARNOLD PROJECT
Early interest in aviation; participation in races; hemis-

pheric flight, 1926–27; transcontinental blind flight; Mitchell court martial case; Army Air Corps and air mail, 1934; Long Beach earthquake; pressure for a separate Air Force; Air Force intelligence; George C. Marshall and air power; relation of Gen. Arnold and Gen. Malin Craig; Winston Churchill and around-the-clock bombing; 8th Air Force Bomber Command, England from 1942: transfer of units to England, relations with RAF, critique of operations; Ploesti and Tokyo raids; pro- and anti-Air Force interests in government in early 1960's; impressions of Gens. Frank Andrews, and Carl Spaatz.
184 pp. *Permission required.* 1959.

EARLE, Genevieve Beavers (Mrs. William P.) (1883–1956) Social worker, politician.

NYC politics, 1917–50; NYC Charter Revision Committee, 1935; Fiorello H. LaGuardia.
126 pp. *Open.* 1950. Papers.

EARLEY, Elisabeth (1917–   ) *See* Richard Hofstadter Project.

EATON, Clement (1898–   ) *See* American Historians.

EBERSTADT, Ferdinand (1890–1969) *See* Robert P. Patterson Project.

EDELMAN, John W. (1893–1971) Labor representative.

Education; early experiences on fringes of Socialist movement; condition of hosiery workers in New Jersey and Pennsylvania during the late 1920's and Depression: role of hosiery workers union in the AFL; AFL conventions; beginnings of Textile Workers Union of America; its role in the CIO; influence of Communist Party in the CIO; merger of the CIO and the AFL; impressions of men and women prominent in the labor movement.
247 pp. *Permission required.* 1957.
See also Social Security.

EDELSTEIN, Julius. *See* Herbert H. Lehman Project *and* New York Political Studies.

EDER, Phanor James (1880–1971) Lawyer.

Education; early experiences in law; banking and law in Latin America; Gold Clause case and others; writings. 110 pp. *Permission required to cite or quote.* 1965. NYT (Part I).

EDISON, Charles (1890–1969) Industrialist.

Family background, childhood, and education; Thomas A. Edison, Inc., its various enterprises, organization, personnel relations; Thomas Alva Edison. 294 pp. *Open.* 1953.

EDISON, Theodore M. *See* Thomas A. Edison Project.

THOMAS ALVA EDISON PROJECT

Interviews with family members and associates of Thomas Alva Edison (1847–1931) illuminate his character, personality, and motivation. The appearance and arrangement of the family home and the laboratory in West Orange, New Jersey, are described, and specific projects carried on in the laboratory are recalled. Earlier recordings prepared by the Edison National Historic Site will be included.

Participants and pages: Edward Daly, 38; Charles Durr, 20; Theodore M. Edison, 26; Madeleine Edison Sloane, 35.

119 pp. *Permission required pending completion of project.* 1972.
Underwritten by the Eastern National Park and Monument Association, Philadelphia.

EDWIN, Ed (1922–   ) Author, journalist.

Armed Forces Network in Germany and military news policy and censorship, 1945–48; US Foreign Service Resi-

dent and Information Officer, 1949–53; television and radio coverage of national and local (including NYC) elections, 1954–70; media reaction to rise of black militancy in northern ghettos from 1958, with recollections of interviews with its leaders; the writing of *Adam Clayton Powell and the Politics of Race;* population problem and related environmental issues, 1966–72; oral history projects.
185 pp. *Permission required to cite or quote.* 1972.
See also Eisenhower Administration.

EDWIN, Edward S. (1889–   ) Physician.

Recollections of his professional and social relationship with Charles M. Russell, the artist.
17 pp. *Permission required.* 1967.

EGNER, Frank (1892–1957) *See* McGraw-Hill.

EISENHOWER, Dwight David (1890–1969) Army officer, President.

EISENHOWER ADMINISTRATION

President of Columbia University, 1948–52; President of the US, 1953–61; labor unions and leaders; state vs. federal controls; China; Cuba; Vietnam; Suez Canal; Open Skies policy; inflation; impressions of Gen. George C. Marshall, Robert A. Taft, Harry Truman, Richard Nixon.
114 pp. *Closed until August 21, 1987.* 1967.

EISENHOWER, Edgar N. (1889–1971) Lawyer.

EISENHOWER ADMINISTRATION

Family and religious background; personal recollections of Dwight Eisenhower and his Presidency; Supreme Court; Sherman Adams, Richard Nixon.
117 pp. *Closed until 1980.* 1967.

EISENHOWER, John Sheldon David (1922–   ) Army officer.

EISENHOWER ADMINISTRATION

Anecdotes and personal recollections of Dwight Eisen-

hower's military career and Presidency; Korea; inauguration, 1953; development of military weapons; Geneva Conference.
In process.

EISENHOWER, Milton Stover (1899–   ) Government official.

EISENHOWER ADMINISTRATION

Latin American relations; Eisenhower brothers; President Eisenhower and his administration; White House staff and organization; Gen. Eisenhower's decisions to run in 1952 and 1956; 1960 campaign; Republican Critical Issues Council; impressions of Harry S. Truman, Richard Nixon, Joseph R. McCarthy, Lyndon B. Johnson, John Foster Dulles, Fidel Castro.
In process.

EISENHOWER ADMINISTRATION

This project has gathered firsthand testimony from those who played major roles in the Eisenhower Administration (1953–61), as well as the recollections of observers and of those knowledgeable about special aspects. In addition to Gen. Dwight D. Eisenhower and members of his family, the list of participants below includes members of the White House staff, cabinet members, political advisers, members of Congress, administrators, scientists, journalists, ambassadors, military and civilian specialists, and others in a position to testify about trends and events of the period.

Among topics well documented in material presently available are the Republican conventions and campaigns of 1952 and 1956, the functioning of White House advisers and staff, the President's relations with his cabinet, the functioning of the Bureau of the Budget and various independent agencies, relations with the press, scientific developments, and other special aspects too numerous to mention, the whole interlaced with anecdotes about major and minor episodes in public life in the 1950's. A series of interviews done in Little Rock, Arkansas on the school integration crisis there is of particular interest.

REFER TO "NOTES ON USE" IN INTRODUCTION

Columbia University

Memoirs are on deposit at the Eisenhower Library in Abilene, Kansas as well as at Columbia under identical stipulations.

The following memoirs are *Permission required to cite or quote* except as noted: Elie Abel, 45; Sherman Adams, 268; Bertha S. Adkins, 72; George D. Aiken, 31 *(open);* H. Meade Alcorn, 159; Joseph Alsop, 18; Dillon Anderson, 130; Evan P. Aurand, 138; Henry S. Aurand, 34; J. Bill Becker, 33; Jack L. Bell, 31; Charles E. Bennett, 18; Ezra Taft Benson, 12; Andrew H. Berding, 38 *(open);* Richard M. Bissell, Jr., 48; Harold Boeschenstein, 24; Charles E. Bohlen, 25; Robert R. Bowie, 51; Omar N. Bradley, 23; Vivion Brewer, 45; Herbert Brownell, 347; Samuel M. Brownell, 83; Percival F. Brundage, 52; E. LaMar Buckner, 18; Carter Burgess, 40 *(open);* James Vincent Burke, Jr., 52; Arthur E. Burns, 45; Prescott Bush, 454; Richard C. Butler, 46; Earl L. Butz, 51 *(open);*

Ralph H. Cake, 78; Lucius DuB. Clay, 113 *(open);* Howard Cook, 16; William G. Cooper, Jr., 48; Kenneth G. Crawford, 26; Thomas B. Curtis, 40; Wesley A. D'Ewart, 136; Edward T. Dicker, 32; George Douhtit, 48; William H. Draper, 18; Roscoe Drummond, 32; Edward Elson, 293; Harold Engstrom, 61; Luther H. Evans, 34 *(open);* Orval Faubus, 135; Leonard Firestone, 15 *(open);* Ralph Flanders, 51; Edward Folliard, 72; Marion B. Folsom, 163; Clarence Francis, 37; William B. Franke, 50; Thomas S. Gates, 59; Andrew J. Goodpaster, 137; Arthur Gray, Jr., 32; Nat R. Griswold, 84; Ernest Gross, 984; L. Richard Guylay, 90; Charles Halleck, 35; John W. Hanes, 27; Wilson Harwood, 52 *(open);* Gabriel Hauge, 130; Loy W. Henderson, 51; Stephen Hess, 41; John M. Hightower, 41; John B. Hollister, 52 *(open);* Patricia House, 46; Elizabeth Huckaby, 62;

Albert Jacobs, 38; Neil Jacoby, 141; Jacob K. Javits, 15 *(open);* Jesse C. Johnson, 36; Roger W. Jones, 73; Kenneth B. Keating, 126; Henry J. Kellerman, 29; Arthur A. Kimball, 104; William F. Knowland, 170; Walter Kohler, 52; Robert Kunzig, 40; William Lacy, 20; James M. Lambie, 49; Alvin H. Lane, 39; Sigurd Larmon, 41; William H. Lawrence, 37; J. Bracken Lee, 70; Barry Leithead, 52; John D. Lodge, 195; Edward A. McCabe, 165 *(open);* Kevin McCann, 158; Carl W. McCardle, 48; Theodore R. McKeldin, 78; Sidney McMath, 31; Henry R. McPhee, Jr., 58; Livingston T. Merchant, 86; Henry L. Miller, 59; L. Arthur Minnich, 34; William Mitchell, 84 *(open);* E. Frederick Morrow, 175; Ancher Nelsen, 34; Arthur Nevins, 87; Dennis O'Rourke, 41;

Bradley H. Patterson, Jr., 65; John S. Patterson, 54; Charles H. Percy, 33; Howard C. Petersen, 68; Richard M. Pittenger, 40; Terrell Powell, 34; Elwood R. Quesada, 89; Ogden R. Reid, 22; Chalmers Roberts, 36; Richard Rovere, 44; Stanley M. Rumbough, Jr., 43 *(open);* Leverett Saltonstall, 151; Irene Samuel, 48; Howland Sargeant, 26; Raymond J. Saulnier, 71 *(open);* Leonard A. Scheele, 44 *(open);* Raymond L. Scherer, 54 *(open);* Gerard David Schine, 24; Dudley Sharp, 67; Joseph S. Sheldon, 28; William T. Shelton, 35; James R. Shepley, 39; Robert Sherrod, 53; Allan Shivers, 58; David M. Shoup, 29; Ellis Slater, 38; Howard K. Smith, 44; William J. Smith, 90; Murray Snyder, 67; Mansfield Sprague, 57; Elmer Staats, 59; Robert Storey, 63; Theodore Streibert, 35; Walter N. Thayer, 52; Edward Thye, 76; Webster B. Todd, 88; Wayne Upton, 64; James J.

The Oral History Collection

Wadsworth, 248; Anne W. Wheaton, 178; Francis O. Wilcox, 63; E. Grainger Williams, 65; Charles F. Willis, Jr., 50; Henry Wriston, 51; Charles R. Yates, 34.

10,994 pp.

The following memoirs are *Permission required:* George V. Allen, 213; Allen V. Astin, 57; Rollin D. Barnard, 60; Edward L. Beach, 470; Earl C. Behrens, 44; Mark W. Clark, 91; Charles A. Coolidge, 35; John A. Danaher, 58; Harry Darby, 73; Clarence A. Davis, 106; Thomas E. Dewey, 43; Douglas Dillon, 94; Robert J. Donovan, 51; Eleanor Lansing Dulles, 973; Robert H. Finch, 69; James M. Gavin, 36; Gordon Gray, 338; James Hagerty, 569; Robert E. Hampton, 57; Raymond Hare, 114; Karl G. Harr, Jr., 41; Robert C. Hill, 105; Eric Hodgins, 162; Katherine Howard, 600; Frederick P. Jessup, 105; Walter H. Judd, 149; David W. Kendall, 85; Goodwin Knight, 94;

Mary Pillsbury Lord, 428; Robert A. Lovett, 21; John Luter, 79; Neil H. McElroy, 88; Thomas Clifton Mann, 60; Robert Merriam, 209; True D. Morse, 144; Robert D. Murphy, 21; Herschel D. Newsom, 108; Roderick O'Connor, 144; Don Paarlberg, 164; Wilton Persons, 161; Maxwell Rabb, 38; Walter S. Robertson, 194; Ilene Slater, 58; Merriman Smith, 79; Arthur Summerfield, 93; Everett Tucker, Jr., 62; Sinclair Weeks, 172.

7,215 pp.

The following memoirs are *Closed during lifetime* except as noted: Dale Alford, 115; James W. Barco, 1,061 *(until January 1, 1984);* Stephen G. Benedict, 137; Douglas M. Black, 53; Ellis O. Briggs, 134 *(until 1978);* Karl Brandt, 69; Wiley Branton, 61; John W. Bricker, 40; William A. M. Burden, 81; Charles D. Cook, 658 *(until 1979);* Ed Edwin, 47 *(until 1990)* Dwight D. Eisenhower, 114 *(until August 21, 1987);* Edgar Eisenhower, 117 *(until 1980);* J. Clifford Folger, 43 *(until January 1, 1977);* Barry M. Goldwater, 85 *(until April 12, 1974);* Robert K. Gray, 38; Alfred Gruenther, 97; Amis Guthridge, 27; Leonard Hall, 59; D. B. Hardeman, 146; Bryce N. Harlow, 144; Brooks Hays, 165; Luther H. Hodges, 39; Leo A. Hoegh, 95; Amory Houghton, 96; A. F. House, 44; James Karam, 29; James R. Killian, 375 *(until 1985);* Herbert G. Klein, 39;

J. E. Lever, 62; R. A. Lile, 31; Clare Booth Luce, 108; James McCrory, 19; Earl Mazo, 52; James B. Mintener, 65; Edward P. Morgan, 53; Gerald D. Morgan, 133; Kenneth D. Nichols, 100; Hugh B. Patterson, Jr., 85; Homa Jack Porter, 47; Wesley Pruden, 33; Howard Pyle (with Charles Masterson), 134; William P. Rogers, 51 *(until 1977);* Clifford Roberts, 878 *(until 20 years after death);* Nelson A. Rockefeller, 40 *(until 1997 or death, whichever is later);* R. Richard Rubottom, 95; Robert L. Schulz, 165 *(until 1993);* Stephen A. Shadegg, 30; Maurice H. Stans, 83; Harold Stassen, 68 *(until 1985);* John R. Steelman, 89 *(until 1990);* Thomas E. Stephens, 98; Lewis L. Strauss, 177 *(until 1985);* Joseph M. Swing, 76; Jessie Thornton, 41; Elbert Tuttle, 113; Nathan Twining, 250; Abbott Washburn, 91; Arthur V. Watkins, 98; W. Walter Williams, 103; Milton R. Young, 30.

7,706 pp.

REFER TO "NOTES ON USE" IN INTRODUCTION

Columbia University

In Process: Winthrop Aldrich, 38; J. Sinclair Armstrong, 94; Wallace R. Brode, 51; Wiley T. Buchanan, 178; Arleigh A. Burke, 180; Clement Conger, 25; Noobar R. Danielian, 51; James H. Douglas, 53; Donald A. Dumont, 75; John S. D. Eisenhower, 144; Milton S. Eisenhower, 115; Peter Grimm, 32; Homer Gruenther, 107; Najeeb E. Halaby, 32; Lyman L. Lemnitzer, 26; John J. McCloy, 47; John A. McCone, 16; Edward Perkins McGuire, 97; Malcolm C. Moos, 41; Robert B. Murphy, 45; Ralph W. E. Reid, 51; Charles Roberts, 35; Robert Roosa, 98; Harrison Salisbury, 23; Irving Salomon, 39; Fred C. Scribner, 83; Bromley Smith, 36; Robert Thayer, 44; David Wainhouse, 33.

1,814 pp.

27,729 pp. 1962–72. Papers.
Underwritten in large part by grants from the National Endowment for the Humanities and the National Archives.

ELDREDGE, Inman F. *See* Forest History Society.

ELEGANT, Robert (1928–   ) *See* International Negotiations.

ELIOT, Martha May (1891–   ) Physician.

SOCIAL SECURITY

Origins of Public Health Service, Children's Bureau, and Social Security Administration; AMA's role in medical care and insurance programs; public health legislation; Committee on Costs of Medical Care, 1920's; Committee on Economic Security, 1930's; Social Security Act; Wagner-Murray-Dingell health insurance bills; Hill-Burton Bill; first National Health Conference, 1938.
115 pp. *Closed during lifetime.* 1966.

ELIOT, Thomas Hopkinson (1907–   ) *See* Social Security.

ELKINS, Stanley (1925–   ) *See* American Historians.

ELLICKSON, Katherine.

SOCIAL SECURITY

Labor efforts toward federal old age, survivors, and Medi-

care legislation since 1953; drafts of legislation and amendments; AFL-CIO relations with HEW and with Ways and Means Committee.
285 pp. *Open.* 1967. Papers inserted in memoir.

ELLIMAN, Douglas Ludlow (1882–1972) Real estate broker.

NYC real estate, 1900–68; development of Park Avenue.
180 pp. *Open.* 1968.

ELSON, Edward Lee Roy (1906-   ) Clergyman.
EISENHOWER ADMINISTRATION
Childhood; experiences as 7th Army chaplain, WWII; relationship of Presidents Harry S. Truman and Dwight Eisenhower with Presbyterian Church; personal knowledge of Middle Eastern countries and leaders; establishment of American Friends of the Middle East; Eisenhower funeral; election as Chaplain of the Senate.
293 pp. *Permission required to cite or quote.* 1969.

EMERSON, Guy (1886–1969) Lawyer, banker.

Episcopal Church Pension League; Roosevelt Non-Partisan League; Liberty Loan campaign; National Hoover League; American Bankers Association convention; Calvin Coolidge campaign; Reserve City Bankers Association.
249 pp. *Permission required to cite or quote.* 1951. NYT (Part I).

EMERSON, Haven (1874–1957) Physician.

NYC politics and the health program; WWI medical corps; national public health and socialized medicine.
103 pp. *Permission required to cite or quote.* 1950.
NYT (Part I). Papers of Ralph Waldo Emerson's brother (microfilm).

EMERSON, Thomas Irwin (1907–   ) Lawyer.

Part I: Family, early youth and high school, Yale College; Yale Law School and *Law Journal;* law practice, NYC; Depression and election of 1932; NRA, 1933–34; drafting National Labor Relations Act; Garrison Board in 1934 textile strikes; cases testing the National Labor Relations Act; Social Security Board and John Winant; formation of National Lawyers Guild; legislative aspects of NLRB; duties as special assistant to Attorney General Francis Biddle; FBI; Martin Dies; Smith Committee; social life in Washington; OPA law enforcement problems; loyalty problems; policy decision of OES; death of Franklin D. Roosevelt; VE Day; Office of War Mobilization and Reconversion; drafting of Atomic Energy Act; teaching at Yale Law School, 1946; political associations; Public Affairs Committee; PAC of CIO; formation of Progressive Party, campaign of 1948. 2,227 pp. *Permission required.* 1953.

Part II: 1953 loyalty cases; Smith Act cases; Owen Lattimore case; research on segregation cases; New Haven branch of ACLU; civil liberties in England, 1955. 279 pp. *Permission required.* 1955.

EMERY, Carlos. *See* Argentina in the 1930's.

EMMET, Jessie (Mrs. Richard) *See* Association for the Aid of Crippled Children.

EMMONS, Delos Carleton (1888–1965) *See* Aviation.

EMSPAK, Julius (1904–1962) Union official.

Comments on labor unionism; early life; development of United Electrical, Radio and Machine Workers from 1936: RCA strike, relations with CIO and Association of Catholic Trade Unionists; labor and government during WWII; Communism and labor movement; labor during the cold war.

363 pp. *Permission required to cite or quote.* 1960. NYT (Part I).

ENDICOTT, Kenneth M. (1916–) *See* Health Science.

ENGLE, Lavinia Government official.

SOCIAL SECURITY

Field Secretary, National American Women's Suffrage Association; executive director, Maryland League of Women Voters; 1932 presidential campaign; member of Maryland legislature until 1932; Frank Bane in Social Security Administration; chief, Social Security division of field operations until WWII; regional director, District of Columbia area; decentralization of Social Security programs; Anna Rosenberg.
184 pp. *Open.* 1967.

ENGSTROM, Harold. *See* Eisenhower Administration.

ENNIS, Thomas G. (1904–) *See* Marine Corps.

ERLANGER, Joseph (1874–1965) *See* Nobel Laureates.

ERNST, Morris Leopold (1888–) *See* Socialist Movement.

ERSKINE, Graves Blanchard (1897–) Marine Corps officer.

Family background, education; WWI, France; sea and foreign duty, 1921–30; Peking, 1935–37; WWII, Attu, Kiska operations, 1941–43; Kwajalein operation; Gen. Holland M. Smith; Saipan, Iwo Jima, Guam, 1944–45; Administrator, Retraining and Reemployment Administration, Department of Labor, 1945–47;Special Joint State-Defense Survey mission to Southeast Asia, 1950; CG, Fleet Marine Force, Atlantic: planning, involvement with NATO.
573 pp. *Permission required.* 1970.

ERSKINE, Helen W. (Mrs. W. H. H. Cranmer) (1896–)
Author.

Early life in Denver, Colorado and NYC; Paris, 1925; NY *World* and *World-Telegram*, 1926–31; Professor John Erskine.
223 pp. *Closed during lifetime.* 1957.

ESPENSCHIED, Lloyd. *See* Radio Pioneers.

ESSELSTYN, Caldwell. *See* Social Security.

EVANS, Carol. *See* Adlai E. Stevenson Project.

EVANS, Clifford. *See* New York Political Studies.

EVANS, Eli (with Alan Pifer) *See* Carnegie Corporation.

EVANS, Francis. *See* Aviation.

EVANS, Luther Harris (1902–) Educator, librarian.

Early life and education: University of Texas, Stanford, Yale, Pennsylvania Military College; instructor at NYU, Dartmouth, Princeton; WPA, 1935–39; director of Historical Records Survey; director of Legislative Reference Service; Librarian of Congress, 1945–53; new projects, programs; establishment of Council of National Library Association; UNESCO: US National Commission, 1946; Executive Board, 1949, director-general, 1953, delegate to General Conference, 1947–51; UNESCO program development: education, agriculture, mass communication, financial aid; Brookings Institution; NEA; automation project; US Commission for Refugees; ACLU. Impressions of Harry Hopkins, Archibald MacLeish, Torres Bodet, Henry Cabot Lodge, Dag Hammarskjold, Lyndon Johnson.
844 pp. *Permission required to cite or quote.* 1965. NYT (Part I).

EISENHOWER ADMINISTRATION

WPA, Historical Records Survey; Library of Congress, 1939 and 1945; UNESCO, 1949–58; first meeting with Dwight D. Eisenhower as President of Columbia University. 34 pp. *Open.* 1970.

EVANS, Rudolph Martin (1890–1956) Agriculturist.

Early life; farmer and livestock raiser, 1921–33; corn-hog program, 1933–36; assistant to the Secretary of Agriculture, 1936–38; AAA, 1938–42.
261 pp. *Permission required to cite or quote.* 1953. NYT (Part I).

EVANS, Walter C. *See* Radio Pioneers.

EWEN, John W. *See* Robert A. Taft Project.

EWING, Oscar Ross (1889–   ) *See* Social Security.

EZEKIEL, Mordecai Joseph Brill (1899–   ) Agricultural economist.

Department of Agriculture and Federal Farm Board; economic adviser to Henry Wallace and Claude Wickard; WPB; FAO of the UN; economic aspects of the New Deal.
137 pp. *Permission required to cite or quote.* 1956. NYT (Part I). Papers.

FABIAN, Bela (1889–1967) Hungarian politician.

Youth and education in Hungary; newspaper work in Budapest, 1907–14; concentration camp experiences, 1914–18; escape to Petrograd; Russia and Hungary in 1918; Hungarian political experiences 1919–39; trip to Spain, 1934; WWII; Hungarian underground, 1940–44; arrest and deportation, 1944.
447 pp. *Permission required to cite or quote.* 1951. NYT (Part I). Papers.

REFER TO "NOTES ON USE" IN INTRODUCTION

FABIAN, Harold Pegram (1885–   ) Lawyer.

JACKSON HOLE PRESERVE

Law practice, Salt Lake City, 1910; Jackson Hole National Park: acquisition of land, opposition, Senate investigation; impressions of John D. Rockefeller, Jr. and Horace M. Albright.
106 pp. *Permission required.* 1966.

FACCIOLO, Jay. *See* Columbia Crisis of 1968.

FACKENTHAL, Frank Diehl (1883–1968) University administrator.

Childhood and education; administrative work at Columbia University, 1902–48; Nicholas Murray Butler and Dwight D. Eisenhower as university presidents.
57 pp. *Permission required to quote.* 1956.

FADIMAN, Clifton (1904–   ) *See* Book-of-the-Month Club.

FAHY, Charles (1892–   ) Lawyer, judge.

Family background; law practice, Washington, D. C., 1914–24, and New Mexico, 1924–33; experiences as WWI naval aviator; Indian affairs and oil in Department of Interior, 1933–35; New Deal; NRA; NLRB; experiences as Assistant Solicitor General and Solicitor General, 1940–45, including London Base-Lease negotiations, 1941; adviser to US delegation, San Francisco Conference, 1945; legal adviser, US military government of Germany, 1945–46; legal adviser, Department of State, 1946–47; Legal Committee, UN General Assembly, 1946; alternate US representative, UN General Assembly, 1947 and 1949; judge, US Court of Appeals for District of Columbia, 1949–58.
451 pp. *Permission required.* 1958.

FAIR, Clinton (1909–   ) *See* Social Security.

FAIRBANK, John (1907–   ) *See* International Negotiations.

137

The Oral History Collection

FAIRFIELD, Leslie and Mary. *See* China Missionaries.

FALK, Isidore Sydney (1899–   ) Public health specialist, medical economist.

SOCIAL SECURITY

Early interest in health insurance; teaching at University of Chicago and service on Chicago Board of Health, 1923–29; Committee on Costs of Medical Care; effect of recommendation for group practice and group payment; voluntary vs. compulsory insurance; New Deal and background of Social Security legislation; Technical Committee and Advisory Council, Committee on Economic Security; Social Security Board, 1936; National Health Survey, 1935–36; National Health Conference, 1938; Technical Committee on Medical Care; legislative efforts to explore and expand role of federal government in health insurance. Impressions of Franklin D. Roosevelt, Harry Hopkins, Frances Perkins, Arthur Altmeyer, Edgar Sydensticker, and many others.
289 pp. *Open.* 1968. Papers.
See also Health Science.

FARLEY, Edward Philip (1886–1956) Shipping executive.

USSB; EFC; US shipping, 1924–50.
44 pp. *Open.* 1949. Papers.

FARLEY, James Aloysius (1888–   ) Politician.

Political activities, 1912–44, with emphasis on his years as National Chairman of the Democratic Party, 1932–40 and Chairman of the NY State Democratic Party, 1930–44; personal impressions of Franklin D. Roosevelt, Wendell L. Willkie, Charles McNary, William E. Borah, and others.
400 pp. *Closed until two years after death.* 1958.
See also Herbert H. Lehman Project.

FARM HOLIDAY ASSOCIATION

Farm Holiday Association pressure on the New Deal in

REFER TO "NOTES ON USE" IN INTRODUCTION

1933–34, as recalled by participants, with descriptions of riots and violence, threats of a farm strike, demands for mortgage relief, and impressions of Milo Reno. The memoirs also include material dealing with the United Farmers League and other Communist-sponsored rivals of the Farm Holiday Association.

Participants and pages: John Bosch, 56; Richard Bosch, 27; Homer Hush, 56; Dale Kramer, 23; Donald Murphy, 32.

194 pp. *Open.* 1960–61.
Contributed by Lowell Dyson, Spirit Lake, Iowa.

FARMAN, Maurice (–1964) *See* Aviation.

FARR, Barclay H. *See* Theodore Roosevelt Association.

FARRELL, Glenda (1904–   ) *See* Popular Arts.

FARRELL, Walter Greatsinger (1897–   ) Marine Corps officer.

Family background, father's experiences with H. H. Kitchener in the Sudan; early Boy Scout movement in US; WWI: France and German occupation, 1918–19; Haiti, 1919–20; US Olympics swimming champion; aviation duty, China and Guam, 1928–30; Bureau of Aeronautics, 1930–33; Naval War College; inventor of rubber landing boat; WWII, Middle East observer, 1941; Commander, Marine Aircraft, Hawaiian area, 1944; major USMC aviation tactical developments.
In process.

FARWELL, Margaret M. (Mrs. John V. III). *See* Adlai E. Stevenson Project.

FAUBUS, Orval Eugene (1910–   ) Governor of Arkansas.
EISENHOWER ADMINISTRATION
Detailed history of the integration of Little Rock High School; integration of institutions of higher education in

the South; National Guard; meeting with President Eisenhower in Newport; federal troops; Arkansas elections of 1958; attitude of the press toward Faubus and the school crisis. Impressions of Dwight Eisenhower, Virgil Blossom, Brooks Hays, Dale Alford.
135 pp. *Permission required to cite or quote.* 1971.

FAURI, Fedele Frederick (1909–   ) *See* Social Security.

FECHTELER, William Morrow (1896–1967) Naval officer.

Education, Naval Academy, training cruises, Yangtze River Patrol; teaching at Naval Academy; Hawaii, 1940–42, Pearl Harbor; Bureau of Naval Personnel; Pacific operations; demobilization problems; Hook Commission; Commander in Chief, Atlantic Fleet, 1951;Chief of Naval Operations, 1951; unification; NATO relationships; impressions of Winston Churchill, Dwight Eisenhower, Dan Kimball, and Forrest Sherman.
266 pp. *Permission required.* 1962.

FEDERATED DEPARTMENT STORES

This project comprises a series of interviews with those who built the largest department store organization in the US, Federated Department Stores. Changes over the years in Federated's policies, methods, and objectives, changes in consumer tastes and buying habits, and the evolution of the organization are traced. There are also interviews with the family and friends of Fred Lazarus, Jr., founder and board chairman.

Participants and pages: Edward Coughlin, 33; Alfred H. Daniels, 46; Dennis Durden, 44; Abe Fortas, 9; Robert Fuoss, 58; Alfred Gruenther, 38; George Hammond, 38; George C. Hayward, 58; Walter Heymann, 22; Harold D. Hodgkinson, 27; Gray Hussey, 18; Mrs. Gray Hussey, 10; Joseph Kasper, 45; Bernard S. Klayf, 42; Herbert Landsman, 81; Celia R. Lazarus, 99; Charles Lazarus, 21; Eleanor and Margaret Lazarus, 47; Fred Lazarus, Jr., 1,039; Fred Lazarus III, 42; Irma M. Lazarus, 40; Jeffrey Lazarus, 32; Maurice Lazarus, 59; Ralph Lazarus, 54; Mrs. Ralph Lazarus, 22; Robert Lazarus, 32; Simon Lazarus, 44; John F. Lebor, 56; Robert Lenhart, 28; Paul Mazur, 59; Leonard Minster, 26; Alfred Neal, 38; Mrs. Jesse Evans Ross, 34; Lewis Saille, 28; Oral Scheaf, 40; Ann Lazarus Schloss, 47; Trent

Columbia University

Sickles, 37; Myron Silbert, 99; William Snaith, 46; Sydney Solomon, 42; Herbert Stein, 29; J. Paul Sticht, 55; Frank Sulzburger, 20; Ann Visconti, 51; George Whitten, 42; Charles Wiedemer, 12; John C. Wilson, 22.

2,911 pp. *Permission required.* 1965. *Underwritten by the children of Fred Lazarus, Jr.*

FEIKER, Frederick Morris (1881–1967) *See* McGraw-Hill.

FEIL, Helen R. *See* Book-of-the-Month Club.

FEJOS, Paul (1897–1963) Anthropologist.

Childhood and education in Hungary; medical training; to US, 1923; Rockefeller Institute, 1924–26; film industry, Hollywood and Europe, during the late 1920's and early 1930's; ethnographic work for Swedish film industry, 1937–40; work with primitive tribes, Madagascar, Seychelles; shipwreck on Komodo Island; archaeology and anthropology in Peru, 1940, with Axel Wenner-Gren; Army Specialized Training Unit, Stanford University, 1943–44; Director, Wenner-Gren Foundation; use of technical aids in anthropology; Yale, 1950–51; Columbia, 1951; international symposia in Austria; *Anthropology Today.*
244 pp. *Permission required.* 1962. Papers.

FELDMAN, Justin N. (1919–   ) Lawyer, politician.

Education: NYC, Columbia; NYC Democratic politics, 1948–65; Mayors William O'Dwyer and Robert F. Wagner; 1960 gubernatorial campaign, with emphasis on roles of Averell Harriman, Franklin Roosevelt, Jr., Eleanor Roosevelt, Carmine De Sapio; county and district leaders; reform movement; Herbert Lehman; Edward Costikyan; Adam Clayton Powell; 1962 state convention; campaign manager for Robert Morgenthau; reapportionment.
330 pp. *Closed during lifetime.* 1968.

FELDMAN, Myer (1917–   ) *See* Social Security.

FELDMAN, Paul. *See* Socialist Movement.

FELICANI, Aldino (1891–1967) Publisher.

A detailed account of the work of the Sacco-Vanzetti Defense Committee, plus some background material on the Italian-American radical press in the first quarter of the 20th century.
160 pp. *Open.* 1954.
Also available at The Boston Public Library.

FELIX, Edgar. *See* Radio Pioneers.

FELIX, Robert (1904–   ) *See* Health Science.

FERGUSON, Homer (1889–   ) *See* Robert A. Taft Project.

FERNANDEZ, Jesus. Labor leader.
ARGENTINA IN THE 1930's
Railway worker from 1916; foreign development of railroads in Argentina; formation of railroad brotherhood, 1912 strike; organization of unions, national officer, opposition to Peron.
31 pp. *Open.* 1970.

FERRELL, Robert (1921–   ) *See* American Historians.

FERRER, José Vicente (1912–   ) *See* Popular Arts.

FERRO, Edward (1895–1968) Immigration inspector.

Early life and education in Italy; emigration to US; life on Lower East Side of Manhattan, early 1900's; immigration interpreter on Ellis Island; immigration procedures, experiences as immigration inspector.
76 pp. *Permission required to cite or quote.* 1968.
Contributed by Harry Kursh, Lakeland Schools, Mohegan Lake, New York.

REFER TO "NOTES ON USE" IN INTRODUCTION

FERTIG, Wendell. *See* Air Force.

FETZER, John Earl (1901–1966) Radio, television executive.

RADIO PIONEERS

Experiments in radio from 1911; license, 1918; early stations in Michigan; controversy with FCC; Broadcasters Victory Council, 1940; radio censorship, 1944; work in Europe for US government, 1945. Impressions of Gen. Dwight D. Eisenhower, various radio personalities.
115 pp. *Open.* 1951.

FEW, Mary Reamey Thomas (Mrs. William Preston).

JAMES B. DUKE PROJECT

Family background in Virginia; education, Trinity College, North Carolina, 1902; friendship with Duke family; graduate studies, Columbia University, 1908; life as wife of president of Trinity College, later Duke University; James B. Duke and Duke University: founding of the university, 1924; Republican National Committeewoman. Impressions of various academic and political figures.
285 pp. *Permission required.* 1963.

FIDANZA, Alfredo.

ARGENTINA IN THE 1930'S

Argentine leather workers' union: foreign influence, strikes, wages, relations with management; General Confederation of Workers, 1942.
21 pp. *Open.* 1970.

FIELD, Betty (1918–) *See* Popular Arts.

FIELD, Ruth (Mrs. Marshall) (1907–) *See* Adlai E. Stevenson Project.

FIELDS, DOROTHY (1905–) *See* Popular Arts.

FIELDS, Gracie (1898–) *See* Popular Arts.

143

FIELDS, Louis J. (1909–   ) Marine Corps officer.

Education, St. John's College; Maryland National Guard, 1925–32; South Pacific, Australia, New Zealand, 1942–44; Aide to USMC Commandant, 1945–47; postwar demobilization; SHAPE, 1954–56; Director of Personnel, HQMC, 1962–65; Vietnam.
267 pp. *Permission required.* 1971.

FIFE, James (1897–   ) Naval officer.

Background and education, Naval Academy; convoy duty, WWI; submarine school, 1918, Yangtze River patrol; fleet problems and training; merchant marine inspections; Director, Submarine School, New London, 1938–40; submarine observer in England, 1940; London Blitz, Portsmouth and Coventry damage; Mediterranean mission, submarine patrol; impressions of Gen. Archibald Wavell, Col. William Donovan, Anthony Eden, Sir John Dill; General Board, Washington, 1941; Pearl Harbor; Philippines, Adm. Thomas Hart, Corregidor; submarine operations, Australia and South Pacific; Battle of Java Sea; Gen. Douglas MacArthur; Task Force 42; Solomons campaign; impressions of Adms. William Leahy, Chester Nimitz, Alan Kirk, Arthur Hepburn, Ernest King, Robert Ghormley, Arthur Carpender, Thomas Kinkaid, Charles Lockwood, and Fairfax Leary.
617 pp. *Permission required to cite or quote.* 1962. NYT (Part I).

FINBERG, Barbara. *See* Children's Television Workshop.

FINCH, Robert Hutchison (1925–   ) Government official.
EISENHOWER ADMINISTRATION

Early association with Richard M. Nixon, 1950 senatorial campaign; California politics; chairman, Los Angeles County Republican Committee; 1960 Presidential primary and campaign.
69 pp. *Permission required.* 1967.
Also available at Occidental College, Los Angeles.

REFER TO "NOTES ON USE" IN INTRODUCTION

FINE, Benjamin (1905–   ) *See* Journalism Lectures.

FINLETTER, Thomas Knight (1893–   ) *See* Adlai E. Stevenson Project.

FINNEY, Burnham (1899–   ) *See* McGraw-Hill.

FINNEY, Thomas. *See* Adlai E. Stevenson Project.

FINUCANE, Peter. *See* Robert P. Patterson Project.

FIORELLO, Albert. *See* Joseph M. Proskauer Project.

FIRESTONE, Leonard Kimball (1907–   ) *See* Eisenhower Administration.

FISHER, Dorothy Canfield (1879–1958) Author.
                    BOOK-OF-THE-MONTH CLUB
   Member, first selection committee of Book-of-the-Month Club; comments on committee members and book selection policies; notable books reviewed, 1926–49; relationship of selection committee to management of club.
   129 pp. *Permission required to cite or quote.* 1955. NYT (Part I).

FISHER, Edwin Shelton (1911–   ) *See* McGraw-Hill.

FISHER, Oliver David (1875–   ) *See* Weyerhaeuser Timber Company.

FISHER, Walter Taylor (1892–   ) *See* Adlai E. Stevenson Project.

FITCH, Lyle C. (1913–   ) *See* New York Political Studies.

FITCH, William Kountz (1889–   ) Government official.
                    SOCIAL SECURITY
   Director, HEW Office of the Aging, 1956; staff director,

White House Conference on Aging; executive director, National Retired Teachers Association and American Association of Retired Persons.
100 pp. *Open.* 1966.

FITTS, William Cochran, Jr. (1905–   ) *See* James Lawrence Fly Project.

FITZGERALD, Alice (Mrs. William) *See* Association for the Aid of Crippled Children.

FLANDERS, Ralph Edward (1880–1969) Senator.
EISENHOWER ADMINISTRATION
Senate investigation of Senator Joseph McCarthy; McCarthy and his effect on the nation and on the Republican Party.
51 pp. *Permission required to cite or quote.* 1967.

FLANIGAN, Mark. *See* Columbia Crisis of 1968.

FLATH, August William (1898–1969) Police inspector.

Career in NYC Police Department; technical improvements; Prohibition; recreation; immigrants; press.
91 pp. *Open.* 1959.

FLEISCHMAN, Harry. *See* Socialist Movement.

FLEMING, Arthur B. *See* Health Science.

FLEXNER, Abraham (1866–1959) Educator.

The career of Simon Flexner; Rockefeller Institute; leaders in American medical history, particularly Doctors William Halsted, Howard Kelly, and William Welch.
36 pp. *Permission required to cite or quote.* 1954. NYT (Part I).

FLEXNER, Carolin A. *See* Herbert H. Lehman Project.

FLOREZ, Luis de. *See* Aviation.

JAMES LAWRENCE FLY PROJECT

Friends and associates recall James L. Fly (1898–1966), particularly his chairmanship of the FCC, 1939–44.

Participants and pages: Thurman Arnold, 16; Edward Brecher, 35; Marcus Cohn, 39; Thomas Corcoran, 29; Norman Corwin, 49; Benedict Peter Cottone, 24; Charles R. Denny, 28; Clifford J. Durr, 32; William C. Fitts, Jr., 52; Abe Fortas, 11; Fred W. Friendly, 14; Lucien Hilmer, 16; Rosel H. Hyde, 19; Leonard H. Marks, 25; Neville Miller, 33; Charles S. Murphy, 13; John Lord O'Brian, 14; Harry Plotkin, 36; Paul A. Porter, 30; Joseph Rauh, 35; James Rowe, 9; Pete Shuebruk, 36; Telford Taylor, 60.

655 pp. *Closed until January 1, 1982. 1967. Contributed by Sally Fly Connell, New York.*

FLYING TIGERS

At the Flying Tiger reunion at Ojai, California, in 1962, pilots, mechanics, radiomen, administrative, and ground crew personnel reminisced of their experiences with Chennault's American Volunteer Group in Burma and China, and with the China National Aviation Corps, during and after WW II. They detail adventurous days in Rangoon, Toungoo and Kunming, retreating over the Burma Road, flying P-40's against Japanese bombers and Zeros, and operating the Mukden shuttle before the fall of Shanghai in 1949. The natural focus of those days was Claire Chennault, and these men and women recount anecdotes and impressions of him. While informal and unstructured, these interviews provide source material on a thinly documented phase of WW II, and the lore that has grown around it.

Participants and pages: Mrs. Anna Chennault and Thomas Corcoran, 4; Thomas Corcundale, 16; Jerry Costello and John Vivian, 12; Tom Cotton, 31; Doreen Davis, 47; Tex Hill, 23; Joe Jordan, 38; Gayle McAlister, 13; Robert Neale, 60; Charley Older, 38; Bob Prescott, 43; Doc Richardson and Bob Blyer, 21; Don Rodewald and Wilfred Schaper, 40; Don Rodewald, Harvey Wirta and Wilfred Schaper, 57; Bob Smith, Tom Trumble, 78; John Vivian, 24.

583 pp. *Permission required to cite or quote.* 1962.

FLYNN, Edward Joseph (1892–1953) Politician.

Democratic Party politics, 1922–40.
24 pp. *Permission required to cite or quote.* 1950. NYT (Part I).

FOGELSON, Robert. *See* Columbia Crisis of 1968.

FOLGER, John Clifford (1896–   ) Investment banker.
EISENHOWER ADMINISTRATION

Citizens' movement; financing 1956 and 1960 Republican campaigns; Milton Eisenhower, Leonard Hall; Ambassador to Belgium.
43 pp. *Closed until January 1, 1977.* 1968.

FOLKS, Homer (1867–1963) Social worker.

American social work; Children's Aid; NYC politics and social work, 1900–35.
98 pp. *Permission required to cite or quote.* 1949. NYT (Part I).

FOLLIARD, Edward Thomas (1899–   ) Newspaperman.
EISENHOWER ADMINISTRATION

President Eisenhower and the press; problems of presidential press coverage; relations between Presidents Harry Truman and Dwight Eisenhower.
72 pp. *Permission required to cite or quote.* 1967.

FOLSOM, Marion Bayard (1893–   ) Executive, government official.
SOCIAL SECURITY

Beginnings of voluntary social security at Eastman Kodak

REFER TO "NOTES ON USE" IN INTRODUCTION

Company; development of philosophy leading to social security program and Medicare.
207 pp. *Permission required to cite or quote.* 1965.

EISENHOWER ADMINISTRATION

Early career; Under Secretary of the Treasury, 1953–55; tax legislation; Secretary of HEW, 1955–58: problems, policies, personalities; National Defense Education Act; Social Security.
163 pp. *Permission required to cite or quote.* 1968.
See also Health Science.

FONDA, Henry (1905–   ) *See* Popular Arts.

FONDILLER, William (1885–   ) Engineer.

Career with Bell System; recollections of Michael Pupin and Albert Einstein.
18 pp. *Permission required.* 1970.

FONER, Eric. *See* Richard Hofstadter Project.

FORAND, Aime Joseph (1895–1972) *See* Social Security.

FORD, George Barry (1885–   ) Priest, student counselor.

Columbia University, 1927–45; personalities in the Roman Catholic community; NYC political figures; American reaction to the Spanish Civil War; Morningside Heights development.
126 pp. *Permission required to cite or quote.* 1956. NYT (Part I).

FORD, Guy Stanton (1873–1962) Historian.

Early life and education; University of Wisconsin, 1892–95 and 1898–99; teaching at Wisconsin Rapids, 1895–98; European travel, 1899–1905; Columbia University, 1900–01; Yale University; illness, 1906; University of Illinois, 1906–13; Dean, University of Minnesota, 1913; sabbatical at Harvard,

1916; Committee on Public Information, 1917–18; *AHR;* SSRC; mission for Rockefeller Foundation, 1924; return to Minnesota; Commission for the Investigation of Social Studies in the Schools; Acting President, University of Minnesota, 1931–32; Stanford University, 1933; Commission of Inquiry on National Policy in International Economic Relations, 1934; achievements at the University of Minnesota as Dean of the Graduate School, 1913–38, Acting President, 1937–38, President, 1938–41; Executive Secretary, AHA; WWII.

963 pp. *Permission required to cite or quote.* 1955. NYT (Part I).

FORD, Katherine. *See* Carnegie Corporation.

FORDYCE, Alice (1905–   ) Foundation officer.

Use of BCG vaccine for tuberculosis in US and in other countries; isoniazid; Lasker Foundation Awards for Medical Journalism.

108 pp. *Permission required.* 1964.

FOREMAN, Carl (1914–   ) *See* Popular Arts.

FOREST HISTORY SOCIETY

These interviews on forestry and logging contain material on conservation, woods safety, fire-fighting and the development of protective associations, old Minnesota logging camps, logging methods and machinery, and the development of the Paul Bunyan legends. Impressions of H. L. Mencken are included, as are impressions of George S. Long and other lumbermen.

Participants and pages: Charles S. Cowan, 54; George W. Dulany, 37; Inman F. Eldredge, 12; Royal S. Kellogg, 55; Donald MacKenzie, 17; Maggie Orr O'Neill, 19; P. J. Rutledge, 10; James Stevens, 33.

237 pp. *Permission required to quote.* 1957.
Contributed by the Forest History Society, Inc., Santa Cruz, California.

REFER TO "NOTES ON USE" IN INTRODUCTION

FORTAS, Abe (1910–   ) *See* Federated Department Stores *and* James Lawrence Fly Project.

FOSSA, Manuel. *See* Argentina in the 1930's.

FOSSA, Mateo (1897–   ) Labor leader.

ARGENTINA IN THE 1930's

Apprentice wood carver; craft unions, following European models; Socialist Party, 1919; effect of WWI on Argentine economy; growth of larger union groupings from 1935, opposition to government; effect of Mexican oil expropriation, 1938; industrial unions, technology; pressures and divisions within General Confederation of Workers; labor support of Peronism; Latin American Workers Congress in Mexico.

77 pp. *Open.* 1970.

FOSTER, Paul F. (1889–1972) Naval officer.

Family background, Oklahoma and the land rush, Utah, Idaho; Naval Academy, cruises; gunnery and fire control; occupation of Vera Cruz, 1914; submarine service; Navy recruiting; engineering duty; resignation from Navy, 1929; Wall Street, adventures in business; Naval service WWII: Panama, Alaska, Puerto Rico, Assistant Naval Inspector General, Navy Manpower Survey Board; merchandising, Mandel Brothers, 1946–50; World Bank, 1950–54; AEC, Atoms for Peace Program, Operations Coordinating Board, general manager, AEC; US representative International Atomic Energy Agency, 1959. Impressions of Adm. Thomas Hart, Lewis L. Strauss, John McCone, Vyacheslav Molotov, and many others.

373 pp. *Permission required.* 1966.

FOULOIS, Benjamin D. (1879–1967) *See* Aviation.

FOUNDATION FOR CHILD DEVELOPMENT *See* Association for the Aid of Crippled Children.

FOWLER, Donald. *See* World Bank.

FOX, John. *See* James B. Duke Project.

FOX, William T. R. (1912–   ) *See* Carnegie Corporation *and* United Nations.

FRADER, Joel. *See* Columbia Crisis of 1968.

FRANCIS, Clarence (1888–   ) Corporation executive.
EISENHOWER ADMINISTRATION
Early career; inter-agency division for disposition of agricultural surpluses.
37 pp. *Permission required to cite or quote.* 1967.

FRANK, Jerome New (1889–1957) Judge.

Education at the University of Chicago; law practice in Chicago and NY; general counsel of AAA; NRA; impressions of Henry A. Wallace, Chester Davis, George Peek, Rexford G. Tugwell, Harry Hopkins, Alger Hiss, and Hugh Johnson.
194 pp. *Permission required.* 1952.

FRANK, Waldo (1889–1967) *See* Hart Crane Project.

FRANKE, William Birrell (1894–   ) *See* Eisenhower Administration.

FRANKEL, Charles (1917–   ) *See* Journalism Lectures.

FRANKFURTER, Felix (1882–1965) Supreme Court Justice.

Life in NYC as an immigrant; Harvard Law School, influence of Professors Samuel Williston and John C. Gray; comments on beginning of legal education; C. C. Langdell, Charles Eliot; association with Henry L. Stimson: US Attorney's Office, NY; War Department; anti-trust activity; minimum wage laws.

REFER TO "NOTES ON USE" IN INTRODUCTION

337 pp. *Permission required to cite or quote.* 1955. NYT (Part I).

FREDERICKSON, A. N.*See* Weyerhaeuser Timber Company.

FREED, Arthur (1894–　) *See* Popular Arts.

FREEDMAN, Max. *See* Journalism Lectures.

FREIDEL, Frank (1916–　) *See* Richard Hofstadter Project.

FREY, John Philip (1871–1957) Union official.

Family background, early life; *Molders' Journal,* 1903–27; Milwaukee Foundry strike, 1906; Thomas Mooney and James McNamara cases; WWI labor and manpower problems; labor consultant to European allies, 1918; Socialist Party; IWW; Metal Trades Department, AFL, 1927–50; relations of AFL with Labor Department; Frances Perkins as Secretary of Labor; NRA; 1934 Wages & Hours Bill and Roosevelt administration; NLRB; Anaconda Copper strike, 1935; 1935 AFL convention; formation of the CIO; Communist Party and the labor movement; Martin Dies Committee; San Francisco strike, 1941; International Association of Machinists; WWII manpower and production; NAM; mobilization in World Wars I and II; relations of labor with political parties and Catholic Church; craft unionism; organizing Negroes. Impressions of Harry Bridges, James J. Davis, Samuel Gompers, William Green, Herbert Hoover, John L. Lewis, Theodore Roosevelt, Franklin D. Roosevelt, William H. Taft.
752 pp. *Open.* 1955.

FRIEDLICH, Herbert Aaron (1893–　) *See* Robert P. Patterson Project.

FRIEDMAN, Samuel. *See* Socialist Movement.

FRIENDLY, Fred W. (1915–) *See* James Lawrence Fly Project *and* Radio Pioneers.

FRIENDLY, Henry Jacob (1903–) *See* Aviation.

FRIENDS OF THE COLUMBIA LIBRARIES

Selected speakers at dinner meetings of The Friends of the Columbia Libraries, generally on literary topics.

Participants and pages: Robert Halsband, 19; Rockwell Kent, 20; Helmut Lehman-Haupt, 36; Ogden Nash, 20.

95 pp. *Permission required to cite or quote.*

FRILLMAN, Paul W. (1912–1972) Missionary.

Missionary experiences, China; Japanese occupation, 1936–41; with Gen. Claire Chennault and the Flying Tigers to Burma and China, 1941; protecting Burma Road and Rangoon; evacuation of Rangoon; Kunming; disbanding of Flying Tigers, 1942; US Army Air Corps, 1942; Combat Intelligence with Chennault and 14th Air Force in China, 1943; OSS; postwar China; USIS.
416 pp. *Permission required to cite or quote.* 1962. NYT (Part I).

FRITCHEY, Clayton. *See* Adlai E. Stevenson Project.

FRY, Guy S. *See* John Robert Gregg Project.

FRYE, Helene. *See* McGraw-Hill.

FUESS, Claude Moore (1885–1963) Educator.

Preparatory school teaching; headmastership at Andover: abolition of fraternities, distinguished Andover graduates; literary recollections and impressions; comments on historians; impressions of Alfred Stearns, Henry Cabot Lodge, Endicott Peabody, Calvin Coolidge, Henry L. Stimson.

REFER TO "NOTES ON USE" IN INTRODUCTION

285 pp. *Permission required to cite or quote.* 1962. NYT (Part I).

FULBRIGHT, James William (1905–   ) Senator.

Childhood and education; Oxford University; Washington, D.C.; University of Arkansas; the Fulbright Act; the House of Representatives and the US Senate.
176 pp. *Closed until 5 years after death.* 1957.

FULLER, Robert. *See* Radio Pioneers.

FULLINGTON, Wayland. *See* Radio Pioneers.

FUOSS, Robert (1912–   ) *See* Federated Department Stores.

GABLER, Milton. *See* Popular Arts.

GALLUP, George Horace (1901–   ) Public opinion statistician.

Family background and education; early newspaper readership surveys; journalism teaching 1929–32; principles of effective advertising; magazine publishing: *Literary Digest, Reader's Digest, Saturday Evening Post, Look,* etc.; postcard polling; Gallup polls from 1933; impressions of Gardner Cowles, Jr., Raymond Rubicam, Douglas Southall Freeman.
158 pp. *Permission required to cite or quote.* 1962.
See also Book-of-the-Month Club.

GALPIN, Perrin Comstock (1889–   ) Educator.

Education; Belgium and WWI; impressions of Brand Whitlock, Hugh Gibson, Herbert Hoover, and others.
40 pp. *Permission required to cite or quote.* 1956. NYT (Part I).

GAMBLING, John. *See* Radio Pioneers.

GANS, Hyram Selig (1905–   ) *See* New York Political Studies.

GARDNER, Grandison. *See* Henry H. Arnold Project.

GARDNER, John William (1912–   ) Foundation executive.

CARNEGIE CORPORATION

First impressions of Carnegie Corporation, 1946; area studies; Harvard Russian Research Center; Afro-American Institute; President of Carnegie Corporation, 1955–67: relations with trustees, other Carnegie organizations, staff selection; evaluation of foundation work. Impressions of Corporation officers and trustees.
221 pp. *Permission required.* 1969.

GARDNER, Ray. *See* Benedum and the Oil Industry.

GAREY, Woodrow Wilson. *See* McGraw-Hill.

GARMES, Lee (1898–   ) *See* Popular Arts.

GARNER, Robert Livingston (1894–   ) International banker.

WORLD BANK

Role of Bank's management and directors, 1947–49; policy developments; history of various loans; staff; organization of Bank and its role as mediator.
100 pp. *Open.* 1961.

GARRISON, Charlotte (1881–1972) Educator.

TC and Horace Mann kindergarten, 1906–38; parents' associations; educational toys; progressive education; Manhattanville Nursery; Russia, 1929; impressions of James E. Russell, Grace Dodge, Patty Hill, Agnes Burke, and John Dewey.
58 pp. *Open.* 1967.

REFER TO "NOTES ON USE" IN INTRODUCTION

GARTNER, William. *See* McGraw-Hill.

GASSER, George. *See* Alaskan Pioneers.

GATES, Thomas Sovereign, Jr. (1906–   ) Cabinet member.
EISENHOWER ADMINISTRATION
Experiences in WWII; Under Secretary and Secretary of the Navy, 1953–59; Deputy Secretary and Secretary of Defense, 1959–60.
59 pp. *Permission required to cite or quote.* 1967.

GAVAGAN, Joseph Andrew (1892–1968) Politician, judge.

NY State politics, 1922–29; Congress, 1929–43; NYC politics in 1950.
70 pp. *Permission required to cite or quote.* 1950. NYT (Part I).

GAVIN, James M. (1907–   ) Army officer.
EISENHOWER ADMINISTRATION
Eisenhower as General and President: decisions, management ability, relations with Gens. George Patton and Walter B. Smith and with Marshal Bernard Montgomery; missiles.
36 pp. *Permission required.* 1967.

GAY, Luis F. Labor leader
ARGENTINA IN THE 1930's
Telephone Workers' union; development of unions during 1920's, political maturing; power of General Confederation of Workers; effect of Depression, rise of Adolf Hitler and Benito Mussolini; Peron's relationship with organized labor, especially 1944–45; formation and dissolution of Labor Party.
107 pp. *Open.* 1971.

GAYNOR, Janet (1906–   ) *See* Popular Arts.

GEER, Bennette Eugene (1873–1964) *See* James B. Duke Project.

GELLES, Gerry. *See* Socialist Movement.

GELLHORN, Edna (Mrs. George).

League of Women Voters, 1919–54: organization, concern with federal and state laws, leaders.
17 pp. *Open.* 1959.

GELLHORN, Walter (1906–   ) Lawyer.

Experience as a student and later faculty member at Columbia University; clerkship with Justice Harlan Stone; Washington, D.C. in the early 1930's; Social Security Board; Attorney General's Committee on Administrative Procedure; OPA; WLB, Region 2.
590 pp. *Closed until 5 years after death.* 1955.

GEORGE, Harold L. *See* Air Force Academy.

GERARD, James Watson (1867–1951) Lawyer, diplomat.

Democratic party and elections, 1902–40; experiences as ambassador to Germany, 1913–17; impressions of Woodrow Wilson, Walter Hines Page, and others.
96 pp. *Permission required to cite or quote.* 1950. NYT (Part I).

GERSTER, John Carl Arpad (1881–   ) *See* Mt. Sinai Hospital.

GHIOLDI, Americo (1900–   ) Political leader, journalist.
ARGENTINA IN THE 1930'S

Early political background, Socialist Party, 1916; delegate, 1st National Socialist Congress, 1923; editor, Socialist periodicals, 1924–56; member of Council for Buenos Aires; review of political and economic situation, 1930–43: role of

military, election of 1932, tax and labor legislation, economic and political crises, relations with Britain, influence of Axis ideology; political philosophy.
50 pp. *Open.* 1971.

GIBBONS, Katherine Clark
ADLAI E. STEVENSON PROJECT
Reminiscences of meetings and correspondence with Stevenson, 1952–65.
73 pp. *Permission required.* 1969.

GIBSON, Edwin T. (1886–1959) Corporation executive.

Development of frozen foods; General Foods organization; defense mobilization in Washington; MSA; American Assembly; Eisenhower Exchange Fellowships.
83 pp. *Permission required to cite or quote.* 1956. NYT (Part I).

GIBSON, Kenneth Allen (1932–   ) Mayor.

Informal record of day in the life of the Mayor of Newark, New Jersey; reflections on first hundred days in office; tax proposals; Trenton riots; Newark's financial, racial, education, and housing problems; Black Panthers; urban violence.
58 pp. *Permission required.* 1970.

GIDEONSE, Harry David (1901–   ) College president.

Experiences as President of Brooklyn College; relationship with NYC Board of Higher Education, Mayor's Office, and presidents of other city colleges; investigations; Russell case, Rapp-Coudert Committee.
118 pp. *Permission required.* 1961.

GIESECKE, Albert Anthony   (1883–1970) Educator, archeologist.

Youth and education; Ministry of Education in Peru, 1909;

Rector of University of Cuzco, 1910–23; Director General of Education of Peru, 1923–31; educational problems and policies in Latin America, student strikes; archeological discoveries and collections; Inter-American Conferences; American Embassy in Lima from 1931; Tacna-Arica Plebiscite Commission, 1925–26. Impressions of Hiram Bingham, Axel Wenner-Gren, Paul Fejos, Gen. John J. Pershing, and many others.

438 pp. *Permission required.* 1962.

GILBERT, James L. *See* McGraw-Hill.

GILBERT, Louis Wolfe (1886–   ) *See* Popular Arts.

GILBERT, Wells. *See* Weyerhaeuser Timber Company.

GILBRETH, Lillian M. (1878–1972) *See* New School Lectures.

GILDERSLEEVE, Virginia C. (1877–1969) *See* Columbiana.

GILE, Elizabeth. *See* McGraw-Hill.

GILES, Bascom. *See* Benedum and the Oil Industry.

GILMAN, Mildred (Mrs. Robert Wohlforth)

Heywood Broun's activities and friends in the 1920's and '30's; Sacco-Vanzetti case; NY *World*; Algonquin Round Table; Newspaper Guild; *Connecticut Nutmeg;* Ruth Hale, Sherwood Anderson, Robert Benchley, H. L. Mencken.
82 pp. *Permission required to cite or quote.* 1969.
NYT (Part II). Papers.

GINGELL, George. *See* Radio Pioneers.

GINOCCHIO, Rafael. *See* Argentina in the 1930's.

REFER TO "NOTES ON USE" IN INTRODUCTION

GINZBERG, Leon. *See* Mt. Sinai Hospital.

GISSEN, Max Journalist.

Childhood and education; book reviewing for *New Republic;* Edmund Wilson; book reviewing for *Time;* Whittaker Chambers, T. S. Matthews, Henry Luce; background of cover stories on Louis Armstrong, J. P. Marquand. 298 pp. *Closed during lifetime.* 1963.

GIUSTI, Roberto F. Editor, legislator.

ARGENTINA IN THE 1930'S

Socialist Party from 1915: factions and divisions, influence of periodicals; leaders of the Socialist Party and other political leaders; Chamber of Deputies, 1928–30, 1932–34: legislative procedures; founder and editor of *Nosotros*. 59 pp. *Open.* 1971.

GIVENS, Willard Earl (1886–   ) Educator.

Early life and education, Columbia, 1915, Union Theological Seminary, 1916; teaching experiences in Hawaii; Superintendent of Schools, Oakland, California, 1925–27; NEA, Executive Secretary, 1935–52. Impressions of Harry Emerson Fosdick, Henry Sloane Coffin. 64 pp. *Permission required to cite or quote.* 1968.

GLADIEUX, Bernard Louis (1907–   ) Government official, management consultant.

Early life and education, Oberlin College and Maxwell School, Syracuse University; administrative consultant in federal government, 1936–40; Chief, special staff on war organization, Bureau of the Budget, 1939–42; administration and budgetary management of the executive branch in wartime; preparation of executive orders for president; formation, operation, and budgets of OPM, BEW, SPAB, WPB, CIAA, ODT, OSS, OCD, OWI, OES; wartime production and manpower problems; leadership and opera-

tional evaluations; later work in WPB, 1943–44; UNRRA, 1944; Department of Commerce, 1945–50; Ford Foundation, 1950–51.
744 pp. *Permission Required.* 1951.

GLASSEN, Mary (Mrs. William H.) *See* James B. Duke Project.

GLOVER, Edward (–1972) Psychoanalyst.
PSYCHOANALYTIC MOVEMENT
History of psychoanalysis; techniques of analysis; research; British Psychoanalytic Society; training analysts; evaluation of Sigmund Freud, Carl Jung, and other analysts; personal background.
108 pp. *Permission required.* 1965.

GODDARD, Esther C. (Mrs. Robert H.) *See* Aviation.

GOELL, Theresa Archeologist.

Early life and education; archeological expedition to Turkey, Numrad Dag; Hartley Lehman.
54 pp. *Permission required.* 1965.
Contributed by Frederick P. Latimer, Jr.

GOLDBERG, Arthur Joseph (1908–   ) Labor lawyer, mediator.
INTERNATIONAL NEGOTIATIONS
Multilateral and bilateral negotiation techniques; changing functions of US ambassadors; "demonstrative diplomacy"; impressions of Cyrus Vance, W. Averell Harriman, and William P. Rogers.
51 pp. *Permission required.* 1970.

GOLDBERG, Jacob. *See* Joseph M. Proskauer Project.

GOLDBLOOM, Maurice. *See* Socialist Movement.

REFER TO "NOTES ON USE" IN INTRODUCTION

GOLDMAN, James. *See* Columbia Crisis of 1968.

GOLDSTEIN, Jonah J. (1886–1967) Judge.

Early life in NYC, NYU Law School, 1909; Educational Alliance, Grand Street Boys; Secretary for Alfred E. Smith, 1911; numerous Jewish philanthropies; administering relief program, Palestine, 1929; NYC Judge: accounts of court cases and work for court reform, 1931–56; Republican candidate for mayor, 1945; relationships with Felix Warburg, Senators Robert F. Wagner and Herbert Lehman, Mayors James Walker, Fiorello LaGuardia, William O'Dwyer. 686 pp. *Open.* 1966.

GOLDWATER, Barry Morris (1909–   ) Senator.
EISENHOWER ADMINISTRATION
Presidency of Dwight Eisenhower; Senate Campaign Committee; Republican Party; impressions of Sherman Adams, Richard Nixon, Lyndon Johnson, Robert Taft, William Knowland. 85 pp. *Closed until April 12, 1974.* 1967.

GOLENPAUL, Dan (1900—   ) Radio producer.

Information Please Almanac; genesis and production of "Information Please"; Heywood Broun, Oscar Levant, Clifton Fadiman, John Kieran, and others on the program; relations with advertising agencies and sponsors. 205 pp. *Permission required to cite or quote.* 1964.

GOOD, George Franklin, Jr. (1901–   ) *See* Marine Corps.

GOODMAN, Benny (1909–   ) *See* Popular Arts.

GOODMAN, Harry. *See* Radio Pioneers.

GOODPASTER, Andrew Jackson (1915–   ) Army officer.
EISENHOWER ADMINISTRATION
White House Staff Secretary, 1954–61: liaison officer with

NSC; relations with Russia, Latin America, Middle East, and Asia during Eisenhower administration.
137 pp. *Permission required to cite or quote.* 1967.

GOODRICH, Lawrence Keith (1906–1968) *See* McGraw-Hill.

GOODRICH, Leland Matthew (1899–   ) Professor of international relations.

Childhood and education in Maine; Bowdoin and Harvard, 1916–25; Brown University; Commission for Belgian Relief, 1923–25; Lafayette University; World Peace Foundation; Columbia University.
151 pp. *Open.* 1967.
See also United Nations Conference.

GOODRICH, Lloyd (1897–   ) Museum officer and art historian.
Amercian Cultural Leaders
Government and foundation support of arts; Whitney Museum; art criticism; White House, 1961–63; visual arts in US.
86 pp. *Closed pending publication of a study.* 1967.

GOODRICH, Luther Carrington (1894–   ) Sinologist.

Early life in China; PUMC after WWI; training in sinology, Columbia University; impressions of Paul Pelliot, J. J. L. Duyvendak and others; research problems of *The Literary Inquisition of Ch'ien-Lung.*
159 pp. *Permission required to cite or quote.* 1959. NYT (Part II).

GOODWIN, Kathryn. *See* Social Security.

GORDEY, Michel (1913–   ) Journalist.

Journalistic experiences, especially in OWI during WWII and in Budapest during Hungarian revolt in 1956. Impressions of Nikita Khrushchev and Gen. Charles DeGaulle. 106 pp. *Permission required.* 1962.

GORDON, Dorothy (1893–   )

RADIO PIONEERS

Childhood and education; concert singer, marriage; children's concerts, 1923; early experience in radio; CBS "Children's Corner," 1930; NBC children's programs; "Yesterday's Children"; Youth Forums for NY *Times* from 1943; impressions of radio personalities and public figures. 168 pp. *Open.* 1951.

GORDON, Joseph. *See* Occupation of Japan.

GORDON, Richard (1882–1956) Actor.

Childhood in Connecticut; playing in stock companies throughout US, 1902–16; impressions of Corse Peyton, Maude Adams, Francis Wilson, William Hodge, Mary Emerson, Anne Sutherland, Thomas Meighan, Frances Ring, Philip H. Lord, Mildred Holland. 203 pp. *Open.* 1951.

GORMAN, Carl. *See* Marine Corps.

GORNEY, Jay. *See* Popular Arts.

GRAEBEL, Richard. *See* Adlai E. Stevenson Project.

GRAFF, Henry F. (1921–   ) *See* Richard Hofstadter Project.

GRAHAM, Frank Porter (1886–1972) University president.

University of North Carolina during presidency, 1930–49. 38 pp. *Permission required to cite or quote.* 1961. *See also* Social Security.

GRAHAM, Sheilah. *See* Popular Arts.

GRANGER, Lester B. (1896–   ) Social worker.

Background and education; experiences as a Negro soldier in WWI; early encounters with discrimination and segregation; extension work, counselling, social work; Urban League, studies of employment structure and placement facilities; racial questions in labor unions; National Negro Congress; segregation in armed forces; Community Relations projects; approaches to leaders of industry; American Association of Social Work; International Conferences; Negroes in international relations; CORE; sit-in movements; Dr. Martin Luther King, NAACP; Negro nationalism; new African leadership; federal record on equal rights in employment.
326 pp. *Permission required.* 1960.

GRANT, John B. (1890–1962) Public health officer.

Education in China, Nova Scotia, University of Michigan, Johns Hopkins; IHB; work on hookworm in North Carolina, China; foundation and early years of PUMC; Peking Health Station; setting up first Ministry of Health in China, 1929; political problems and relationships; public health organization in Japan; Rockefeller Foundation program; Institute of Public Health in Tokyo, 1932; public health work in Yugoslavia; rural reconstruction in China and India; problems of social medicine in US, Europe, and Canada; international organizations. Impressions of Victor Heiser, Joseph Mountin, Selskar Gunn, Roger Greene, and Wickliffe Rose.
1,223 pp. *Permission required.* 1961.
Underwritten by the Rockefeller Foundation.

GRANVILLE, Bonita (1923–   ) *See* Popular Arts.

GRAUER, Alvin.
OCCUPATION OF JAPAN
Experience in advertising; Army Industrial Services dur-

ing WWII; public relations for occupation forces in Yokohama and Tokyo, 1945; Visitors Bureau, 1946; American soldier in Japan: attitude of Japanese, fraternization; Gen. Douglas MacArthur.
139 pp. *Permission required to cite or quote.* 1961.

GRAUER, Ben (1908–   ) Radio reporter.

RADIO PIONEERS

Early days of radio; experiences as radio reporter.
65 pp. *Permission required to cite or quote.* 1968.

GRAY, Arthur Jr. (1922–   ) Investment broker.

EISENHOWER ADMINISTRATION

Chairman of special events, Citizens for Eisenhower-Nixon, 1952; 1952 convention and campaign.
32 pp. *Permission required to cite or quote.* 1967.

GRAY, Gordon (1909–   ) Government official.

EISENHOWER ADMINISTRATION

Education, University of North Carolina, Yale Law School; early legal practice; publishing; North Carolina State Senate, 1938–42, 1946–47; service in WWII; Assistant Secretary and Secretary of the Army, 1947–50; unification of services, civilian control of Department of Defense; Special Assistant to President Harry Truman, 1950; President, University of North Carolina, 1950–55; Assistant Secretary of Defense for International Security Affairs, 1955–57; service intelligence operations; Director, Office of Defense Mobilization, 1957–58; Special Assistant to President Eisenhower for National Security Affairs, 1958–61; Robert Oppenheimer Case and Personnel Security Board for AEC, 1954; National Trust for Historic Preservation; Commission for Financing Hospital Care; Research Triangle Institute.
338 pp. *Permission required.* 1967. Papers.

GRAY, Gordon. *See* Radio Pioneers.

GRAY, Robert Keith

EISENHOWER ADMINISTRATION

Background of *Eighteen Acres Under Glass;* impressions of President Eisenhower, Richard Nixon, Sherman Adams. 38 pp. *Closed during lifetime.* 1970.

GREB, Gordon. *See* Radio Pioneers.

GREEN, Adolph (1915–   ) *See* Popular Arts.

GREENBAUM, Edward Samuel (1890–1970) Lawyer.

Family background, education, NYC; Williams College; Columbia Law School; NYC practice, Greenbaum, Wolff & Ernst from 1915; WWI; Johns Hopkins Institute of Law and survey of litigation in NY, 1930's; impressions of legal and political figures, including Felix Frankfurter, Henry Morgenthau, Sr., and Herman Oliphant.
266 pp. *Permission required to cite or quote.* 1965. NYT (Part II).
See also Robert P. Patterson Project.

GREENE, Jack P. *See* American Historians.

GREENE, Rosaline. *See* Radio Pioneers.

GREENSTEIN, Robert (1924–   ) Architect.

Work with Charles Le Corbusier on Unity House, Marseilles.
40 pp. *Permission required to cite or quote.* 1950. NYT (Part I).

GREGG, Alan (1890–1957) Physician.

Early life and education at Harvard College and Harvard Medical School; internship at MGH; experiences in WWI; work for Rockefeller Foundation as a public health officer in Brazil, 1919–22; work in Division of Medical Sciences,

NY, 1923–25; survey of medical needs of Colombia, 1924; beginnings of survey of medical education in Italy, 1925; Rockefeller Foundation; legal medicine.
259 pp. *Permission required to cite or quote.* 1956. NYT (Part I).

JOHN ROBERT GREGG PROJECT

This is a compilation of interviews with friends and associates of John Robert Gregg (1867–1948), the man who developed the Gregg shorthand system.

Participants and pages: Guy S. Fry, 46; W.W. Lewis, 23; Louis Pfeiffer, 17; Margaret Richards Shimko and Charles Lee Swem, 82.

168 pp. *Permission required.* 1956. *Underwritten by Mrs. Alfred C. Howell, New York.*

GREITZER, Herman S. (1919–   ) Lawyer, politician.

NYC politics; detailed account of his candidacy for Democratic District Leader, First Assembly District South, Manhattan, in 1957, against incumbent Carmine DeSapio.
101 pp. *Permission required.* 1962.

GRIFFITH, Samuel Blair (1906–   ) Marine Corps officer.

Naval Academy, 1925–29; early assignments; Chinese language studies, Peking, 1935–38; British Commando training; WWII: Tulagi, Guadalcanal, New Georgia; postwar withdrawal of Marines from North China; American Advisory Group, Greece.
205 pp. *Permission required.* 1970.

GRIFFITH, William Morris (1897–   ) *See* Benedum and the Oil Industry.

GRIMM, Peter (1886–   ) Real estate executive.

Family background, growing up in NYC; Columbia College, 1911; beginnings in NYC real estate; WWI, balloon

training; William A. White and Sons; John D. Rockefeller, Jr.
181 pp. *Permission required.* 1972.
See also Eisenhower Administration.

GRISCOM, Lloyd Carpenter (1872–1959) Diplomat.

Business and political association of Clement Griscom with steamship transportation, the Pennsylvania Railroad, Theodore Roosevelt, Marcus A. Hanna, and others; diplomatic experiences, 1893–1909; NYC politics, 1910–11; subsequent career as newspaper proprietor.
123 pp. *Permission required to cite or quote.* 1951. NYT (Part I). Papers: 13 letters (copies).

GRISWOLD, Nat R. *See* Eisenhower Administration.

GROGAN, Thomas (1922–   ) *See* McGraw-Hill.

GROSS, Ernest A. (1906–   ) Lawyer.
EISENHOWER ADMINISTRATION
Family background; Harvard, Oxford, Harvard Law School; counsel to various government agencies, 1933–47; Deputy Assistant Secretary of State for Occupied Areas, 1946; State Department legal adviser and Assistant Secretary of State for Congressional Relations, 1947–49; Deputy representative to UN, 1949; drafting of Marshall Plan and Economic Cooperation Act; full account of UN and other activities, including NATO, Military Assistance Program, India-Pakistan dispute, 1965; Korea; reminiscences of Dean Rusk, John Foster Dulles, Trygve Lie, and others.
984 pp. *Permission required to cite or quote.* 1968. NYT (Part II).
See also Dag Hammarskjold Project.

GROSS, Robert Ellsworth (1897–1961) *See* Henry H. Arnold Project.

GROSSMAN, James. *See* Columbia Crisis of 1968.

GROVES, Leslie A. (1896–1970) *See* Robert P. Patterson Project.

GRUENTHER, Alfred M. (1899–   ) Army officer.
EISENHOWER ADMINISTRATION
Recollections of Gen. Eisenhower; Operation Torch; NATO; pre-campaign discussions and New Hampshire primary, 1952; SHAPE.
97 pp. *Closed during lifetime.* 1967.
See also Federated Department Stores.

GRUENTHER, Homer H. (1900–   ) *See* Eisenhower Administration.

GUARDO, Ricardo. *See* Argentina in the 1930's.

GUGGENHEIM, Harry F. (1890–1971) *See* Aviation.

GUION, Connie Myers (1882–1971) Physician.

Family background and childhood; education; internship at Bellevue; experiences as assistant to Dr. James Babcock and Dr. Frank S. Meara; Cornell Pay Clinic, 1922–32; Cornell Medical College, 1932–41; the Family Comprehensive Care Program.
260 pp. *Permission required to cite or quote.* 1956. NYT (Part I). Papers.

GULICK, Luther Halsey (1892–   ) City administrator.

Reorganization of NYC government, 1950–56; origin, development and comment upon the Mayor's Committee on Management Survey; personal observations as City Administrator.
90 pp. *Permission required to quote.* 1956. Papers.
See also New York Political Studies.

GUNZENDORFER, Wilton. *See* Radio Pioneers.

GUSTAFSON, John Kyle (1906–) *See* Mining Engineers.

GUSTAFSON, Phyllis. *See* Adlai E. Stevenson Project.

GUTHRIDGE, Amis. *See* Eisenhower Administration.

GUTHRIE, Virgil B. (1886–1968) *See* McGraw-Hill.

GUY, Raymond Frederick (1899–) *See* Radio Pioneers.

GUYLAY, L. Richard (1913–) Public relations counselor.

EISENHOWER ADMINISTRATION

Robert A. Taft; 1952 Republican Convention; Fair Play Amendment; Dwight D. Eisenhower; public relations in campaign of 1956.
90 pp. *Permission required to cite or quote.* 1967.
See also Robert A. Taft Project.

HAAS, Robert K. (1890–) *See* Book-of-the-Month Club.

HAAS, Victor (1924–) *See* Health Science.

HABER, William (1899–) *See* Social Security.

HABIAGUE, Esteban

ARGENTINA IN THE 1930'S

Experiences in journalism and politics; account of Alberto Barcelo and his political control in Avellaneda; illustrative anecdotes of Argentine development, 1910–45.
147 pp. *Open.* 1971.

HACKETT, Albert (1900–) *See* Popular Arts.

HADLEY, Morris (1894–) *See* Carnegie Corporation.

REFER TO "NOTES ON USE" IN INTRODUCTION

HAEFFNER, Joseph Anthony (1907–   ) *See* Radio Pioneers.

HAGER, Kolin. *See* Radio Pioneers.

HAGERTY, James C. (1909–   ) Journalist.

EISENHOWER ADMINISTRATION

1952 convention and campaign; trip to Korea; effect of television on politics, campaigns, and press conferences; relations with news media and press conferences; advance trips and travels with President Eisenhower in US and abroad; elections of 1954, 1956, 1960; President Eisenhower's heart attack; Sherman Adams; impressions of Winston Churchill, Nikita Khrushchev, Charles De Gaulle; cabinet meetings; impressions of Eisenhower's associates and aides.

569 pp. *Permission required.* 1968.

HALABY, Najeeb E. (1915–   ) Lawyer. *See* Eisenhower Administration.

HALL, John Lesslie Jr. (1891–   ) Naval officer.

William and Mary, Naval Academy, athletics; early cruises; instructor, Naval Academy; Naval War College 1937–40; North African campaign 1942–43; Commander Amphibious Forces, landings in North Africa, Sicily, Italy; invasion of Normandy, Omaha Beach, 1944; commands in Pacific, 1945; Okinawa; Commandant, Armed Forces Staff College 1948–51. Impressions of military leaders, especially Adms. Ernest King and Thomas Hart and Gens. George Patton, Dwight Eisenhower, and Omar Bradley.

338 pp. *Permission required to cite or quote.* 1963. NYT (Part I).

HALL, Leonard (1900–   ) Politician.

EISENHOWER ADMINISTRATION

Republican Party politics; chairman of National Republican Committee; campaigns of 1956 and 1964.

59 pp. *Closed during lifetime.* 1965.
Contributed by James Cannon, New York.

HALL, Samuel Stickney, Jr. (1894–) Financial consultant.
CARNEGIE CORPORATION

Father's role in teachers' insurance program of Carnegie
Foundation; Assistant Treasurer, TIAA, 1919; investment
officer for Carnegie philanthropies, 1921–40; impressions of
Mrs. Andrew Carnegie and various associates.
115 pp. *Permission required.* 1967.

HALLANAN, Walter Simms (1890–1962) *See* Benedum and
the Oil Industry.

HALLECK, Charles A. (1900–) Congressman.
EISENHOWER ADMINISTRATION

1952 Republican Convention and campaign; President
Eisenhower's relations with Congress.
35 pp. *Permission required to cite or quote.* 1967.

HALLER, Edouard de. *See* Pedro de Azcarate *and* League
of Nations.

HALSBAND, Robert. *See* Friends of the Columbia Libraries.

HAMILTON, Carl (1914–) Agricultural journalist.

Early life in Iowa; AAA information work; assistant to
Secretary of Agriculture Claude Wickard; assistant to the
Food Administrator; assistant on REA matters.
735 pp. *Closed until 5 years after death.* 1953. Papers.

DAG HAMMARSKJOLD PROJECT

Colleagues recall their association with Dag Hammarskjold, his personal qualities, his training and experience in
Sweden and elsewhere in Europe, his abilities and interests, and his approach to the administrative and executive

REFER TO "NOTES ON USE" IN INTRODUCTION

challenges of the post of Secretary General of the UN, particularly staffing the Secretariat, the Congo crisis, and the Russian troika proposal.

Participants and pages: Sven Ayman, 11; Andrew Cordier, 22; Ernest Gross, 100; C.V. Narasimhan, 48.

181 pp. *Permission required to cite or quote. 1962. Underwritten by the Institute for International Order, New York.*

HAMMERSTEIN, Oscar II (1895–1960) *See* Popular Arts.

HAMMOND, George. *See* Federated Department Stores.

HAMMONS, Earle Wooldridge (1886–1962) *See* Popular Arts.

HAMPTON, Robert Edward (1922–   ) Government official.

EISENHOWER ADMINISTRATION

White House staff; processing Presidential appointments; Civil Service Commission.

57 pp. *Permission required. 1967.*

HAND, Learned (1872–1961) Judge.

Family background and childhood; Harvard College and Law School; impressions of Augustus Hand, Louis D. Brandeis, Felix Frankfurter, and others; views on politics, world events, religion, history, and the law.

169 pp. *Permission required to cite or quote. 1957.* NYT (Part I).

HANDOVER, Dennis. *See* Aviation.

HANDSFIELD, Hugh (1911–   ) *See* McGraw-Hill.

HANES, John Wesley, Jr. (1925–   ) *See* Eisenhower Administration.

HANKINS, Frank Hamilton (1877–1969) Sociologist.

Columbia University during early 1900's; Franklin H. Giddings; Sociology Department.
20 pp. *Open.* 1968.
Contributed by Neal De Nood, Northampton, Massachusetts.

HANSELL, Heywood S.

AIR FORCE ACADEMY

WWII experiences, especially B-29 wing, Marianas, 1944–45; air tactics.
28 pp. *Open.*

HANSEN, Alvin Harvey (1887–   ) *See* Social Security.

HANSEN, Clifford Peter (1912–   ) *See* Jackson Hole Preserve.

HANSEN, Edward S. (1889–   )

JAMES B. DUKE PROJECT

Childhood in Norway, arrival in US, 1909; footman and butler, for the Duke family; description of mansion, daily household routine, parties; impressions of Mr. and Mrs. James B. Duke, Doris Duke.
176 pp. *Permission required.* 1963.

HANSER, Richard Frederick (1909–   ) Writer.

RADIO PIONEERS

WWII; the newspaper *PM* magazine; OWI, psychological warfare unit; Normandy after D-Day; *Frontpost;* capture of Radio Luxembourg; *Fieldpost;* "Tom Jones" radio program; Battle of the Bulge; SHAEF; "This is America"; "Victory at Sea."
32 pp. *Open.* 1967.

HARBACH, Otto (1873–1963) *See* Popular Arts.

REFER TO "NOTES ON USE" IN INTRODUCTION

HARDEMAN, D. B.

EISENHOWER ADMINISTRATION

Texas politics; Tidelands issue; Adlai Stevenson Campaigns, 1952 and 1956; 1960 Democratic Convention; impressions of Adlai Stevenson, Sam Rayburn, Estes Kefauver, Lyndon Johnson, Price Daniel, Allan Shivers.

146 pp. *Closed during lifetime.* 1970.

HARDMAN, J.B.S. (1882–1968) Labor leader.

Early life in Vilna; Russia, 1900–10; Social Democratic Party Conference, 1907; Leon Trotsky; union organization; Amalgamated Clothing Workers.

83 pp. *Open.* 1962.

HARE, Raymond Arthur (1901–) *See* Eisenhower Administration.

HARKNESS, William E. (1873–)

RADIO PIONEERS

Network radio; educational radio; advertisers, sales; radio and music rights; patent infringements; recorded programs; recollections of many early radio figures.

99 pp. *Open.* 1951.

HARLAN, John Marshall (1899–1972) *See* Adlai E. Stevenson Project.

HARLOW, Bryce Nathaniel (1916–) Government official.

EISENHOWER ADMINISTRATION

White House staff and organization under President Eisenhower; a typical week in the White House; press conferences; preparation of State of the Union messages and other speeches; relations with Congress.

144 pp. *Closed during lifetime.* 1967.

HAROLD, John. *See* Occupation of Japan.

HARR, Karl Gottlieb, Jr. (1922–   ) Lawyer.
EISENHOWER ADMINISTRATION

Deputy Assistant Secretary of Defense; National Security Planning Board; special assistant to President Eisenhower for security operations coordination; Operations Coordinating Board.
41 pp. *Permission required.* 1967.

HARRAR, J. George (1906–   ) Foundation executive.

Early life and family; education, Oberlin and Iowa State College; University of Puerto Rico, 1929–30; impressions of University of Minnesota department of plant pathology under Edward M. Freeman and E. C. Stakman; corn smut and wheat rusts; teaching at Virginia Polytechnic Institute and Washington State College; reflections on education in US; origins of Rockefeller Foundation agriculture program; experiences of Rockefeller research team, Mexico, 1943–46.
In process.

HARRIMAN, Florence Jaffray (Mrs. J. Borden) (1870–1967) Politician, diplomat.

Democratic Party politics, 1912–45.
40 pp. *Permission required to cite or quote.* 1950. NYT (Part I).

HARRIMAN, W. Averell (1891–   ) Government official.
INTERNATIONAL NEGOTIATIONS

Extensive discussion of process of international negotiations with illustrations from his diplomatic career, especially the test ban agreement, WWII conferences, Vietnam peace talks; effects of national and world opinion; roles of the military, Congress, and the press; choice of negotiating personnel, training for professional diplomats; assessment of the use of the Presidency in international affairs, 1933–69; "Good officer" experiences: Iran oil concession case and India-Pakistan disputes. Many vignettes of international leaders.

REFER TO "NOTES ON USE" IN INTRODUCTION

353 pp. *Permission required to cite or quote.* 1969.
See also Henry H. Arnold Project.

HARRIS, Sir Arthur. *See* Henry H. Arnold Project.

HARRIS, Joseph. *See* Social Security.

HARRIS, Julie (1925–   ) *See* Popular Arts.

HARRIS, Marvin. *See* Columbia Crisis of 1968 *and* Columbia Television Lectures.

HARRISON, Sir Geoffrey. *See* International Negotiations.

HART, Fred J. *See* Radio Pioneers.

HART, Herschell. *See* Radio Pioneers.

HART, John Neely (1902–1970) *See* Marine Corps.

HART, Thomas Charles (1877–1971) Naval Officer.

Childhood and education; Spanish-American War; ordnance, teaching, submarines; Army War College; command of *Mississippi;* submarine command; Superintendent, Naval Academy, 1931–34; heavy cruisers, 1934–36; General Board, 1936–39 and 1942–45; Asiatic Fleet, 1939–41; Hart Investigation of Pearl Harbor; Senator from Connecticut, 1945–47. Impressions of many political and military figures, including Theodore Roosevelt, Franklin Roosevelt, Frank Knox, James Forrestal, Gen. Douglas MacArthur and Adms. William Leahy, Harry Ervin Yarnell, Ernest King, Arthur Hepburn, Chester Nimitz, and Harold Stark.
284 pp. *Permission required to cite or quote.* 1962. NYT (Part I). Papers.

HARTE, Houston (1893–1971) *See* Benedum and the Oil Industry.

HARTMANN, Heinz (1894–1970) Psychoanalyst.

PSYCHOANALYTIC MOVEMENT

Early education, Vienna; development of interest and training in psychoanalysis in Berlin and Vienna; analysis by Sigmund Freud; early associations with leading figures in European and American psychoanalytic movement; *Ego Psychology and the Problem of Adaptation,* 1939; effect of ego metapsychological writings on current psychoanalytic theory and technique; New York Psychoanalytic Institute; collaborative work with Drs. Rudolph Loewenstein and Ernst Kris.

145 pp. *Open except for specified pages.* 1963.
Open portions also available at New York Psychoanalytic Institute.

HARWOOD, Wilson.

EISENHOWER ADMINISTRATION

National Science Foundation; National Bureau of Standards; McCarthyism and scientific community; meetings with President Eisenhower.

52 pp. *Open.* 1968.

HASKINS, Caryl Parker (1908–   ) Educator, scientist.

CARNEGIE CORPORATION

History of Carnegie Institution of Washington; Carnegie Corporation grant for psychophysical research, 1948; consultant for Carnegie Corporation, 1950, trustee, 1955; President, Carnegie Institution, 1956; evaluation of grants and programs; views on Andrew Carnegie; relations between Institution and Corporation; impressions of Devereux Josephs, Charles Dollard, John Gardner, and other Carnegie officers and trustees.

251 pp. *Permission required.* 1967.

HASS, Eric. *See* Socialist Movement.

HASSIALIS, Menelaos D. (1909–) *See* Nuclear Energy.

HAUBERG, John Henry (1916–) Lumber company executive.

WEYERHAEUSER TIMBER COMPANY

History of Denkmann and Weyerhaeuser families from 1860; Mississippi River Logging Company, Southern Lumber Company.

127 pp. *Permission required.* 1949.

HAUGE, Gabriel (1914–) Economist.

EISENHOWER ADMINISTRATION

Preconvention activity and 1952 campaign; President Eisenhower's cabinet appointments; economic policies; Council of Economic Advisors; Departments of Agriculture and Interior; Arthur Burns.

130 pp. *Permission required to cite or quote.* 1967.

HAUPTLI, Albert (1894–1964)

McGRAW-HILL

Magazine work, McGraw-Hill, from 1920: paid vs. free circulation publications; growth of advertising agencies, role of salesmen, special media publications; *American Machinist, Product Engineering;* automation.

103 pp. *Permission required.* 1956.

HAUSMAN, Louis (1906–) *See* Children's Television Workshop.

HAVENS, Beckwith. *See* Aviation.

HAVERLIN, Carl (1899–) Radio executive.

Early years in the Southwest; touring with a theatrical troupe, 1916–17; radio in Los Angeles in the 1920's.

38 pp. *Closed during lifetime.* 1955.

See also Allan Nevins Project.

HAWKES, John. *See* American Cultural Leaders.

HAWKINS, Laurence Ashley (1877–1958) *See* Radio Pioneers.

HAY, Marley Fotheringham (1880–1963) Naval architect.

Submarine construction and warfare in WWI.
19 pp. *Open.* 1950.

HAYAKAWA, Sessue (1890–   ) *See* Popular Arts.

HAYDEN, Philip M. *See* Columbiana.

HAYES, Albert John (1900–   ) Labor union executive.

Early life; International Association of Machinists; NIRA;
formation of CIO; merger of AFL-CIO; Ethical Practices
Committee, AFL-CIO; Truman Commission on Health;
impressions of John L. Lewis, William Green, Arthur
Wharton.
216 pp. *Permission required to cite or quote.* 1957.
NYT (Part I).

HAYES, Carlton J. H. (1882–1964) *See* Columbiana.

HAYES, Charles Harold (1906–   ) Marine Corps officer.

Education; early assignments; WWII: Guadalcanal, Green
Island, Emirau, Leyte, Luzon, Palau, 1943–45; occupation of Japan; Korea; Assistant USMC Commandant, 1961–65.
239 pp. *Permission required to cite or quote.* 1970.

HAYES, Edward Pearce (1895–   ) *See* China Missionaries.

HAYES, George Francis (1885–   ) *See* Popular Arts.

REFER TO "NOTES ON USE" IN INTRODUCTION

HAYS, Brooks (1898–   ) Congressman, lawyer.
EISENHOWER ADMINISTRATION

Early career; Little Rock school crisis; Newport meeting
with President Eisenhower and Orval Faubus.
165 pp. *Closed during lifetime.* 1970.

HAYWARD, George C. *See* Federated Department Stores.

HEACOX, E.F. *See* Weyerhaeuser Timber Company.

HEALTH SCIENCE

This project is laying the foundations for a study of the
growth of the biological and medical sciences in the US, of
the changing role of the federal government in relation to
research and training in the health field, and of changing
public attitudes toward such activities. Interviews have
been conducted with persons closely associated with the
National Institutes of Health (NIH) and its predecessors,
upon which the study is primarily focused, but others
prominent as researchers, administrators, and philanthro-
pists in the field are included.

Participants and pages: Ernest Allen, 77; Carl Baker, 172; W. Ray Bryan,
82; Leroy Burney, 46; George Robert Coatney, 90; L.T. Coggeshall, 52;
Martin Cummings, 28; Warren Palmer Dearing, 95; Warren Draper, 77;
Rolla Dyer, 24; Kenneth Endicott, 45; I.S. Falk, 79; Robert Felix, 63;
Arthur B. Fleming, 42; Marion Folsom, 101; Victor Haas, 137; John R.
Heller, 50; Herman Hilleboe, 147; Vane Hoge, 33; Mark D. Hollis, 58;
James Hundley, 62;

Carlyle Jacobson, 59; Charles V. Kidd, 59; Lawrence Kolb, 66; Alexander
Langmuir, 56; Esmond Long, 119; Jack Masur, 30; Leonard Mayo, 54;
Joseph Murtaugh, 44; Thomas Parran, 133; John Paul, 34; George Perrott,
58; David Price, 41; Leonard Scheele, 57; William H. Sebrell, 72; W.P.
Shephard, 40; Roscoe Spencer, 142; Harold Stewart, 63; Frederick L.
Stone, 41; Norman Topping, 64; Wilson Smillie, 50; C.J. Van Slyke, 63.

2,905 pp. *Permission required.* 1962–67.
*Underwritten by the National Institutes of Health. Also
available at the National Library of Medicine.*

HEARTT, Philip Brewster (1896–   ) *See* James B. Duke
Project.

HECHT, Ben (1894–1964) *See* Popular Arts.

HEDGES, William Saxby (1895–   ) Radio executive.
RADIO PIONEERS
Early experiences in radio; formation of National Association of Broadcasters, code of decency, 1928; channel allocations; NBC from 1930's: relations of network companies and affiliates, planning and development, soap operas, television; President, NBC Integrated Services Department.
123 pp. *Open.* 1951.

HEFFERNAN, John A. (1871–1952) Newspaperman.

Impressions of Bird S. Coler; Brooklyn politics, 1900–20.
87 pp. *Open.* 1950.

HEILBRONER, Robert (1919–   ) *See* American Historians.

HEIN, Marjorie. *See* Robert A. Taft Project.

HEISKELL, Marian (Mrs. Andrew) (1918–   ) *See* Adlai E. Stevenson Project.

HELD, Adolph. *See* Socialist Movement.

HELLER, John Roderick, Jr. (1905–   ) *See* Health Science.

HENDERSON, Harold Gould (1889–   ) *See* Occupation of Japan.

HENDERSON, Loy Wesley (1892–   ) *See* Eisenhower Administration.

HENDERSON, Ray. *See* Popular Arts.

REFER TO "NOTES ON USE" IN INTRODUCTION

HENDRICK, Burton Jesse (1870–1949) Writer, editor.

Magazine publishing, 1900–20; S. S. McClure, Ida Tarbell and the "muckrakers"; Walter Hines Page, Andrew Carnegie.
59 pp. *Permission required to cite or quote.* 1949. NYT (Part I).

HENNEY, Keith. *See* McGraw-Hill.

HENRIKSON, Carl H., Jr. (1899–   ) Business executive.

Lumbering in Minnesota; WWI naval service.
145 pp. *Permission required to cite or quote.* 1955. NYT (Part I).

HENRY, Ray

SOCIAL SECURITY

Drive for Medicare legislation: publications, consultation with Congressmen, encounters with AMA members. Impressions of Blue Carstenson, Nelson Cruikshank, Zalman J. Lichtenstein.
135 pp. *Closed during lifetime.* 1966.

HENRY, S.T. (1882–1957) *See* McGraw-Hill.

HENSHAW, Frederick W. (1898–1953) Journalist.

Youth and education; Michigan State; Detroit *News*, 1923–28; *Magazine of Michigan*, 1929–33; Division of Information, AAA, 1933–38; George Peek; Henry Wallace; Chester Davis; Alfred Stedman; Howard Tolley; Franklin Roosevelt; BEW, 1940; *US News*.
175 pp. *Open.* 1953.

HERBERG, Will (1909–   ) *See* Danforth Lectures.

HERMLE, Leo David (1890–   ) *See* Marine Corps.

HERRING, Edward Pendleton (1903–) Educator.
CARNEGIE CORPORATION

Carnegie Corporation and social sciences; American Political Science Association; case study method in public administration; investigation of polling procedures following 1948 election; impressions of Devereux Josephs and James T. Shotwell.
129 pp. *Permission required.* 1967.

HERZFELD, Willie. *See* Civil Rights in Alabama.

HESS, Arthur E.
SOCIAL SECURITY

Bureau of Old Age and Survivors' Insurance; efforts toward disability legislation.
102 pp. *Open.* 1966.

HESS, Stephen (1933–) *See* Eisenhower Administration.

HETTRICK, John T. (1868–) Newspaperman, lawyer.

Leading figures on Brooklyn *Eagle*, NY *World*, NY *Times*, 1889–1900; NY sporting life; NYC under Mayor Robert Van Wyck; NYC subways, building and development; secretary to August Belmont, 1900–15; Lockwood Investigating Committee; impressions of Theodore Roosevelt, John W. Keller, P. J. Donahue.
202 pp. *Open.* 1949. Papers.

HEURTAUX, A. *See* Aviation.

HEWITT, F.W. *See* Weyerhaeuser Timber Company.

HEWITT, H. Kent (1887–1972) Naval officer.

Youth and education, Naval Academy; world cruise, 1907; teaching at Naval Academy; hydrographic survey work; Cuban Revolution, 1917; destroyer duty, 1918; Naval Institute; War College; President Franklin Roosevelt's trip to Buenos Aires, 1936; fleet exercises, ammunition depot, Bremerton; Panama Canal Zone; Pearl Harbor; neutrality patrol; amphibious training; training for combined operations, London; Operation Torch; Commander US Naval Forces, Mediterranean, 1943; Operation Husky; Salerno. Impressions of many political and military figures.

478 pp. *Permission required to cite or quote.* 1961. NYT (Part I).

HEYMANN, Walter M. (1892–   ) *See* Federated Department Stores.

HIBBERD, Christy. *See* James B. Duke Project.

HICKENLOOPER, Bourke Blakemore (1896–1971) *See* Robert A. Taft Project.

HICKMAN, Harry B. (1889–   ) *See* Benedum and the Oil Industry.

HICKMAN, Leon Edward (1907–   ) *See* James B. Duke Project.

HIGGINS, Joe. *See* Popular Arts.

HIGGINS, Juanda. *See* Adlai E. Stevenson Project.

HIGHET, Gilbert Arthur (1906–   ) *See* Book-of-the-Month Club.

HIGHTOWER, John Murmann (1909–   ) Newspaperman.
EISENHOWER ADMINISTRATION

Foreign policy under Eisenhower; John Foster Dulles.
41 pp. *Permission required to cite or quote.* 1968.

HILL, Frank Ernest (1888–1969) Journalist, author.

Family background and boyhood in California; Stanford

University and Columbia, 1913–17; editorial writer, NY *Globe* and NY *Sun,* literary editor *Sun,* 1925; editor, Longmans, Green Company, 1925–31: authors, manuscripts, NYC literary and publishing circles; *The Winged Horse,* 1927; adult educational programs, CBS; lecturing and freelance writing, poetry and prose; *Westward Star, The Canterbury Tales,* texts and young people's books; collaboration with Allan Nevins on biographies of Rockefeller and Ford; Radio Pioneers project for the Oral History Research Office. Comments on publishing, books, and authors, especially Allan Nevins, Don Marquis, Edwin Markham, Vachel Lindsay, Carl Sandburg.

605 pp. *Permission required to cite or quote.* 1961. NYT (Part I).

HILL, Harry W. (1890–1971) Naval officer.

Naval Academy; early cruises, gunnery training; WWI: Scapa Flow, German Fleet surrender; Navy Department reorganization; arms limitation, naval budget, congressional liaison; Hoover good will cruise to South America, 1928; Naval War College, 1937; War Plans Division, 1940; WWII: US-Canada Joint Board Armed Defense, convoys and patrols, Murmansk, Iceland; Pacific theater commands: detailed analysis of amphibious assault at Tarawa; operations at Saipan, Tinian, Iwo Jima, Okinawa; plans for assault on Japan; National War College, Naval Academy superintendent; Naval Home. Accounts of Gens. Douglas MacArthur and Holland M. Smith; Adms. Ernest King, Chester Nimitz, Raymond Spruance, Kelly Turner, and other military, naval, and political figures.

955 pp. *Permission required to cite or quote.* 1967. Papers.

HILL, John E. *See* Radio Pioneers.

HILL, Lister (1894–   ) Senator.

Boyhood and early political experiences in Alabama.
18 pp. *Closed during lifetime.* 1958.

REFER TO "NOTES ON USE" IN INTRODUCTION

HILL, Robert Charles (1917–) *See* Eisenhower Administration.

HILL, Tex. *See* Flying Tigers.

HILL, Tom F. *See* James B. Duke Project.

HILLEBOE, Herman Ertresvaag (1906–) *See* Health Science.

HILMER, Lucien. *See* James Lawrence Fly Project.

HINGLE, Pat (1924–) *See* Popular Arts.

HIRSCHHORN, Kurt. *See* Mt. Sinai Hospital.

HISS, Alger (1904–) Lawyer.
CARNEGIE CORPORATION
Carnegie Endowment for International Peace and its relations with Carnegie Corporation; role of trustees; impressions of Robert Leffingwell, Arthur Page, Whitney Shepardson.
67 pp. *Permission required.* 1968.

HO, Franklin L. *See* Chinese Oral History.

HOCHWALT, Frederick George (1909–1966) Priest.

Administrator, Cincinnati parochial schools, 1940's; federal aid to education; National Catholic Education Association; UNESCO.
47 pp. *Open.* 1962.

HOCTOR, Alice. *See* Carnegie Corporation.

HODGES, Luther Hartwell (1898–   ) Cabinet member.
EISENHOWER ADMINISTRATION

Southern Governors' Conference, 1957; Little Rock crisis; visit to Russia; Governor of North Carolina; Secretary of Commerce; Adlai E. Stevenson; President Eisenhower.
39 pp. *Closed during lifetime.* 1968.

HODGINS, Eric (1899–1971) Author.
EISENHOWER ADMINISTRATION

Paley Commission; speech writing for Adlai Stevenson campaign, 1952; education, early experien:e in journalism: *Youth's Companion,* 1920's; *Fortune* in the 1930's; *Time* during WWII; Henry R. Luce; writing of the *Blandings* books and *Episode.*
162 pp. *Permission required.* 1969.

HODGKINSON, Harold Daniel (1890–   ) *See* Federated Department Stores.

HOEGH, Leo Arthur (1908–   ) Lawyer, politician.
EISENHOWER ADMINISTRATION

Iowa politics; 1952 Republican Convention; Director of Civil and Defense Mobilization, 1958–61; relations with President Eisenhower; 1960 and 1964 elections.
95 pp. *Closed during lifetime.* 1968.

HOEY, Jane Margueretta (1892–1968) Government official.
SOCIAL SECURITY

Assistant Director of Welfare Council, NYC; experiences as federal director of Public Assistance, 1936–54.
102 pp. *Permission required to cite or quote.* 1965.

HOFFER, Willi (1897–1967) Psychoanalyst.
PSYCHOANALYTIC MOVEMENT

Creating a children's home; analysis by H. Nunberg, 1921–22; use of play in education; remedial educator; emigration to London, 1938; scientific journals; behaviorism; case histories; ego, defense, and other problems of psychoanalysis; impressions of Anna and Sigmund Freud. 116 pp. *Permission required to cite or quote.* 1965.

HOFFMAN, Michael Lindsay (1915–   ) (with William Diamond) *See* World Bank.

HOFFMAN, Paul Gray (1891–   ) Government official, industrialist.

Family background, education in Illinois; early interest in automobiles; Studebaker salesman, California, 1912; regional manager, 1917; OTC, WWI; establishment of own company to distribute automobiles, 1920–25; vice president, Studebaker, 1925; receivership, 1933, and reorganization; Studebaker in WWII; new designs, labor relations, merger with Packard.
In process.

HOFSTADTER, Richard (1916–1970) *See* American Historians; Columbia Crisis of 1968; *and* Richard Hofstadter Project.

HOFSTADTER, Robert (1915–   ) *See* Nobel Laureates.

RICHARD HOFSTADTER PROJECT

This project brings together the recollections of students, faculty colleagues, and others who knew Richard Hofstadter, for the most part during his years at Columbia (1946–70), where he became DeWitt Clinton Professor of American History. Contributors recall him as teacher, social observer, writer, and friend, tracing the intellectual development of a major scholar. Specifics include comment on *Social Darwinism in American Thought, The American Political Tradition, The Age of Reform, Anti-Intellectualism in Amerian Life,* and other works, as well as insights into the mind and character of the man.

Participants and pages: Daniel Bell, 42; Elisabeth Earley, 24; Eric Foner, 21; Frank Freidel, 22; Henry F. Graff, 35; H. Stuart Hughes, 23; Alfred Kazin, 28; Walter Metzger, 29; Arthur M. Schlesinger, Jr., 14.

238 pp. *Permission required to cite or quote.* 1972–

HOGABOOM, Robert Edward (1902–   ) Marine Corps officer.

Family background, education; early duty in Nicaragua, Shanghai; Sino-Japanese War; amphibious warfare doctrine, 1939–42; WWII: Attu and Kiska operations, Marianas, Iwo Jima, preparations for invasion of Japan; reminiscences of Gens. Holland Smith and Graves Erskine, Adm. Kelly Turner; staff, National War College; CG, NATO exercises, phase-out operations in Korea; Deputy Chief of Staff (Plans) and Chief of Staff, HQMC, 1955–59.
357 pp. *Permission required to cite or quote.* 1970.

HOGE, Alicia (Mrs. Michael Arlen). *See* Adlai E. Stevenson Project.

HOGE, Vane. *See* Health Science.

HOHAUS, Reinhard Arthur (1896–   ) Actuary.
SOCIAL SECURITY

Apprentice actuary, Metropolitan Life Insurance, 1921; Committee on Economic Security; chairman, Advisory Council on Social Security, 1953; social adequacy concept; actuarial science, experience rating, other concepts of social insurance legislation; impressions of Vincent Miles, Abraham Epstein, John Winant.
141 pp. *Closed during lifetime.* 1965.

HOLCOMB, Bankson T. (1908–   ) *See* Marine Corps.

HOLLAND, Kenneth (1907–   ) *See* Carnegie Corporation.

HOLLAND, Lawrence La Motte (1895–   ) *See* Radio Pioneers.

HOLLANDER, Louis. *See* Journalism Lectures.

HOLLEMAN, Clarence H. (1890–   ) *See* China Missionaries.

HOLLIS, Mark D. (1908–   ) *See* Health Science.

HOLLISTER, John Baker (1890–   ) Congressman, lawyer.
EISENHOWER ADMINISTRATION
Service in House, 1931–36; Senator Robert A. Taft; ICA, 1955–57; visit to Vietnam, 1955.
52 pp. *Open.* 1970.
See also Robert A. Taft Project.

HOLLOWAY, James Lemuel, Jr. (1898–   ) Naval officer.

Education, Naval Academy; convoy duty, WWI; Atlantic Fleet; WWII, exercises off Puerto Rico, Operation Torch; Bermuda training exercises; Director of Training, 1943–44; Holloway Plan for Naval Academy; Superintendent Naval Academy; Chief of Naval Personnel; reserve officers; relationship with Congress; impressions of Harry Truman, James Forrestal, Adm. Louis Denfeld.
187 pp. *Permission required.* 1962.

HOLM, Celeste (1919–   ) *See* Popular Arts.

HOLMAN, Charles William (1886–1971) Agriculturist.

Childhood, family background and education; early newspaper work; National Conference on Marketing and Farm Credit; farmers' cooperatives; Herbert Hoover in Woodrow Wilson's WFA.
69 pp. *Permission required to cite or quote.* 1953. NYT (Part II).

HOLMES, Lulu.
OCCUPATION OF JAPAN
Adviser to SCAP on Higher Education for Women in Japan, 1946–48.

54 pp. *Permission required to cite or quote.* 1966. *Contributed by the Regional Oral History Office, University of California, Berkeley.*

HONEY, John C. *See* Carnegie Corporation.

HOOVER, Herbert Clark (1874–1964)

RADIO PIONEERS

Role in developing policy on radio broadcasting as Secretary of Commerce, 1921–27; annual radio conference, 1922–25; allocation of wave lengths, problems of monopoly, censorship, commercial use; Federal Radio Act, 1927; Aimee Semple McPherson; Federal Radio Commission; amateur operators.
21 pp. *Open.* 1950.

HOOVER, John Howard (1887–1970) Naval officer.

Family background; Annapolis; US Navy of 1910–30; early cruises, torpedo training, destroyer duty; growth of naval aviation; WWI duty at Channel ports and in eastern Mediterranean; submarine training, Submarine Desk, 1923–28; the *Lexington* and carrier duty; naval air stations, San Diego and Norfolk; WWII and Caribbean Sea Frontier, 1941–43; convoying and anti-submarine efforts; impressions of Adms. Ernest King, John R. Edwards, Raymond Spruance, and Henry Wilson.
432 pp. *Permission required to cite or quote.* 1964. NYT (Part I).

HOPKINS, Terence K. *See* Columbia Crisis of 1968.

HOPPOCK, Robert (1901–   ) *See* Carnegie Corporation.

HORD, Stephen Y. (1897–   ) *See* Adlai E. Stevenson Project.

HORNBLOW, Arthur, Jr. (1893–   ) *See* Popular Arts.

REFER TO "NOTES ON USE" IN INTRODUCTION

HORNER, H. Mansfield (1903–   ) *See* Aviation.

HOTZ, Robert (1914–   ) *See* McGraw-Hill.

HOUGHTON, Amory (1899–   ) Ambassador, executive.
EISENHOWER ADMINISTRATION
Ambassador to France during President Eisenhower's visits; Charles De Gaulle; NATO; aborted summit meeting; relations with State Department; impressions of John Foster Dulles.
96 pp. *Closed during lifetime.* 1968.

HOUSE, A. F. *See* Eisenhower Administration.

HOUSE, Patricia. *See* Eisenhower Administration.

HOUSTON, Lyda Suydam (1891–   ) *See* China Missionaries.

HOWARD, Ben Odell (1904–   ) *See* Aviation.

HOWARD, Ernest (1910–   ) AMA official.

AMA since 1948; mission to Peru, 1946–48; AMA positions on: national health, public health insurance program; Congressional hearings; involvement in political campaigns; disability legislation; Forand bill; impact of President Kennedy's assassination; Kerr-Mills bill; votes on health bills; AMA support from American Farm Bureau, Blue Shield; Madison Square Garden rally; civil rights and Medicare; analysis of Senators' positions on health legislation; 1964 campaign.
302 pp. *Permission required.* 1967.

HOWARD, Katherine Graham (Mrs. Charles P.) (1898–   )
EISENHOWER ADMINISTRATION
Republican National Committee; 1952 Republican Convention; Deputy Civil Defense Administrator; NATO Civil

Defense Committee; Eisenhower campaign, 1952; vignettes of Gen. and Mrs. Eisenhower.
600 pp. *Permission required.* 1971.

HOWE, Quincy (1900–   ) Journalist.

Childhood and education; *The Living Age, Atlantic Monthly, Atlas;* radio broadcasting. Impressions of A. Lawrence Lowell and Ellery Sedgwick.
127 pp. *Permission required to cite or quote.* 1962. NYT (Part I).

HOWELL, William F. *See* World Bank.

HOWSON, Albert Sidney (1881–1960) *See* Popular Arts.

HU, C. T. *See* International Negotiations.

HU, Shih. *See* Chinese Oral History.

HUANG, Fu. *See* Chinese Oral History.

HUCKABY, Elizabeth. *See* Eisenhower Administration.

HUDGENS, Robert Watts (1896–   ) Government official.

Early life; Citadel College; religious, economic, and political conditions in the South; RA and FSA; important New Deal personalities, policies, and problems.
290 pp. *Permission required to cite or quote.* 1954. NYT (Part II).

HUEBSCH, Ben W. (1876–1964) Publisher.

NYC in the 1890's; schooling; apprenticeship with a lithographer; work as a printer; early ventures in publishing; Gelett Burgess; Francis Hackett; first US publication of Sherwood Anderson and James Joyce; friendship with

Joyce, Franz Werfel, Stefan Zweig; editing and publishing *The Freeman;* correspondence with D. H. Lawrence, 1916–23; Henry Ford Peace Expedition, 1915–16; genesis of Viking Press; H. G. Wells; Hendrik Willem Van Loon; origins of ACLU; correspondence with John Quinn on Joyce and others; letters from H. L. Mencken; general comments on book publishing.

492 pp. *Permission required to cite or quote.* 1955. NYT (Part I).

HUFFMAN, Roy. *See* Weyerhaeuser Timber Company.

HUGHES, Everett Cherrington (1897–   ) *See* Carnegie Corporation.

HUGHES, H. Stuart (1916–   ) *See* Richard Hofstadter Project.

HULL, Albert Wallace (1880–1966) Physicist.

RADIO PIONEERS

Early life; General Electric Laboratory, dynatron and magnetron; development of tubes during WWII; cathodes; Irving Langmuir, Willis R. Whitney.

31 pp. *Open.* 1951.

HUMPHREY, Hubert Horatio, Jr. (1911–   ) *See* Herbert H. Lehman Project.

HUNDLEY, James Manson (1915–   ) *See* Health Science.

HUNSAKER, Jerome Clarke (1886–   ) Aeronautical engineer.

AVIATION

Naval Academy, 1904–08; naval architecture, MIT; research in Europe, stability analysis and wind tunnels; Navy duty, WW I: flying boat, Material Division; first aircraft carrier, 1922; non-rigid air ships; Zeppelins; Goodyear, 1929–30; coordinator of research for Navy, 1940; impressions of Gen. William Mitchell, Adm. William Moffett. 112 pp. *Permission required to cite or quote.* 1960.

HUNT, Robert W. *See* Weyerhaeuser Timber Company.

HUNT, Roy Arthur (1881–1966) *See* James B. Duke Project.

HUNTER, Marjorie. *See* Social Security.

HUSH, Homer. *See* Farm Holiday Association.

HUSSEY, George Frederick, Jr. (1894–   ) Naval officer.

Background and education; Naval Academy; *Pennsylvania,* 1920; courses in ordnance, ballistics; Australian cruise, 1925; Bureau of Ordnance, Armor and Projectile Section, Proof Officer, Naval Proving Ground; Gunnery Officer *Salt Lake City,* destroyer command; command of Mine Division and Mine Squadron; command off-shore patrol, Pearl Harbor, December, 1941—April, 1942; Bureau of Ordnance: Director of Production, Assistant Chief, later Chief of Bureau until September, 1947; contractor-operated ordnance plants; basis for postwar ordnance research; many military and naval vignettes.

582 pp. *Permission required to cite or quote.* 1965. NYT (Part II).

HUSSEY, Gray. *See* Federated Department Stores.

HUSSEY, Mrs. Gray. *See* Federated Department Stores.

HUTCHINS, Robert Maynard (1899–   ) University president.

Election as President of University of Chicago, 1929; concept of a university; relationships with faculty, students, trustees, alumni, and the general public; experiments: Great Books courses, divisions, liberal arts college; professional schools and the university; Rush Medical College;

attacks on University of Chicago program; effect of WWII nuclear research; *Encyclopedia Britannica;* Gen. Robert E. Wood; William Benton.

110 pp. *Permission required to cite or quote.* 1967. NYT (Part II).

Contributed by Donald McDonald, Center for the Study of Democratic Institutions, Santa Barbara, California.

HUTSON, John B. (1890–1964) Government official.

Education; University of Kentucky; problems of the South; tobacco farming; AAA; Agricultural Adjustment Acts, 1933 and 1938; BAE; AAA tobacco program; Kerr Tobacco Control Act; Bankhead Cotton Control Act; Soil Conservation; CCC; private farm organizations; WWII; OPA; parity; Steagall Amendment; Production and Marketing Administration; Office of Agricultural Defense Relations; price stabilization; WFA; UN Secretariat; Tobacco Associates, Inc.

559 pp. *Permission required to cite or quote.* 1954. NYT (Part I).

HUTTON, William. Public relations counsellor.

SOCIAL SECURITY

Public relations work with Master Newspaper Syndicate; information director, National Council of Senior Citizens for Health Care; efforts toward Medicare legislation.

113 pp. *Open.* 1966.

HYDE, Edd. *See* Adlai E. Stevenson Project.

HYDE, Rosel Herschel (1900–   ) *See* James Lawrence Fly Project.

HYLE, Gordon. *See* Book-of-the-Month Club.

HYMAN, Abraham. *See* Mt. Sinai Hospital.

HYMAN, Harold M. (1924–   ) *See* Civil War Centennial.

IANNI, Francis A. J. (1926–   ) Educator.

Office of Education, 1960–65, particularly Bureau of Research; new developments under Commissioners Sterling McMurrin and Francis Keppel: team research and development, curriculum reform, cognitive psychology; effects of Sputnik and of civil rights movement on education; Elementary and Secondary Education Act, 1965.
66 pp. *Permission required to cite or quote.* 1967.

IBARGUREN, Carlos. Politician.

ARGENTINA IN THE 1930'S

Rise of nationalist groups in Argentina: Liga Republicana, 1929, opposition to foreign influence, effects of immigration, role in 1930 revolution; Juan Carlos Uriburu's regime; provincial economic councils; effect of world events on Argentine nationalist groups, 1930–45.
49 pp. *Open.* 1971.

ILIFF, Sir William Angus Boyd (1898–   ) Banker.

WORLD BANK

Background in finance; World Bank, 1948; divisions of Bank; Bank dealings with India and Egypt: Aswan Dam, Suez Canal, Kashmir, and Indus water dispute.
76 pp. *Permission required to cite or quote.* 1961.

INDEPENDENCE NATIONAL HISTORICAL PARK

The story of the Independence Hall Association from 1942 and the development of the Independence National Historical Park are recounted by those who played the major parts, in particular Judge Edwin O. Lewis. Accounts of the ensuing urban redevelopment, and of historic preservation and restoration in Philadelphia explore the legal, financial, architectural, and procedural problems and how they were surmounted. Park historians and superintendents describe the role of the National Park Service.

Participants and pages: M.O. Anderson, 38; Roy Appleman, 27; Edmund Bacon, 47; Lysbeth Borie, 27; Michael J. Bradley, 27; Mrs. Joseph Carson, 22; Herbert Kahler, 13; Arthur Kaufmann, 21; Dennis Kurjack, 58; Roy

REFER TO "NOTES ON USE" IN INTRODUCTION

Larson, 39; Edwin O. Lewis, 70; M. Joseph McCosker, 33; Isidor Ostroff, 40; Charles Peterson, 47; Edward Riley, 40; Leon Sacks, 14; Hardy Scott, 11.

574 pp. *Permission required.* 1970. *Underwritten by the Eastern National Park and Monument Association, Philadelphia, Pennsylvania.*

INGERSOLL, Royal E. (1883–   ) Naval officer.

Naval Academy; early cruises; Paris Peace Conference; War Plans Division, 1935; London Naval Conference, 1935; Commander in Chief, Atlantic Fleet, 1942–44; Operation Torch; Atlantic convoys.

126 pp. *Permission required to cite or quote.* 1964. NYT (Part II).

INGRAM, Charles H. (1892–   ) *See* Weyerhaeuser Timber Company.

INTERNATIONAL NEGOTIATIONS

Edward W. Barrett, director of the Communications Institute of the Academy for Educational Development, conducted a series of interviews with practitioners in the field of international negotiations and mediation of disputes. The interviews are preserved by the Oral History program and will be drawn on in delineating guidelines that may be useful to those mediating and negotiating international differences in the future. The work is part of a continuing study of international negotiation and mediation conducted by the Academy under a grant from Dr. and Mrs. John S. Schweppe of Chicago.

Participants and pages: Manuel Brosio, 24; Arthur J. Goldberg, 51; W. Averell Harriman, 353; Sir Geoffrey Harrison, 34; Joseph E. Johnson, 66; Theodore H. Kheel, 43; John J. McCloy, 24; Llewellyn Thompson, 29; Vladimir Velebit, 80.

704 pp. *Permission required.* 1970–72.

The Academy has also canvassed academic and journalistic specialists for their views on future relations between countries, particularly in the Far East, in interviews by Professor Frederick T. C. Yu of Columbia. The interviews, which have been contributed to the Oral History program, include recorded conversations with the following:

John M. Allison, 23; Davis Bobrow, 41; Emerson Chapin, 25; Theodore Chen, 26; Tillman Durdin, 20; Robert S. Elegant, 33; John Fairbank, 25; C. T. Hu, 18; Harold Isaacs, 9; T. B. Koh, 28; Daniel Lerner, 15; John Lindbeck, 18; Sidney Liu, 28; Ithiel de Sola Pool, 20; Lucien Pye, 32; Milton Sacks, 26; Sol Sanders, 52; Ezra Vogel, 23.

462 pp. *Permission required. 1970.*
Contributed by the Academy for Educational Development, New York.

IRAZUSTA, Julio. *See* Argentina in the 1930's.

IRVIN, Lawrence.
ADLAI E. STEVENSON PROJECT

Patronage system; Democratic Party in Illinois, 1952; relationship between Adlai Stevenson and Paul Douglas; Stevenson and party politics; Stevenson as governor.
72 pp. *Permission required.* 1969.

IRVIN, Leslie LeRoy (1895–1966) *See* Aviation.

IRWIN, David. *See* Mining Engineers.

IRWIN, Leo (1917–   ) *See* Social Security.

IRWIN, R. E. *See* Weyerhaeuser Timber Company.

ISAACS, Harold (1910–   ) *See* International Negotiations.

ISAACS, Julius (1896–   ) Lawyer, politician.

NYC politics during the Fiorello LaGuardia administration.
28 pp. *Permission required to cite or quote.* 1949. NYT (Part II).
See also New York Political Studies.

REFER TO "NOTES ON USE" IN INTRODUCTION

ISAACS, Stanley Myer (1882–1962) Lawyer, Politician.

Columbia University, New York Law School, 1905; settlement house work; Republican political activity, 1900–12; fusion movement; Theodore Roosevelt and National Progressive Party, 1912, Convention, 1916; Draft Board, War Department under Secretary Newton D. Baker, 1917–18; Republican platform, 1920; NY real estate, 1919–37: mortgage participation, Lockwood Committee investigation, Tenement House Law, United Neighborhood Houses; campaign manager for Congresswoman Ruth Pratt, 1928, '30; La Guardia mayoralty campaigns, 1929, '33; Samuel Seabury investigation; State Constitutional Convention, 1938; Manhattan Borough President, 1938–41; East River Drive, acquisition of riparian rights; Robert Moses, WPA; City Council from 1941; NYC mayoralty election, 1945; NY election, 1949. Recollections of Herbert Parsons, Ogden Mills, Kenneth Simpson, Irving Ives, Fiorello La-Guardia, Thomas Dewey, William O'Dwyer, Newbold Morris.
260 pp. *Permission required to cite or quote.* 1950. NYT (Part I).
See also Theodore Roosevelt Association.

IVES, Elizabeth Stevenson (Mrs. Ernest) (1898–   )
ADLAI E. STEVENSON PROJECT

Last year of Stevenson's life; Cuba missile crisis; 1960 Democratic Convention; family homes, Libertyville and Bloomington; evaluation of brother's biographers; 1948 Illinois gubernatorial campaign; governorship, 1949–53; 1956 campaign; UN mission, 1961–65; family anecdotes and childhood recollections; impressions of Stevenson's personal friends and recollections of his relationships with John F. Kennedy and Robert F. Kennedy, Richard J. Daley, Hubert H. Humphrey, Lyndon B. Johnson, William McCormick Blair, Jr., Willard Wirtz, and others.
Part I: 52 pp. *Permission required.* 1966.
Part II: 257 pp. *Permission required.* 1969.

IVES, Ernest (1887–1972) *See* Adlai E. Stevenson Project.

JABARA, James. *See* Aviation.

JABLONOWER, Joseph (1888–1971) Educator.

Childhood in Austria; NYC, Lower East side, 1896; Teachers Union, 1916; Ethical Culture School, 1919; influence and development of Ethical Culture; views on WWI; Vienna, 1932–33; teachers union, 1930's; Communist influence; Board of Examiners, NYC Board of Education, 1940–59; choosing teachers, salaries, state control vs. autonomy, underprivileged neighborhoods, strikes; progressive education. Impressions of Felix Adler, David Muzzey, George Counts.
379 pp. *Permission required to cite or quote.* 1965.

JACK, Samuel Sloan (1905–   ) *See* Marine Corps.

JACKSON, Frederick Herbert (1919–   )
CARNEGIE CORPORATION

Carnegie Corporation, 1955–64; mathematics program, university self-studies, honors programs, Chinese and Japanese language programs; evaluation of grants, daily routine, board of trustees; role of foundation officer; Negro education; administrator at NYU, 1964. Impressions of John Gardner, James Perkins, Florence Anderson.
305 pp. *Permission required.* 1967.

JACKSON, Gardner (1896–1965) Public official.

Youth, family background, education; newspaper reporter, Boston and Washington; Sacco-Vanzetti defense; Mooney report; Bonus Army; AAA; New Deal; liberalism in the 1930's, labor movement; impressions of Henry Wallace, Claude Wickard, Herbert Parisius, John L. Lewis, Felix Frankfurter, Louis D. Brandeis, Jerome Frank, Alger Hiss, Drew Pearson, Arthur Schlesinger.
786 pp. *Permission required to cite or quote.* 1955. NYT (Part I).
See also La Follette Civil Liberties Committee.

JACKSON, Robert Houghwout (1892–1954) Supreme Court Justice.

Lawyer, upper NY State; General Counsel, Bureau of Internal Revenue; Assistant Attorney General, Tax Division and Anti-Trust Division of the US Department of Justice; Solicitor General; Attorney General; Justice of the US Supreme Court; US Prosecutor at Nuremberg War Crimes Trials.

1,672 pp. *Closed until June 1, 1980.* 1952.

JACKSON HOLE PRESERVE

This project relates the history of Jackson Hole Preserve, describing the Rockefeller family's interest in preserving and protecting the area and problems encountered in acquiring the land which was eventually added to the National Park System. Included are memoirs of people who knew Jackson Hole as their home and who have experienced the transformation of the area since it became part of the National Park System in the 1940's.

Participants and pages: Horace M. Albright, 238; Mrs. Struthers Burt, 91; Kenneth Chorley, 160; Harold Fabian, 106; Clifford P. Hansen, 53; Harry E. Klissold, 50; W. C. Lawrence, 51; Leslie A. Miller, 122; Homer C. Richards, 53; Laurance Rockefeller, 42; Conrad L. Wirth, 76; Mike Yokel, 38.

1,080 pp. *Permission required.* 1966.
Underwritten by Jackson Hole Preserve, Inc.

JACOBS, Albert Charles (1900–   ) *See* Eisenhower Administration.

JACOBS, CARLYLE. *See* Health Science.

JACOBY, Neil H. (1909–   ) Economist.
EISENHOWER ADMINISTRATION

University of Chicago, 1937–42; Dean, College of Business Administration, University of California, 1948; Council of Economic Advisors, 1953–55: functions, personnel, philosophy, goals; relationship with UN Department of Economic Affairs; US representative to UNESCO, 1957; comments on Federal Reserve system, Commodity Credit Corporation, agricultural economics, social legislation. Impressions of President Eisenhower, Arthur Burns, Raymond Saulnier, Walter Stewart, George Humphrey.

141 pp. *Permission required to cite or quote.* 1970.
Also available at the University of California at Los Angeles.

JACQUITH, James. *See* Civil Rights in Alabama.

JAMES, E. P. H. *See* Radio Pioneers.

JAMES, George (1915–1972) *See* Mt. Sinai Hospital.

JAMIESON, Francis Anthony (1904–1960) Newspaperman.

Reporter in Albany; Lindbergh kidnapping; New Jersey politics during Frank Hague's rule and Charles Edison's governorship; work in the NY office of the AP and founding of the Newspaper Guild; public relations adviser, Office of Inter-American Affairs under Nelson Rockefeller; admission of Argentina to the UN; role of the Rockefeller family in locating the UN in NYC.

205 pp. *Permission required.* 1952.

JANIN, Ernesto. Labor leader.

ARGENTINA IN THE 1930'S

Socialists, syndicalists, Communists, and anarchists in Argentine labor during 1930's: influence, strength, shifting alliances, organization of new unions; strikes, increase in union membership; Angel Borlenghi and Jose Domenech.

57 pp. *Open.* 1970.

JANIS, Eddie. *See* Radio Pioneers.

JANSEN, William (1887-1968) Educator.

Early years and education; teacher, principal, assistant superintendent, superintendent of schools in NYC, 1947-58; impressions of William Kilpatrick, George Strayer, and other TC professors; Communist purge in NYC schools; Bronx Park experiment; banning of the *Nation*.
163 pp. *Permission required to cite or quote*. 1963. NYT (Part I).

JASON, Hillard. *See* Mt. Sinai Hospital.

JASTROW, Robert (1925–   ) *See* Columbia Television Lectures.

JAURETCHE, Arturo. Politician.
ARGENTINA IN THE 1930'S

Participation in several revolutionary movements as politician and writer; FORJA, 1936; association with Peronist movement in 1943; break with Peron, 1950.
221 pp. *Open*. 1971.

JAVITS, Jacob Koppel (1904–   ) *See* Eisenhower Administration *and* Social Security.

JEFFORD, Jack. *See* Aviation.

JENSEN, Oliver (1914–   ) Editor, writer.

Career as a picture book publisher; editor, *Life* magazine; founding *American Heritage;* impressions of Joseph J. Thorndike and James Parton.
29 pp. *Open*. 1959.

JERSILD, Arthur T. (1902–   ) Psychologist, educator.

Education, South Dakota and Nebraska; T C, 1929; consulting psychologist to CBS, 1935-48; Institute for Educational

Leadership in Japan, 1948–49; school consultant; impressions of educators James Russell and William Russell, William H. Kilpatrick, and Edward R. Thorndike.
255 pp. *Permission required to cite or quote.* 1967. NYT (Part I).

JESSUP, Frederick P. (1920–) Government official.
EISENHOWER ADMINISTRATION

The politics and growth of intelligence operations, 1946–72, with reference to CIA; Germany in the 1950's; US diplomatic personnel, Switzerland and Israel, 1957–63; NSC staff work, 1963–72; US-Israeli relations; impressions of Robert A. McClure, Lucian Truscott, Allen Dulles, McGeorge Bundy, Walt Rostow, Henry Kissinger, and others.
105 pp. *Permission required.* 1972.

JESSUP, Philip Caryl (1897–) Diplomat, scholar.

Early years and education; teaching international law at Columbia University; State Department; research on neutrality; setting up Naval School of Military Government and Administration at Columbia; work with Herbert Lehman organizing OFRRO and later UNRRA; international conferences (UNRRA, Bretton Woods, San Francisco); US delegation to the UN; impressions of personalities in American government; Joseph McCarthy charges and Senate investigations.
388 pp. *Permission required.* 1958.
See also Journalism Lectures.

JOFRE, Emilio (1907–) Politician.
ARGENTINA IN THE 1930'S

Lawyer, joined Democratic Party, 1931; economics and politics of Mendoza, Argentina; relation of provincial and national governments; foreign agricultural workers, sharecropping, viniculture; petroleum development; Peronism; Governor Ricardo Videla.
40 pp. *Open.* 1971.

REFER TO "NOTES ON USE" IN INTRODUCTION

JOHNS, S. P., Jr. *See* Weyerhaeuser Timber Company.

JOHNSON, Alfred Wilkinson (1876–1963) Naval officer.

Naval family background; Annapolis; Spanish-American War; early cruises; naval inventions; instructor at Naval Academy 1907–10.
88 pp. *Permission required to cite or quote.* 1962. NYT (Part I).

JOHNSON, Alvin (1874–1971) Writer, educator.

Early years in the Middle West; education; teaching at Columbia; impressions of Nicholas Murray Butler and faculty members; *New Republic* and impressions of Walter Lippmann and Herbert Croly; New School.
195 pp. *Permission required to cite or quote.* 1960. NYT (Part I).
See also New School Lectures.

JOHNSON, David Dean (1899–   ) *See* Benedum and the Oil Industry.

JOHNSON, Guion Griffis (Mrs. Guy B.) *See* Carnegie Corporation.

JOHNSON, Guy Benton (1901–   ) Sociologist.
SOUTHERN INTELLECTUAL LEADERS

Childhood and education in rural Texas; graduate work, University of Chicago, University of North Carolina; research on race relations in the South; St. Helena Island Study, 1928–29; teaching career, University of North Carolina; research associate, *An American Dilemma;* Director, Southern Regional Council, 1945–47; trustee, Howard University. Impressions of Gunnar Myrdal and Howard W. Odum.
171 pp. *Closed pending publication of a study.* 1972.
See also Carnegie Corporation.

JOHNSON, Jesse Charles (1894–   ) *See* Eisenhower Administration.

JOHNSON, Joseph Esrey (1906–   ) Professor of History.

Activities in Latin American diplomacy; Dumbarton Oaks Conference; Division of International Security Affairs. 58 pp. *Closed during lifetime.* 1951. *See also* Carnegie Corporation, International Negotiations, *and* United Nations Conference.

JOHNSON, Lydia (1893–   ) *See* China Missionaries.

JOHNSON, Nelson Trusler (1887–1954) Diplomat.

Family background and early life; experiences as student interpreter for Consular Service in China, 1907; Battle of the Concessions, Open Door Policy; Manchuria, 1909–10; concession railways; Tai-ping rebellion; Revolution of 1911; Yale-in-China activities; Chinese social life and attitudes, early 1900's; recall to Washington and preparations for the Washington Conference; appointment as inspection officer in China, 1923. 730 pp. *Permission required to cite or quote.* 1954. NYT (Part I).

JOHNSON, Nunnally (1897–   ) *See* Popular Arts.

JOHNSON, Robert S. *See* Aviation.

JOHNSON, Walter (1915–   ) *See* Adlai E. Stevenson Project.

JOHNSTON, Eric A. (1896–1963) *See* Popular Arts.

JOLLY, Thomas David (1891–   ) *See* James B. Duke Project.

JONES, Caswell S. *See* Benedum and the Oil Industry.

JONES, Charles Sherman (1894–   ) *See* Aviation.

JONES, Francis Price (1890–   ) *See* China Missionaries.

JONES, Louis Reeder. *See* Marine Corps.

JONES, Lucile Williams (Mrs. Francis) (1889–   ) *See* China Missionaries.

JONES, Marvin (1880–   ) Jurist, legislator.

Youth and education; early law practice in Amarillo, Texas; US Congress; WWI; legislative organization and procedure; farm legislation; Farm Bureau; National Grange; Farmers' Union; McNary-Haugen Bill; House Agricultural Committee; state and national elections, 1928–40; Agricultural Adjustment Act; Franklin D. Roosevelt and the New Deal; Emergency Farm Mortgage Act; Farm Credit Act; Federal Farm Bankruptcy Act; Soil Conservation and Domestic Allotment Act; RA; OES; WFA; President, Hot Springs Food Conference, 1943; WFA, 1943–45; US Court of Claims; impressions of Henry A. Wallace, George Peek, James F. Byrnes, Claude Wickard, Chester Davis, and others.
1,453 pp. *Permission required to cite or quote.* 1953. NYT (Part I).

JONES, Roger Warren (1908–   ) Government official.
EISENHOWER ADMINISTRATION
WWII experience with Combined Chiefs of Staff; Bureau of the Budget; US Civil Service Commission; legislation and personnel in the Eisenhower administration.
73 pp. *Permission required to cite or quote.* 1967.

JONES, William J. *See* Benedum and the Oil Industry.

JORALEMON, Ira Beaman (1884–) *See* Mining Engineers.

JORDAHL, Russell Nelton (1903–) Marine Corps officer.

Family background; Nicaragua, 1928–30; Shanghai, 1932–35; Personnel Officer, HQMC, 1941–44, Pacific, 1944–47; Parris Island, 1947–50; Korea, 1951–52; USMC administrative and personnel matters, WWII and Korea; vignettes of associates.
202 pp. *Open.* 1970.

JORDAN, Joseph. *See* Flying Tigers.

JOSEPHS, Devereux Colt (1893–) Executive.
CARNEGIE CORPORATION
Personal background; vice president, later president, of TIAA, 1939–45; president, Carnegie Corporation, 1946–48; philosophy of Corporation; projects, selection of staff; Alger Hiss; impressions of trustees and staff.
150 pp. *Permission required.* 1967.

JOSEPHSON, Matthew (1899–) *See* LaFollette Civil Liberties Committee.

JOURNALISM LECTURES

Guest lecturers at the Graduate School of Journalism of Columbia University occasionally provide firsthand accounts of pivotal events. Benjamin Fine's account of the integration crisis of Central High School in Little Rock, Harrison Salisbury's description of Nikita Khrushchev's visit to the US and the "Battle of Coon Rapids," and Tom Wicker's recitation of the aftermath of the assassination of John F. Kennedy are examples. Other lectures grouped under this heading range from Watson Berry's on NYC journalism in the 1890's to discussions of the role of the news media from the 1950's on.

Participants and pages: Dean Acheson, 39; Brooks Atkinson, 29; Hanson Baldwin, 17; Ross Barnett, 23; Watson Berry, 25; Herbert Block, 34; Rob-

REFER TO "NOTES ON USE" IN INTRODUCTION

ert Briscoe, 24; Ted Cott, 36; Norman Cousins, 26; Clifton Daniel, 76; Allen W. Dulles, 27; Benjamin Fine, 25; Max Freedman, 29; John V. Lindsay, 22; Walter Lippmann, 58; Samuel Lubell, 127; Malcolm X, 38; Lester Markel, 46; Herbert Mayes, 29; Sig Mickelson, 31; James Reston, 46; William Rusher, 66; Harrison Salisbury, 65; David Schoenbrun, 46; Harry S. Truman, 13; Tom Wicker, 40.

1,037 pp. *Permission required to cite or quote.*

A. BASIC ISSUES IN THE NEWS

In these lectures, given at the Graduate School of Journalism (1959–1963) each scholar has undertaken to tell newsmen something of what they need to know in his area of specialization.

Participants, topics, and pages: Adolf Berle on economics, 29; John Ray Dunning on nuclear energy, 104; Louis Hollander on the labor movement, 58; Philip Jessup on the national state and the international community, 85; Polykarp Kusch on physics, 17; Wallace Sayre on the problems of the city, 136.

429 pp. *Permission required.*

B. CONSUMER REPORTING

Two conferences at the Graduate School of Journalism examined problems facing journalists in covering the consumer movement. Aspects of reporting product analysis, consumer research, and ecological questions are discussed.

982 pp. *Permission required to cite or quote.* 1971–72.

C. FORUMS

Two Columbia forums assess American journalism in the 1960's, the first from the several vantage points of learned observers, the second from those of professionals in the field.

Forum I: Grayson Kirk, moderator; Charles Frankel, Polykarp Kusch, Margaret Mead, Leo Rosten.
Forum II: Edward W. Barrett, moderator; Hodding Carter, Max Lerner, Marya Mannes, Michael J. Ogden, Eric Sevareid.

105 pp. *Permission required to cite or quote.* 1963.

JOYCE, George J. *See* New York Political Studies.

JUDD, Walter H. (1898–   ) Physician, Congressman.
EISENHOWER ADMINISTRATION

Personal background, religion; University of Nebraska, 1916, Medical School, 1919; missionary doctor in China, 1925–31, 1934–37; lecturing against Communism, 1937–40; Congressman from Minnesota, 1943; Chiang Kai-shek and Nationalist government; Marshall Plan; nomination of Dwight D. Eisenhower; Geneva Conference, 1955; State Department; US foreign policy. Impressions of John Foster Dulles, Richard Nixon, John F. Kennedy.
149 pp. *Permission required.* 1970.

JUDSON, Arthur (1881–   ) *See* Radio Pioneers.

KADES, Charles Louis (1906–   ) *See* Occupation of Japan.

KAHLER, Herbert. *See* Independence Park.

KAILO, Meyer. *See* New York Political Studies.

KALAND, William J. *See* Radio Pioneers.

KALTENBORN, Hans V. (1878–1965) Editor, radio commentator.
RADIO PIONEERS

Childhood and early occupations; Harvard; Brooklyn *Eagle;* radio broadcaster with several NYC stations and CBS and NBC networks, 1921–50; organized Association of Radio News Analysts, 1942; views on past and future roles of radio; visits to Russia, 1926, 1929; impressions of Adolf Hitler, Calvin Coolidge, and others.
248 pp. *Permission required to cite or quote.* 1950. NYT (Part I).

KAMARCK, Andrew Martin (1914–   ) *See* World Bank.

REFER TO "NOTES ON USE" IN INTRODUCTION

KANDEL, Isaac Leon (1881–1965) Educator.

Education in US and abroad; TC, 1913–46: comparative, permissive, and progressive education; foreign students, travel, pensions. Impressions of John Dewey, W. H. Kilpatrick, George Counts, and other educators.
85 pp. *Permission required to cite or quote.* 1962. NYT (Part I).

KAPLAN, Joseph (1892–   ) Physicist.

National Academy of Science; government support and influence for basic research facilities; IGY, National Committee: panels, chairman's role, international program, space questions, use of IGY information.
82 pp. *Permission required.* 1960.

KAPLOW, Jeffrey. *See* Columbia Crisis of 1968.

KAPP, Dave. *See* Popular Arts.

KARAM, James. *See* Eisenhower Administration.

KARDINER, Abram (1891–   ) Psychoanalyst.
PSYCHOANALYTIC MOVEMENT
Early childhood and education in NYC; Cornell Medical College; analysis by Sigmund Freud; Vienna in the 1920's, association with leading figures in the psychoanalytic movement; work with Drs. W. H. Frink, A. A. Brill, Otto Rank, Franz Alexander; New York psychoanalytic movement, 1920's and 1930's; activities and associations as lecturer in anthropology, Columbia University; chairman of Columbia Psychoanalytic Clinic's research seminar on comparative analysis of cultures, 1939–51; director, 1955–57; development as practicing psychoanalyst, interest in anthropology; research in the relation of psychiatry and the social sciences; discussion of his major books.
712 pp. *Open except for specified pages.* 1963.

215

KARK, Alan Eugene (1921–   ) *See* Mt. Sinai Hospital.

KARTVELI, Alexander (1896–   ) *See* Aviation.

KASPER, Joseph Phillip (1897–   ) *See* Federated Department Stores.

KAUFMAN, Boris. *See* Popular Arts.

KAUFMAN, Ralph. *See* Mt. Sinai Hospital.

KAUFMANN, Arthur. *See* Independence Park.

KAUL, Brij Mohan (–1972) Indian Army officer.

Education, Royal Military College, Sandhurst, 1933; Rajputana Rifles; Secretary, Nationalization Committee, India, 1946–47; India's Military Attaché, Washington, D.C., 1947; adviser, Indian delegation to UN Security Council, 1948; fought in the Kashmir War till the end of 1948; commander, infantry brigade and division, 1948–56; Chief of Staff, Neutral Nations Repatriation Commission, Korea, 1953–54; visits to Peking and other parts of China, 1954; Quartermaster General, 1959–61; Chief of the General Staff, Indian Army, 1961–62; Chinese invasion of India, 1962; premature resignation from the Indian Army, December, 1962; impressions of Jawaharlal Nehru, Krishna Menon, and many others.
445 pp. *Permission required.* 1964.

KAZAN, Abraham (–1971) Labor leader.

Early life; immigration to US; ILGWU; Union Welfare Fund; ILGWU Cooperative Ventures; union housing; problems in cooperative housing; Twin Lake Cooperative Farm; United Housing Foundation; self help in cooperatives. Recollections of Sidney Hillman, Robert Moses, Jacob Potofsky.
554 pp. *Permission required.* 1968.

REFER TO "NOTES ON USE" IN INTRODUCTION

KAZIN, Alfred (1915–   ) *See* American Historians *and* Richard Hofstadter Project.

KEATING, Kenneth B. (1900–   ) Senator, ambassador.
EISENHOWER ADMINISTRATION
Service in House and Senate; President Eisenhower's relations with Congress; 1958 NY Senate campaign; Judiciary and Space Committees.
126 pp. *Permission required to cite or quote.* 1968.

KEATON, Buster (1896–1966) *See* Popular Arts.

KEENEY, Barnaby (1914–   ) *See* American Cultural Leaders.

KEEZER, Dexter Merriam (1896–   ) *See* McGraw-Hill.

KEFAUVER, Estes (1903–1963) *See* Herbert H. Lehman Project.

KELLAND, Clarence Budington (1881–1964) Author, politician.

Family background; life in Michigan in 1900; Henry Ford and the Ford Motor Company; writer, editor of *American Boy*, publicity director of the YMCA in France, WWI; beginnings in politics; presidential conventions, especially 1952; experiences in Arizona as Republican National Committeeman.
164 pp. *Open.* 1952.

KELLERMAN, Henry Joseph (1910–   ) *See* Eisenhower Administration.

KELLEY, Nicholas (1885–1965) Lawyer.

Family background; Harvard College and Law School; experiences at Cravath, Henderson & De Gersdorff and other firms; war loan staff of the Department of the Treasury during WWI; business reorganization work; trip to Peru as head of mission on behalf of American banking interests; reorganization of the Maxwell Company into the Chrysler Corporation; detailed description of the Chrysler Corporation, including production, finances and labor; Automobile Labor Board during the New Deal; Chrysler strikes in 1937 and 1939; anti-trust action against the automobile industry in 1937; Chrysler's war contracts; philanthropic activities.

522 pp. *Permission required to cite or quote.* 1953. NYT (Part I). Papers.

KELLOGG, Royal S. (–1965) *See* Forest History Society.

KELLY, Gene Curran (1912–   ) *See* Popular Arts.

KELLY, Hugh Joseph (1905–   ) *See* McGraw-Hill.

KELSO, Winchester (1895–   ) *See* Benedum and the Oil Industry.

KEMPER, John Mason (1912–1971) Army officer, educator.

Family background, education; West Point.
113 pp. *Permission required to cite or quote.* 1963.

KENDALL, David Walbridge (1903–   ) *See* Eisenhower Administration.

KENDALL, Edward Calvin (1886–1972) *See* Nobel Laureates.

KENEN, Peter B. (1932–   ) *See* Columbia Crisis of 1968.

KENNEDY, Elsie Parsons (Mrs. John D.) (1903–1966)

Recollections of parents and grandparents; Newport and

NY society; Republican Convention, 1920; real estate developments, NYC, 1920's. Also a brief interview with John D. Kennedy.
58 pp. *Permission required to cite or quote.* 1962. NYT (Part II).

KENNEDY, John D. *See* Elsie Parsons Kennedy.

KENNEDY, Ken. *See* Radio Pioneers.

KENT, Rockwell (1882–1971) *See* Friends of the Columbia Libraries.

KEOGH, Eugene James (1907–   ) Congressman.

NY State politics, 1930–36; national politics, 1937–50.
82 pp. *Permission required to cite or quote.* 1950. NYT (Part I).

KEPPEL, Francis (1916–   ) *See* Carnegie Corporation.

KERR, Barbara. *See* Adlai E. Stevenson Project.

KHEEL, Theodore Woodrow (1914–   ) Lawyer, mediator.
INTERNATIONAL NEGOTIATIONS
General philosophy of mediation; examples from his career.
43 pp. *Permission required to cite or quote.* 1969.

KIDD, Charles Vincent (1914–   ) *See* Health Science.

KIEFFER, Jarold Alan (1923–   ) *See* Social Security.

KILLIAN, James R., Jr. (1904–   ) Scientist.
EISENHOWER ADMINISTRATION
Special Assistant to President Eisenhower for Science and Technology; President's Science Advisory Committee;

Technological Capabilities Panel; Department of Defense; State Department; CIA; NSC; National Science Foundation; relations with President Eisenhower; effect of Sputnik; science and government; influence and limitations of a science adviser; Defense Communications Agency; Advanced Research Projects Agency; Geneva Conference on nuclear test detection.
375 pp. *Closed until 1985.* 1970.
Contributed by Stephen White, New York.

KILPATRICK, William Heard (1871–1965) Educator.

Georgia during Reconstruction; Mercer University; Johns Hopkins; John Dewey and theories of teaching; board of trustees, Bennington College; General Education Board; Lincoln and Horace Mann Schools; education experiments at TC; impressions of William Russell and James Russell, Edward Thorndike, Nicholas Murray Butler, Harold Rugg, George Counts, John Childs, Montessori system; project method.
212 pp. *Open.* 1961.

KIMBALL, Arthur Alden (1908–   ) Government official.
EISENHOWER ADMINISTRATION
Early career; International Information Administration; Senator Joseph McCarthy; USIA; President's Advisory Committee on Government Organization.
104 pp. *Permission required to cite or quote.* 1967.

KIMBALL, Doris Fleeson. *See* Adlai E. Stevenson Project.

KIMBRELL, Marvin. *See* James B. Duke Project.

KIMMEY, J. E. *See* Columbia Television Lectures.

KINDELBERGER, James Howard (1895–1962) *See* Henry H. Arnold Project.

KING, Jimmy, Sr. *See* Marine Corps.

Columbia University

KINKAID, Thomas Cassin (1888–1972) Naval officer.

Education, Naval Academy; world cruise, 1908; Turkey, burning of Smyrna; Geneva Conference, 1932; Naval Attaché, Rome and Belgrade, 1938–41; Benito Mussolini, Galeazzo Ciano, Bernard Berenson, Spanish royal family; destroyer squadron, convoy duty; Pearl Harbor, 1941; Task Force II, carrier operations, Coral Sea, Midway, Guadalcanal, Eastern Solomons; Commander North Pacific Fleet, Aleutians; combat intelligence; preparations for Philippine campaign; detailed description of Leyte Gulf and subsequent operations; Yellow Sea and Korea; Shanghai, Chungking; impressions of Gen. Douglas MacArthur, Chiang Kai-shek, many prominent naval and political figures.
450 pp. *Permission required.* 1961.

KIRCHHOFER, Alfred Henry (1892–) *See* Radio Pioneers.

KIRK, Alan Goodrich (1888–1963) Naval officer.

Background and education, Naval Academy; European cruises, Asiatic Fleet, Canton, 1911, Sun Yat Sen; WWI, fleet exercises; Naval Proving Ground, testing ordnance; Presidential yacht *Mayflower*, Warren G. Harding; Bureau of Ordnance; Australia, 1925; fleet gunnery officer; Naval War College, 1928–29; Naval Attaché, London, 1939–41; Joseph P. Kennedy; Director of Naval Intelligence, 1941; codes and war plans; Atlantic Fleet; naval mission to London, 1942–43; Mediterranean; amphibious force, 1943; John Mason Brown; North African landings; Operation Husky; planning for Normandy; impressions of many outstanding naval and political figures.
386 pp. *Permission required to cite or quote.* 1961. NYT (Part I).

KIRK, Grayson Louis (1903–) *See* Columbia Crisis of 1968 *and* United Nations Conference.

KIRKLAND, Edward Chase (1894–   ) *See* American Historians.

KIRKPATRICK, Sidney Dale (1894–   ) *See* McGraw-Hill.

KLAYF, Bernard Spencer (1921–   ) *See* Federated Department Stores.

KLEIN, Herbert George (1918–   ) Newspaper editor.
EISENHOWER ADMINISTRATION
Richard M. Nixon's elections to the House and Senate; 1952 campaign and election; Nixon fund.
39 pp. *Closed during lifetime.* 1967.

KLEIN, Joseph J. (1884–   ) Accountant.

Recollections of CCNY as student, teacher, member of NYC Board of Higher Education; Council for National Defense and Internal Revenue Service, WWI; career as accountant: certification, founding of Klein, Hines, and Fink; taxation work; Ivar Kreuger International Match Co. case. Impressions of Julius Rosenthal, Felix Warburg, Morris Raphael Cohen.
193 pp. *Permission required to cite or quote.* 1969.

KLEIN, Samuel. *See* Mt. Sinai Hospital.

KLEIN, Solomon A. Lawyer.
NEW YORK POLITICAL STUDIES
Immigration to US; education, Cornell College, Harvard Law School; association with Harry G. Anderson, 1935–39; Kings County District Attorney's office from 1940; chief of Appeal Bureau; views on religion, ethics, politics; Manton case; organized crime; Murder, Inc. cases; blue ribbon juries; selection of jurors. Impressions of William O'Dwyer, Burton Turkus, Samuel Liebowitz.
160 pp. *Permission required.* 1962.

REFER TO "NOTES ON USE" IN INTRODUCTION

This photo essay on Oral History's first 25 years opens with our favorite picture of its founder, Allan Nevins (q.v.) in the office, 1958.

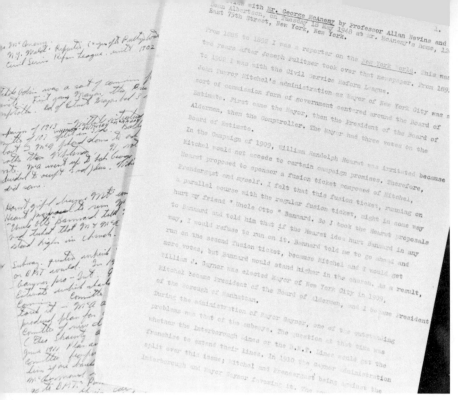

*Page one of the first transcript is shown
with the notes from which it was composed,
May 18, 1948—before the dawn of
tape recording.*
Below: *Wire recorders came first, as these
transcribers show, along with 1949's
"New Look."*

Allan Nevins interviews Herbert Lehman (q.v.) *in the study of the Governor's Park Avenue apartment, December, 1949. Later interviews led to Nevins's biography of Lehman, and ultimately to the beautiful suite where the Lehman papers now live at Columbia.*

Above: *Henry A. Wallace affixes his signature to one of Oral History's longest memoirs, 1951.* Below: *Transcribers work from tape recorders, 1953, Claudine Tillier Knight in foreground.*

*Dean Albertson, left, a Nevins
graduate student who became
Oral History's first employee,
interviews James P. Warburg
(q.v.), 1953.*

*Elizabeth Mason, associate director,
examines a transcript in the office. Boxes in
the background hold thousands of pages
awaiting editing by interviewees or indexing.*

*Two previous editions of this
work, with a supplement
published in between, are
flanked by reports dating from
1960 (top right) to 1971
(top left). These have spread
the gospel.*

James C. Hagerty (q.v.) *recalls Eisenhower Administration experiences for Ed Edwin and Oral History in his New York office, 1967.*

Dwight Eisenhower scribbled this note on yellow foolscap (slightly revised in type) about our project on his administration (q.v.).

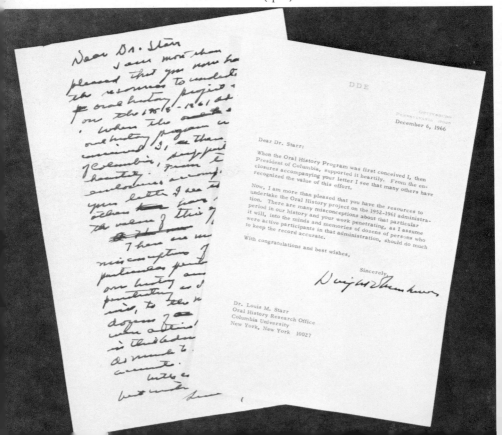

DDE

December 6, 1966

Dear Dr. Starr:

When the Oral History Program was first conceived I, then President of Columbia, supported it heartily. From the enclosures accompanying your letter I see that many others have recognized the value of this effort.

Now, I am more than pleased that you have the resources to undertake the Oral History project on the 1952-1961 administration. There are many misconceptions about that particular period in our history and your work penetrating, as I assume it will, into the minds and memories of dozens of persons who were active participants in that administration, should do much to keep the record accurate.

With congratulations and best wishes,

Sincerely,

Dwight Eisenhower

Dr. Louis M. Starr
Oral History Research Office
Columbia University
New York, New York 10027

Anna Lord Strauss (q.v.) *in the study of her New York apartment, comes to a vital episode in the series obtained for Oral History by Mrs. Walter Gellhorn, right, in 1973. By now, tape recorders are barely in evidence.*

A selection of history titles published in the early 1970s suggests the widely varying interests of scholars who draw upon the Collection.

Open" memoirs line the galleries of the Manuscript Reading Room, a secluded retreat on the 8th floor of Butler Library.

Chester M. Lewis, archivist of the New York Times,
presents the first microfiche of an Oral History memoir
to Professor Louis M. Starr as Mrs. Mason looks on,
June, 1972. In this form, other libraries share
unrestricted memoirs.

Mrs. Mason reads a transcript in a new portable microfiche reader. Each fiche holds 98 pages, and Part One of the micro edition, 200 memoirs running to 55,000 pages, fits into the box in the foreground.

Biographies make up the largest category of books drawing upon Oral History at Columbia, as suggested by these notable ones of the '70s. Shown with them are autobiographies that originated as Oral History memoirs, by Cass Canfield and Warren Weaver.

Professor Starr, director of Oral History since 1956, interviews Joan Seligman, Columbia Library Systems analyst, to plan this first computerized edition of The Oral History Collection.

Considerable use of memoirs in the Collection is made in each of these volumes, winners of Pulitzer Prizes, top to bottom, for 1971, 1970, and 1972.

KLINGENSTEIN, Percy (1896–   ) *See* Mt. Sinai Hospital.

KLISSOLD, Harry E. *See* Jackson Hole Preserve.

KLOPFER, Donald Simon (1902–   ) Publisher.

William Faulkner's funeral in Oxford, Mississippi.
11 pp. *Open.* 1962.

KLOPSTEG, Paul Ernest (1889–   ) *See* American Association of Physics Teachers.

KNAPP, James. *See* Mining Engineers.

KNAPP, Joseph Burke (1913–   ) *See* World Bank.

KNIGHT, Goodwin (1896–1970) Government official.
EISENHOWER ADMINISTRATION
California politics; Presidential campaigning; Republican Party politics, 1950's; Elephant-Eagle Mine. Recollections of Richard M. Nixon, Dwight D. Eisenhower, William F. Knowland, Earl Warren.
94 pp. *Permission required.* 1967.

KNIGHT, Kirk. Program manager.
RADIO PIONEERS
Early days in radio announcing at WJBK, Ypsilanti, and WEXL, Detroit; television programing from 1948, WWJ, Detroit.
34 pp. *Open.* 1951.

KNOERR, Alvin. *See* McGraw-Hill.

KNOPF, Alfred A. (1892–   ) Publisher.

Early life in NYC; Columbia College; years with Doubleday, Page & Co. and Mitchell Kennerley; founding of own firm, 1915; notable early publications; Anthony Comstock and other book censors; H. L. Mencken, George Jean Nathan, and the *American Mercury;* book design; growth of the firm; vignettes of Charles A. Beard, Willa Cather, Clarence Day, Joseph Hergesheimer, Thomas Mann, Katherine Mansfield, and others.

325 pp. *Permission required.* 1961.

KNOWLAND, William Fife (1908–   ) Senator, publisher.

EISENHOWER ADMINISTRATION

1952 convention; California delegation; Nixon fund; President Eisenhower's relations with Congress; domestic legislation; foreign policy; Richard M. Nixon and the 1956 convention; 1960 campaign; Senator Knowland's career; 1958 gubernatorial campaign; California politics; "right to work" issue; relations with President Eisenhower: appointments, role of Senate Majority Leader, president as party leader; Senator Joseph McCarthy; Joint Committee on Atomic Energy.

170 pp. *Permission required to cite or quote.* 1970.

KOBACK, Edgar (1895–1962) Business consultant.

MCGRAW-HILL

McGraw-Hill from 1916; business manager of *Electrical World;* aviation, electronics, and nucleonics; stock participation; corporate building erected during Depression; NBC vice president.

120 pp. *Permission required.* 1956.

KOENIG, Robert P. (1904–   ) Engineer, geologist, executive.

Education; early experience in mining in Latin America, 1925–35; Lehman Brothers and Electric Shovel Corporation, 1935–39.

121 pp. *Closed during lifetime.* 1964.

See also Mining Engineers.

REFER TO "NOTES ON USE" IN INTRODUCTION

KOENIG, Samuel S. (1872–1955) Lawyer, politician.

NY politics, 1905–35: state elections, Republican nominations, and party background.
53 pp. *Permission required to cite or quote.* 1950. NYT (Part I).

KOH, T. B. *See* International Negotiations.

KOHLER, Walter Jodok, Jr. (1904–   ) *See* Eisenhower Administration.

KOHLMAN, Edwina. *See* Book-of-the-Month Club.

KOHN, Louis A. (1907–   ) *See* Adlai E. Stevenson Project.

KOLB, Lawrence Coleman (1911–   ) *See* Health Science.

KOO, Vi Kyuin Wellington (1888–   ) *See* Chinese Oral History.

KORNBERG, Arthur (1918–   ) *See* Nobel Laureates.

KRAFT, Alice E. *See* McGraw-Hill.

KRAMER, Dale (–1966) *See* Farm Holiday Association.

KRAMER, Kenneth (1904–   ) *See* McGraw-Hill.

KRANTZ, Aron. *See* Aviation.

KROCK, Arthur (1887–   ) Newspaperman.

NY Democratic Party, 1920's; Charles F. Murphy; NY *World*, 1923–27; NY *Times*, 1927; reporting Washington politics for NY *Times*, 1932–50: campaigns of 1932 and 1936, Brain Trust, NRA, foreign policy, preparations for war; Pearl Harbor, Yalta Conference; impressions of many political figures.

102 pp. *Permission required to cite or quote.* 1950. NYT (Part I).

KROLL, Leon (1884–   ) Artist.

Family background and early education in NYC; studies in Europe; experiences exhibiting and teaching; associations with the McDowell group; technique and philosophy of painting; work as a muralist; illustrated discussion of 158 of his paintings, drawings, and murals.
259 pp. *Permission required to cite or quote.* 1957. NYT (Part II). Papers.

KRULAK, Victor Harold (1913–   ) Marine Corps officer.

Education; early assignments, Shanghai, 1937–39, Sino-Japanese War; Aide to Gen. Holland M. Smith; Okinawa operation and Tsingtao occupation; unification fight; Korea: Inchon landing, Chosin reservoir operation; Secretary of the General Staff, HQMC, 1951–55, Lemuel Shepherd Commandancy; Special Assistant for Counter-insurgency Matters to Secretary of Defense Robert McNamara, 1962–64; CG, Fleet Marine Force, Pacific, 1964–68; reminiscences of USMC personalities.
227 pp. *Permission required.* 1970.

KRULEWITCH, Melvin Levin (1895–   ) *See* Marine Corps.

KUME, Ai. *See* Occupation of Japan.

KUNG, Hsiang-hsi (1881–1967) *See* Chinese Oral History.

KUNZIG, Robert Lowe (1918–   ) *See* Eisenhower Administration.

KUPER, Theodore Fred (1886–   ) Lawyer.

Education, NYU Law School; early practice, NYC; oil busi-

ness; Thomas Jefferson Memorial Foundation, 1923–32; acquisition of Monticello; efforts to preserve other Virginia antiquities; consultant to NYC Board of Education, 1927–43. Impressions of Fiorello LaGuardia and Claude G. Bowers.
186 pp. *Permission required to cite or quote.* 1963. NYT (Part I).

Account of 1911 insurgency in the NY Legislature.
17 pp. *Open.* 1968.

Creation of the Fashion Institute of Technology and Educational Foundation for the Fashion Industry.
16 pp. *Open.* 1971.

KURJACK, Dennis. *See* Independence Park.

KUSCH, Polykarp (1911–   ) Physicist.

Part I: Family background and early education; Cleveland Public Library; Case Institute and University of Illinois; research assistant, University of Minnesota, 1936; Columbia University, 1937–41; Westinghouse Electric, 1941–42; Columbia Radiation Laboratory, 1942–44; Bell Telephone Laboratories; Columbia University, from 1946; research program, head of Physics Department and Radiation Laboratory; description of receiving the Nobel Prize, 1955.
212 pp. *Permission required.* 1962.

Part II: Account of experiences as Executive Vice President for Academic Affairs and Provost of Columbia University, 1969–71.
297 pp. *Permission required.* 1972.
See also Columbia Crisis of 1968, Journalism Lectures, *and* Nobel Laureates.

KYLE, Wood Barbee (1915–   ) Marine Corps officer.

Education, Texas A & M, 1932–36; Shanghai, 1937–39;

WW II: Tulagi-Guadalcanal, Tarawa, and Saipan operations, Command and General Staff School, Fort Leavenworth; Fleet Marine Force, Pacific, 1947–49; mobilization of reserves for Korea; Army War College; Joint Plans Branch, 1958–61; Lebanon.
226 pp. *Permission required.* 1969.

LACY, William Sterling Byrd (1910–   ) *See* Eisenhower Administration.

LA FOLLETTE CIVIL LIBERTIES COMMITTEE

These interviews deal with labor and civil liberties during the New Deal, with discussion of the roles of the NLRB and the CIO, anti-union practices in industry and agriculture, the functioning of the committee, and recollections of Senator Robert M. La Follette, Jr.

Participants and pages: John J. Abt, 16; Gardner Jackson, 24; Carey McWilliams, 20; Luke Wilson, 28; Robert Wohlforth and Matthew Josephson, 75.

163 pp. *Permission required to cite or quote.* 1963. *Contributed by Jerold S. Auerbach, Waltham, Mass.*

LAGOS, Julio A. *See* Argentina in the 1930's.

LaGUARDIA, Marie M. (Mrs. Fiorello H.) (1896–   )

Mayor Fiorello LaGuardia: some personal reminiscences.
56 pp. *Permission required to cite or quote.* 1950. NYT (Part I).
See also New York Political Studies.

LAHEY, Edwin A. (1906–1969) Columnist.

Early days on the Chicago *Daily News;* Frank Knox; Al Capone and John Dillinger cases; work as labor specialist and relations with Philip Murray; impressions of Lee Pressman, James Carey, John L. Lewis, Robert A. Taft, and Thomas E. Dewey.

REFER TO "NOTES ON USE" IN INTRODUCTION

161 pp. *Permission required to cite or quote.* 1959. NYT (Part I).
See also Robert A. Taft Project.

LAHM, Frank Purdy (1877–1963) *See* Henry H. Arnold Project.

LAIDLER, Harry Wellington (1884–1970) *See* Socialist Movement.

LAMBIE, James McClurg, Jr. (1914–   ) Executive.
EISENHOWER ADMINISTRATION

Eisenhower Headquarters Committee, 1952 campaign; Advertising Council; CARE; impressions of President Eisenhower and his administration.
49 pp. *Permission required to cite or quote.* 1968.

LAMONT, Corliss (1902–   ) Author, teacher.

Childhood and education; interest in civil liberties and ACLU; conflicts with Congressional committees; passport difficulties; visits to Russia; Senator Joseph McCarthy; contempt citation; humanism.
165 pp. *Permission required.* 1960.

LAND, Emory Scott (1879–1971) Naval officer.

Naval Academy, athletics; early cruises; naval architecture, MIT; Bureau of Ships, Bureau of Aeronautics; Harry Guggenheim and air research; Charles A. Lindbergh; Fleet Naval Construction, 1930–32; Chief, Bureau of Ships, 1933–37; Maritime Commission, 1937; Joseph Kennedy; Merchant Marine Academy; shipbuilding for National Defense Agency; William Knudsen; Liberty Ships; War Shipping Administration; Air Transport Association, 1946–53. Impressions of Theodore Roosevelt, Franklin D. Roosevelt, Harry Hopkins, Bernard Baruch, Jesse Jones.
227 pp. *Permission required to cite or quote.* 1963. NYT (Part I).
See also Aviation.

LANDIS, James McCauley (1899–1964) Lawyer, government official.

Family background; childhood and education in Japan and US; Harvard Law School; early legal writings; secretary to Justice Louis Brandeis; professor, Harvard, 1926–34; government service, 1933–37; Dean, Harvard Law School, 1937–46; later government service: Civil Defense, WWII, Civil Aeronautics Board; Middle East; government studies and reports, 1953–60; 1956 and 1960 campaigns, elections; presidential adviser. Comments on Justices Felix Frankfurter, Oliver W. Holmes, and Benjamin Cardozo; Samuel Williston, Roscoe Pound, Franklin Roosevelt, Joseph P. Kennedy, John L. Lewis, Fiorello LaGuardia, King Farouk, Lord Moyne.
685 pp. *Permission required.* 1964.

LANDON, Alfred Mossman (1887–   ) *See* Robert A. Taft Project.

LANDSMAN, Herbert Samuel (1918–   ) *See* Federated Department Stores.

LANE, Alvin Huey (1895–   ) Lawyer, business executive.
EISENHOWER ADMINISTRATION

Texas delegation to 1952 Republican Convention; Republican Party in Texas.
39 pp. *Permission required to cite or quote.* 1969.

LANE, Burton. *See* Popular Arts.

LANE, Chester Tevis (1905–1958) Lawyer.

Childhood and early education; Harvard Law School; Milbank, Tweed, Hope and Webb, 1930–35; corporate trusteeship NYC; General Counsel's office of the SEC, 1935–42; drafting Securities Act; relationship between SEC General Counsel, Attorney General, and Solicitor General; Trans-

america Corporation cases; special assistant to the Attorney General, 1942–45; war policies unit, War Division, Justice Department; Solicitor General's office; legal consultant, Army–Navy Liquidation Commission; Lend-Lease administrator and deputy foreign liquidation commissioner, 1946–47.
869 pp. *Permission required to cite or quote.* 1951. NYT (Part I).

LANE, W. B. (1898–   ) *See* Benedum and the Oil Industry.

LANG, Chester Henry (1893–1961) Corporation official.
RADIO PIONEERS
Early life and education; WWI; traveling auditor for General Electric, 1919; WGY, Schnectady; memorable broadcasts; impressions of David Sarnoff, Martin P. Rice, Owen D. Young, Harry S. Truman.
29 pp. *Open.* 1951.

LANGDON, Jesse (1881–   ) Rough Rider.
THEODORE ROOSEVELT ASSOCIATION
Enlistment in the Rough Riders; San Antonio, Tampa; crossing from Florida to Cuba; landing at Daiquiri; Kettle Hill; San Juan Hill; postwar experiences; Philippine action; Storey-Langdon Foundation.
67 pp. *Permission required to cite or quote.* 1970.

LANGMUIR, Alexander Duncan (1910–   ) *See* Health Science.

LANING, Clair. *See* Holger Cahill.

LANSDALE, Edwin. *See* Air Force Academy.

LARGE, Arlen. *See* Social Security.

LARMON, Sigurd Stanton (1891–   ) *See* Eisenhower Administration.

LARRABEE, Eric (1922–   ) Editor, writer.
CARNEGIE CORPORATION

Carnegie Corporation's African studies program; music and art in West Africa; American studies program; American Shelf Project; European Unity Conference in Italy; International Education Act; foundation policies.
89 pp. *Permission required.* 1967.

LARSEN, Harold. *See* World Bank.

LARSON, Arthur (1910–   ) *See* Social Security.

LARSON, August. *See* Marine Corps.

LARSON, Roy Frank (1893–   ) *See* Independence Park.

LASKER, Albert Davis (1880–1952) Advertising man.

Early adventures as a newspaper reporter; career in advertising; George Washington Hill and others; reorganization of professional baseball, 1920; Republican politics, 1918–30; USSB.
180 pp. *Open.* 1950. Papers.

LASKER, Bruno (1880–1965) Social researcher.

Early life in Germany, England, and US; University Settlement, Manchester, England; social work in England and US from 1916; Seebohm Rowntree and the Rowntree Trust; "The Inquiry", WWI; Henry Street Settlement, 1916; *The Survey* and *The Survey Graphic;* Service Bureau for International Relations; IPR; Southeast Asia Institute; travels in Southeast Asia; 50 years of political, social, and charitable endeavor.
543 pp. *Permission required to cite or quote.* 1956. NYT (Part I). Papers.

REFER TO "NOTES ON USE" IN INTRODUCTION

LASKER, Mary (Mrs. Albert D.) (1900–   ) Promoter of medical research, philanthropist.

Part I: Family background, University of Wisconsin, Radcliffe; interest in fine arts; European travel, study at Oxford; art dealer; Hollywood dress pattern business; interest in and promotion of Planned Parenthood Federation, other voluntary agencies in the field of health; fund-raising: American Cancer Society, American Heart Association; attempts to secure adequate appropriations to implement existing legislation for medical research; US Public Health Service: National Science Foundation; formation and development of national institutes for cancer, heart, arthritis, mental health, neurological diseases, blindness; aid to medical education; interest in psychoanalysis; medical research in NY; large scale clinical trials through Veterans Administration; activities of Lasker Foundation to promote health through medical research; health insurance; HIP in NY; Presidential Health Commission; support of performing arts; art collection. Impressions of many statesmen, legislators, and medical and scientific pioneers.

1,157 pp. *Closed until 25 years after death.* 1965.

Part II: A continuing account, bringing up to date the major activities described in Part I: federal aid to medical research, development of regional medical centers, Cancer, Heart and Stroke Commission, NIH appropriations; beautification: plans for National Horticultural Park and Garden, activities in NY, District of Columbia, and elsewhere; visits to Johnson ranch; Medal of Freedom; health and medical research, from 1968: national health insurance, family planning, alcoholism, passage of 1971 cancer bill; Kennedy Center for the Performing Arts; restoration of Versailles.

368 pp. *Closed until 25 years after death.* 1972. Papers.

LASSWELL, Alva Bryan (1905–   ) *See* Marine Corps.

LATHROP, John Howland (1880–1967) Clergyman.

Ministry in Massachusetts, California, and Brooklyn; commission to investigate minority rights in Rumania; travels in India; Unitarian Service Missions to Czechoslovakia, Hungary, Yugoslavia, and the Middle East. 330 pp. *Permission required to cite or quote.* 1953. NYT (Part I).

LATIMER, Murray Webb (1901–) *See* Social Security.

LAURENCE, William Leonard (1888–) Science editor.

Part I: Early years in Czarist Russia and Germany; dreams of flying; arrival in US, 1905; and first jobs; experience at Harvard as student and tutor, 1908–17; WWI experiences. 148 pp. *Permission required to cite or quote.* 1954. NYT (Part I).

Part II: Experiences in NYC journalism: NY *World*, 1926–30; science reporter, NY *Times*, 1930–64; notable stories covered, including discovery of neutron, new elements, Harvard 300th Anniversary Conference; coverage of development of atomic energy: Manhattan Project, tests, dropping of bomb; Pulitzer Prizes, medical reporting. 395 pp. *Permission required to cite or quote.* 1964. NYT (Part I).

LAWRENCE, Don. *See* Weyerhaeuser Timber Company.

LAWRENCE, W. C. *See* Jackson Hole Preserve.

LAWRENCE, William Howard (1916–1972) Journalist.
EISENHOWER ADMINISTRATION
President Eisenhower and the news media; impressions of Eisenhower, Richard Nixon, Sherman Adams, Harold Talbot, and others. 37 pp. *Permission required to cite or quote.* 1967.

LAZARSFELD, Paul Felix (1901–) Sociologist.

Vienna during and after WWI; instructor in social psychology, University of Vienna, 1927; empirical studies; Rocke-

REFER TO "NOTES ON USE" IN INTRODUCTION

feller Foundation traveling fellowship in US, 1933–35; University of Newark Research Center, 1935; Director, Rockefeller Princeton Radio Project, 1937; Columbia, 1940; Bureau of Applied Social Research, 1941; market research; impressions of Hadley Cantril, Frank Stanton, Samuel Stouffer, Robert Lynd, Luther Fry. 377 pp. *Closed during lifetime.* 1962.

LAZARUS, Celia Rosenthal (Mrs. Fred, Jr.) *See* Federated Department Stores.

LAZARUS, Charles. *See* Federated Department Stores.

LAZARUS, Eleanor and Margaret. *See* Federated Department Stores.

LAZARUS, Fred, Jr. (1884–   ) Merchandising executive.
                    FEDERATED DEPARTMENT STORES
Family background; F. & R. Lazarus Co., Shillito's; philosophy of retailing and merchandising; development of Federated Department Stores; Filene's; Committee on Economic Development; Ohio Retail Merchants' Council; American Retail Federation; US Chamber of Commerce; detailed discussion of operation of a department store: personnel, customer service, selling, layout, design of fixtures, credit, stock, service departments, discount houses, special sales, night and Sunday shopping, computerization, area research, resources, retail accounting and applied statistical procedures, business forecasting, revolving credit, unionization, family financing; charitable and philanthropic undertakings; Retail Research Association; Associated Merchandising; Red Cross, American Jewish Committee. 1,039 pp. *Permission required.* 1965.

LAZARUS, Fred III (1912–   ) *See* Federated Department Stores.

LAZARUS, Irma Mendelson (Mrs. Fred III) *See* Federated Department Stores.

LAZARUS, Jeffrey L. (1894–) *See* Federated Department Stores.

LAZARUS, Maurice (1915–) *See* Federated Department Stores.

LAZARUS, Paul N., Jr. (1913–) *See* Popular Arts.

LAZARUS, Ralph (1914–) *See* Federated Department Stores.

LAZARUS, Mrs. Ralph. *See* Federated Department Stores.

LAZARUS, Reuben Avis (1895–1971) Lawyer.

NYC and State politics including the administrations of Mayors James Walker, Fiorello LaGuardia, and William O'Dwyer, 1926–49; NY State legislature; the Liberal Party; rent control; election of 1950; the Senate crime investigation.
502 pp. *Permission required.* 1951.
See also New York Political Studies.

LAZARUS, Robert (1890–1973) *See* Federated Department Stores.

LAZARUS, Simon. *See* Federated Department Stores.

LEAGUE OF NATIONS

The recollections of a number of officials of the League of Nations have been recorded through the cooperation of the Carnegie Endowment for International Peace. The interviews, obtained in Geneva, describe the early days of organizing the League Secretariat and record many international problems and negotiations. The memoirs are in French.

Participants and pages: Thanassos Aghnides, 506; Pablo de Azcarate, 80; Pablo de Azcarate with Edouard de Haller, and W. Van Asch Van Wijck, 156; Branko Lukac, 124.

REFER TO "NOTES ON USE" IN INTRODUCTION

866 pp. *Individual restrictions apply.* 1966–69. *Copies of the memoirs are also available at The Carnegie Endowment for International Peace, New York City and Geneva, Switzerland.*

LEAR, William Powell (1902–) *See* Aviation.

LEBOR, John Francis (1906–) *See* Federated Department Stores.

LeCRON, James D. (1885–1961) Government official.

Childhood and education; Des Moines *Register & Tribune,* 1913–33; US Department of Agriculture, 1934–40; the "purge"; election of 1940; Agricultural Marketing Service, 1940–42; Institute of Inter-American Affairs, 1942–43, Henry A. Wallace, 1913–48.
181 pp. *Open.* 1953.

LEE, Carl. *See* James B. Duke Project.

LEE, Joseph Bracken (1899–) Government official.
EISENHOWER ADMINISTRATION

Governor of Utah; Mayor of Salt Lake City; 1952 Republican Convention; impressions of Dwight D. Eisenhower, Robert A. Taft, and others; Republican Party; John Birch Society.
70 pp. *Permission required to cite or quote.* 1967.

LEE, Lila. *See* Popular Arts.

LEE, Tsung-Dao (1926–) *See* Nobel Laureates.

LEE, Warren Isbell (1874–1955) Congressman.

Brooklyn Republican politics, 1900–22.
20 pp. *Open.* 1950.

LEHMAN, Herbert Henry (1878–1963) Governor, Senator.

HERBERT H. LEHMAN PROJECT

Family background, boyhood in NYC; Williams College; Lehman Brothers; textile business; WWI, Army and Navy Quartermaster Corps; Lillian Wald, UJA, ORT; Alfred E. Smith; election in 1928 as Lieutenant Governor under Franklin D. Roosevelt; Governorship of NY, 1932–42: Prohibition and Repeal, crime investigation, public housing, labor and social welfare, relations with Tammany Hall, significant legislation, gubernatorial campaigns, Geoghan trial, Druckman case. Director General, UNRRA and post WWII problems. NY Reform movement; election to US Senate, 1949, and fight against McCarthyism; impressions of many public figures. This memoir has a full topical index.

785 pp. *Permission required to cite or quote.* 1961. NYT (Part I).
See also New York Political Studies.

LEHMAN, Maxwell. *See* New York Political Studies.

HERBERT H. LEHMAN PROJECT

Herbert Lehman's own memoir, described above, is supplemented by a series of interviews with persons who were closely associated with him through various stages of his career.

Participants and pages: Helen Altschul, 13; Emanuel Celler, 3; Paul Douglas, 22; Julius Edelstein, 45; James A. Farley, 44; Carolin Flexner, 67; Hubert Humphrey, 25; Estes Kefauver, 12; Herbert H. Lehman, 785; George Meany, 13; Henry Morgenthau, Jr., 8; Wayne Morse, 29; Charles Poletti, 32; Eleanor Roosevelt, 17; Anna M. Rosenberg, 14; Samuel I. Rosenman, 23; Marc Tanenbaum, 38; Roy Wilkins, 26.

1,184 pp. *Permission required to cite or quote.* 1959.

LEHMAN-HAUPT, Helmut. *See* Friends of the Columbia Libraries.

REFER TO "NOTES ON USE" IN INTRODUCTION

Columbia University

LEITHEAD, Barry T. (1907–   ) Business executive.
EISENHOWER ADMINISTRATION
Fund raising in the 1952 and 1956 campaigns; personal associations with President Eisenhower.
52 pp. *Permission required to cite or quote.* 1968.

LEKACHMAN, Robert (1920–   ) *See* Danforth Lectures.

LELAND, Waldo Gifford (1879–1966) Historian.

AHA and *AHR;* state and regional historical societies; Public Archives Commission; International Committee of Historical Sciences; origin of the ACLS and of the *DAB*.
63 pp. *Permission required to cite or quote.* 1955. NYT (Part I).

LE MAISTRE, George. *See* Civil Rights in Alabama.

LeMAY, Curtis E. (1906–   ) *See* Air Force Academy.

LEMMON, Jack (1925–   ) *See* Popular Arts.

LEMNITZER, Lyman L. (1899–   ) Army officer. *See* Eisenhower Administration.

LENHART, Robert (1913–   ) *See* Federated Department Stores.

LENROOT, Katharine Fredrica (1891–   ) Social worker.
SOCIAL SECURITY
Family background, childhood in Wisconsin, University of Wisconsin, 1912; Wisconsin Industrial Commission, 1913–14; US Children's Bureau from 1915: studies on infant mortality and child labor, early Mother's Aid laws, development of Social Security Act, Bureau's relations with states and Congress; Reorganization Act, 1945; Bureau under Social Security Administration. Impressions of Emma Lundberg,

239

Edwin Witte, Frances Perkins, Harry Hopkins, Eleanor Roosevelt, and others.
173 pp. *Open.* 1965.

LEOPOLD, Richard W. (1912–   ) *See* American Historians.

LERNER, Daniel (1917–   ) *See* International Negotiations.

LERNER, Max (1902–   ) *See* Journalism Lectures.

LESLIE, Edgar. *See* Popular Arts.

LESSER, Allen. *See* Social Security.

LESSER, Leonard. *See* Social Security.

LESSER, Sol (1890–   ) Motion picture executive.

San Francisco earthquake and fire, 1906; early days in motion picture industry: film exchange and distribution, dealer in feature films, financing, production, laboratory, ownership of a studio; foreign markets; theater circuits; consultant; anecdotes of many industry personalities; relationship of producer and author: Thornton Wilder and *Our Town;* Edgar Rice Burroughs and *Tarzan* series; seminar at University of Southern California.
154 pp. *Permission required to cite or quote.* 1970. NYT (Part II).
Contributed by Theodore Fred Kuper, Los Angeles.

LESTER, Robert MacDonald (1889–1969) Foundation executive.

CARNEGIE CORPORATION

Detailed account of operations, personnel policies, relationships of Carnegie Corporation, 1926–54. Impressions of Andrew Carnegie, Walter A. Jessup, Devereux Josephs, Nicholas Murray Butler, Frederick Keppel, and many other prominent educators and public figures.
872 pp. *Permission required.* 1967. Papers.

REFER TO "NOTES ON USE" IN INTRODUCTION

LEUCHTENBURG, William Edward (1922–   ) *See* American Historians.

LEVENSALER, Lewis. *See* Mining Engineers.

LEVENSTEIN, Aaron J. *See* Socialist Movement.

LEVENTHAL, Harold (1915–   ) *See* Stanley Reed.

LEVER, J. E. *See* Eisenhower Administration.

LEVINE, Jack (1915–   ) Artist.

Childhood and early training; life of an artist; philosophy of art; painting techniques; the creative process; illustrated commentary on some of his own work; etchings, drawings; abstract art.
150 pp. *Permission required to cite or quote.* 1956. NYT (Part I).

LEVINE, Manuel. *See* Social Security.

LEVY, Leonard W. (1923–   ) *See* Allan Nevins Project.

LEWIS, Edwin Owen (1879–   ) *See* Independence Park.

LEWIS, Frederica Crane. *See* Hart Crane Project.

LEWIS, Freeman (1908–   ) Publisher.

The founding of Pocket Books, Inc., and observations on the publishing trade, literacy, and economics of retailing paperbound books. Joint interview with Leon Shimkin.
63 pp. *Permission required to cite or quote.* 1955. NYT (Part II).

LEWIS, John. Civil rights leader.

SNCC, 1960–66: voter registration campaigns, relations

with Justice Department and other civil rights organizations; Mississippi delegation, Democratic Convention, 1964; March on Washington; Selma; role of white sympathizers during 1960's; Martin Luther King.
38 pp. *Permission required. 1970.*
Contributed by Stephen Lawson of New York City.

LEWIS, Katherine H. *See* Popular Arts.

LEWIS, Kathryn (1911–   ) *See* Adlai E. Stevenson Project.

LEWIS, Mort. Author.

ALLAN NEVINS PROJECT

Recollections of Allan Nevins, especially after 1960; anecdotes of Nevins at the Huntington Library and at the Pen Club; methods of work; associates in California.
173 pp. *Closed until March 5, 1976. 1970.*

LEWIS, Robert (1909–   ) *See* Popular Arts.

LEWIS, W. W. *See* John Robert Gregg Project.

LI, Han-hun. *See* Chinese Oral History.

LI, Huang (1895–   ) *See* Chinese Oral History.

LI, Shu-hua (1890–   ) *See* Chinese Oral History.

LI, Tsung-jen (1890–   ) *See* Chinese Oral History.

LIBBY, Rudolf F. *See* Nobel Laureates.

LICHTENFELD, Leon. *See* Radio Pioneers.

LIEBERSON, Goddard (1911–   ) Composer, business executive.

AMERICAN CULTURAL LEADERS

Early life, Seattle; Eastman School of Music; Columbia Re-

cording Corporation and Columbia Records, 1940–66; US recording industry.
95 pp. *Closed pending publication of a study.* 1966.

LILE, R. A. *See* Eisenhower Administration.

LINDBECK, John. *See* International Negotiations.

LINDBERG, Jaffet. *See* Mining Engineers.

LINDSAY, John V. (1921–   ) *See* Journalism Lectures.

LINDSAY, Samuel McCune (–1959) *See* Theodore Roosevelt Association.

LINK, Arthur S. (1920–   ) *See* American Historians.

LIPMANN, Fritz Albert (1899–   ) *See* Nobel Laureates.

LIPPMANN, Walter (1889–   ) Editor, author.

Early years in journalism; Treaty of Versailles; Harvard; the Fabian Socialists; outbreak of WWI; psychological warfare; politics and journalism in the 1920's; Franklin D. Roosevelt's candidacy for President; outbreak of WWII; US-Britain-Russia and the peace; books.
265 pp. *Permission required.* 1956. Papers: typescript of diary of Mr. Lippmann's journeys to Europe and India, 1948 and 1949 (169 pp. *Permission required).*
See also Journalism Lectures.

LITTAUER, Kenneth (–1968) *See* Aviation.

LITTLE, Donald G. (1893–   ) Business executive.
RADIO PIONEERS

Family background, education; amateur radio work in Kalamazoo, Michigan; US Signal Corps; radio engineering

at Westinghouse; work with Dr. Frank Conrad; broadcast of 1920 election; station KDKA; short wave and FM broadcasting; studio techniques.
101 pp. *Open.* 1951. Papers.

LITVAK, Michael Anatole (1902–   ) *See* Popular Arts.

LIU, J. Heng (1890–1961) *See* Chinese Oral History.

LIU, Sidney. *See* International Negotiations.

LLOYD, Glen Alfred (with Mrs. Lloyd) (1895–   ) *See* Adlai E. Stevenson Project.

LLOYD, Harold Clayton (1893–1971) *See* Popular Arts.

LLOYD, R. McAllister. *See* Carnegie Corporation.

LLOYD, Trevor (1906–   ) Geographer.
CARNEGIE CORPORATION
Founding of the Canadian Association for Adult Education; Arctic Institute of North America at McGill University. Impressions of Whitney Shepardson and Morse Cartwright.
45 pp. *Permission required.* 1968.

LOBOS, Roberto. *See* Argentina in the 1930's.

LOCKWOOD, Charles A. (1890–1967) Naval officer.

Youth in Missouri, Naval Academy, early cruises; Asiatic Fleet, submarine duty and command; Philippines, Command of 1st Asiatic Submarine Division, 1917; Japan, 1918; New London submarine base; captured German submarines; interwar training cruises and submarine experiences; fleet operations; Naval Mission, Rio de Janeiro, 1929; *Squalus* rescue operations; Naval Attaché, London, 1941; Commander Submarines, Pacific Fleet, 1943; wolfpack techniques, sonar and radar, periscope photography, rescue operations; postwar career; nuclear propulsion, development of atomic submarine.

720 pp. *Permission required to cite or quote.* 1965.

LODGE, John Davis (1903–) Government official.

EISENHOWER ADMINISTRATION

WWII experiences; member of Congress; Governor of Connecticut; 1952 Republican Convention; Ambassador to Spain; impressions of Gen. Francisco Franco.

195 pp. *Permission required to cite or quote.* 1969.

LOEMKER, Dorothy Rowden. *See* Carnegie Corporation.

LOENING, Grover (1888–) Aircraft engineer.

Recollections of Wilbur Wright; early days in aviation.

43 pp. *Permission required to cite or quote.* 1967. *Contributed by E. W. Robischon, Washington, D. C. See also Air Force Academy.*

LOEWENSTEIN, Rudolph Maurice (1898–) Psychoanalyst.

PSYCHOANALYTIC MOVEMENT

Childhood; studies at the Universities of Zurich, Berlin, Paris; Berlin Psychoanalytic Institute, 1923–25; analysis by Dr. Hans Sachs; founding of Paris Psychoanalytic Society, 1926; collaboration with Princess Marie Bonaparte in translating Freud's five case histories into French, 1935; New York Psychoanalytic Institute since 1943; work with Drs. Heinz Hartmann and Ernst Kris; theory and technique of psychoanalysis.

149 pp. *Open except for specified pages.* 1963. Papers. *Copy of open portion on deposit at New York Psychoanalytic Institute.*

LONG, E. B. *See* Civil War Centennial *and* Allan Nevins Project.

LONG, Esmond Ray (1890–   ) *See* Health Science.

LONG, George S., Jr. *See* Weyerhaeuser Timber Company.

LONGWORTH, Alice Lee Roosevelt (1884–   ) *See* Theodore Roosevelt Association.

LOOMIS, Francis Butler, Jr. (1903–   ) *See* Marine Corps.

LOOMIS, Milton Early (1887–   ) Educator.

NYU School of Education and Washington Square College, 1916–39; Associate Commissioner of Education, NY State, 1939–40.
63 pp. *Permission required.* 1966.

LOOS, Anita (Mrs. John Emerson) (1893–   ) *See* Popular Arts.

LORD, Henry Gardner (1865–1961) *See* McGraw-Hill.

LORD, Mary Pillsbury (Mrs. Oswald B.) (1904–   ) Government official.

EISENHOWER ADMINISTRATION

Citizens for Eisenhower; NATO; years with UN; refugee problems; Planned Parenthood Association; travels; political and social conditions in Africa, Middle East; experiences in Iron Curtain countries; Atlantic Institute; Ethiopia uprising of 1960; student riots in Paris; impressions of prominent women.
428 pp. *Permission required.* 1969.

LORWIN, Lewis L. (1883–1970) Economist.

Professor of economics, University of Montana, 1918; mine tax study and resignation, 1920; survey of Russia, 1921–23; Chicago *Daily News;* Brookings Institution, 1925–35; National Planning Association; Franklin D. Roosevelt ad-

ministration; chief economist, ILO, 1935; ILO and League of Nations, 1935–39; BEW, 1943–45; IPR; recollections of John Winant.
479 pp. *Permission required.* 1961.

LOVE, Edgar (1905–   ) *See* Radio Pioneers.

LOVELACE, William R. III (1907–1965) *See* Aviation.

LOVEMAN, Amy (1881–1955) *See* Book-of-the-Month Club.

LOVEMAN, Samuel A. (–1963) *See* Hart Crane Project.

LOVETT, Robert Abercrombie (1895–   ) *See* Eisenhower Administration *and* Henry H. Arnold Project.

LOWDERMILK, Walter Clay (1888–   ) Conservationist.

Childhood and education; Forest Service, 1915–17; Lumberjack Regiment, 1917–20; Forest Service, Missoula, Montana, 1920–22; China, 1922–27: studies of erosion, Nanking incident; Soil Erosion Service, Washington, 1933–35; Soil Conservation Service, 1935–37; consultant on soil, forest, and water conservation and reclamation in China, Israel, Africa, and US.
684 pp. *Permission required to cite or quote.* 1968.
Acquired from the Regional Oral History Office, University of California, Berkeley.

LOWELL, Ralph (1890–   ) Foundation executive.

History of Lowell Institute; trustee, 1938 on; public lectures, University Extension Courses; Lowell Institute School at MIT; educational radio station; Cooperative Broadcasting Council, 1946; National Educational Television and Ford Foundation.
98 pp. *Permission required to cite or quote.* 1964.
NYT (Part I).

LOWRY, W. McNeil (1913–   ) Foundation executive.

AMERICAN CULTURAL LEADERS.

Childhood and education; service in OWI, domestic branch, 1942–43; political correspondent, Washington, 1947–52; career as program director and vice president, humanities and the arts, Ford Foundation, 1957–1967. 296 pp. *Closed pending publication of a study.* 1967.

LOY, Myrna (1905–   ) *See* Popular Arts.

LUBELL, Samuel (1911–   ) *See* Journalism Lectures.

LUBIN, Isador (1896–   ) Economist.

Early life; Missouri University and Thorstein Veblen; statistical branch of the WIB in WWI; the Brookings Institution; Bureau of Labor Statistics, 1939–44; other wartime federal posts, impressions of associates, New Deal legislation; UNESCO.
168 pp. *Permission required to cite or quote.* 1957. NYT (Part I).
See also Social Security.

LUCE, Clare Boothe (Mrs. Henry R.) (1903–   ) Government official.

EISENHOWER ADMINISTRATION

Impressions of President Eisenhower; 1952 campaign; foreign service; Ambassador to Italy; Trieste; Ambassador to Brazil; Republican Party; John Foster Dulles.
108 pp. *Closed during lifetime.* 1968.

LUCKEY, Robert Burneston (1905–   ) Marine Corps officer.

Education, University of Maryland, 1923–27; expeditionary duty, Nicaragua, 1929; early assignments, artillery training; US Embassy Guard, Peking, 1936–38; aide to Gen. James Breckinridge, 1938–39; WWII: Guadalcanal, Cape Gloucester, and Okinawa operations, occupation of Tsing-

tao; USMC in interwar period; postwar assignments: Marine Barracks, Washington, D.C., 1949–51; USMC Schools, Quantico; Hogaboom Board, 1953–54; Fleet Marine Force, Atlantic, 1954–55; amphibious warfare operations; USMC Recruit Depots, Parris Island, 1957–59; 3d Marine Division, 1959–60; Far Eastern situation; Camp Lejeune, 1960–61; CG, Fleet Marine Force, Atlantic, 1961–63; contingency planning.
228 pp. *Open.* 1969.

LUKAC, Branko. League of Nations official.

LEAGUE OF NATIONS

Role of Secretary General and leaders in League of Nations before WWII; Manchuria, Germany's entrance; relations with Switzerland as host country; Russo-Finnish War, fall of France; detailed analysis of use of sanctions in Ethiopia conflict, 1935; impressions of Sir Eric Drummond and Joseph Avenol.
124 pp. *Permission required to cite or quote.* 1966.

LUMBER INDUSTRY. *See* Forest History Society *and* Weyerhaeuser Timber Company.

LUMET, Sidney (1924–   ) *See* Popular Arts.

LUNTZ, Jerome (1923–   ) *See* McGraw-Hill.

LUSK, William (1901–   ) Corporation executive.

Tiffany and Lusk family background; education, Groton, and Yale; Tiffany and Co., 1837–1955: expansion of manufacturing and retail trade, personnel, effects of Depression, closing of Paris office, 1955 stock sale and reorganization under Walter Hoving, upgrading of various departments, franchises for sale of Tiffany silver, publicity innovations, synthetic gems, buying trips to Europe after WWII, memorable sales; *The Tiffany Touch.* Impressions of many figures in Tiffany's history including Louis Moore, Walter Hoving.
395 pp. *Closed for 20 years after death.* 1972.

LUTER, John (1919–   ) *See* Eisenhower Administration.

LUTES, Leroy (1890–   ) *See* Henry H. Arnold Project.

LUXFORD, Ansel Frank (1911–   ) Lawyer.
WORLD BANK
Early experience with Bank; British loan; planning for
Bretton Woods conference: education of Congress and
public; comparison of International Monetary Fund and
World Bank; John Maynard Keynes' attitude toward Bank;
bond marketing; Bank and other financing organizations;
Army, Lend-Lease, Marshall Plan, UNRRA; effects of
Roosevelt's death; internal organization of Bank; Savannah
conference; selection of president; loan application procedure; legal interpretations; evolution of policy making department.
61 pp. *Open.* 1961.

LYNCH, John J. *See* New York Political Studies.

LYNCH, Warren. *See* Book-of-the-Month Club.

LYONS, Ruth. *See* Radio Pioneers.

McALISTER, Gayle. *See* Flying Tigers.

McANENY, George (1869–1953) Banker, civic leader.

NYC history; subway construction; rewriting the city charter; zoning law; Negro education; historical monuments;
NY World's Fair, 1939–40.
102 pp. *Permission required to cite or quote.* 1949. NYT
(Part I).

McAULIFFE, Anthony C. (1898–   ) Army officer.

Childhood and education; West Point; early Army training; Command and General Staff School, War College;

General Staff, Research and Development, Service of Supply; OSRD; origins of dukw, jeep; WWII: 101st Airborne Division, 1942; gliders; training in US and Europe; Normandy; Arnhem; Battle of the Bulge, Bastogne; Korea; atomic tests at Bikini; General Staff, 1946; Japan, 1948; Chief of Chemical Corps, G-1; Army integration; Deputy Chief of Staff, 1951–53; 7th Army, Commander US Forces in Europe; American Cyanamid, 1956–63.

267 pp. *Open.* 1963.

McCABE, Edward Aeneas (1917–) Lawyer.
EISENHOWER ADMINISTRATION

Early career; general counsel, House Committee on Education and Labor, 1953–55; associate counsel, later administrative assistant to the President, 1956–61; coordinating interests of executive and legislative branches; Eisenhower and legislation, 1958–60; Landrum-Griffin Act; transition period, 1960; campaigns of 1960 and 1964; Sherman Adams and Bernard Goldfine; impressions of the President and White House staff.

165 pp. *Permission required to cite or quote.* 1967.

McCAMMAN, Dorothy. *See* Social Security.

McCANDLESS, Alex U. (–1954) *See* Benedum and the Oil Industry.

McCANN, Kevin (1904–) Author.
EISENHOWER ADMINISTRATION

Impressions of Dwight Eisenhower, Sherman Adams; evaluation of the influence of White House aides, staff, Cabinet, friends, and other associates on President Eisenhower.

158 pp. *Permission required to cite or quote.* 1966.

McCANN, Richard H. *See* Robert P. Patterson Project.

McCARDLE, Carl Wesley (1904–1972) Government official.
EISENHOWER ADMINISTRATION

Journalism background; Assistant Secretary of State for

Public Affairs, 1953–57; impressions of John Foster Dulles and President Eisenhower; SEATO; Senator Joseph McCarthy and State Department. 48 pp. *Permission required to cite or quote.* 1967.

MACARTNEY, R. R. *See* Weyerhaeuser Timber Company.

McCLINTOCK, Charles Arbuthnot (1883–1968) *See* Benedum and the Oil Industry.

McCLOY, John Jay (1895–   ) *See* Eisenhower Administration *and* International Negotiations.

McCONE, John A. (1902–   ) *See* Eisenhower Administration.

McCONNELL, John P. *See* Air Force Academy.

McCONNELL, Thomas Raymond (1901–   ) *See* Carnegie Corporation.

McCORD, Robert. *See* American Cultural Leaders.

McCREA, Joel (1905–   ) *See* Popular Arts.

McCRORY, James. *See* Eisenhower Administration.

McCOSKER, M. Joseph. *See* Independence Park.

McCUE, Constance. *See* Carnegie Corporation.

McDERMOTT, Robert Francis (1920–   ) Air Force officer.
AIR FORCE ACADEMY
Experiences as vice dean, later dean of faculty, USAF Academy, 1954–68; with detailed discussions of his rela-

tions with the superintendents, commandants of cadets, and faculty serving at the Academy during this period. 207 pp. *Permission required.* 1972.

MacDONALD, Jeanette (1907–1965) *See* Popular Arts.

McDOUGAL, Edward Dickinson, Jr. (1896–   ) *See* Adlai E. Stevenson Project.

McDOUGAL, Katherine (Mrs. Edward) *See* Adlai E. Stevenson Project.

McDOWALL, Roddy (1928–   ) *See* Popular Arts.

McELROY, Neil Hoosier (1904–1972) Business executive.
EISENHOWER ADMINISTRATION
White House Conference on Education, 1954–56; Secretary of Defense, 1957–59; Senate Preparedness Subcommittee; missiles and satellites; 1958 Defense Reorganization Bill.
88 pp. *Permission required.* 1967.

McEVOY, Nan. *See* Adlai E. Stevenson Project.

McFARLAND, Emily (Mrs. Ross). *See* Association for the Aid of Crippled Children.

McGOUGH, Charles J. *See* Weyerhaeuser Timber Company.

McGOWAN, Carl (1911–   ) Judge.
ADLAI E. STEVENSON PROJECT
Youth in Chicago, WWII naval service; Stevenson as Governor of Illinois: divorce, recruitment of staff, relationship with Democratic Party, patronage system; 1952 campaign; Elks Club group; Stevenson's speeches; press relations; 1956 campaign; UN. Recollections of John F. Kennedy,

Hubert Humphrey, Joseph McCarthy, Richard Nixon, Richard Daley, and others.
252 pp. *Permission required.* 1969.

McGRATH, Earl James (1902–   ) Educator.

Childhood and education; teaching and administration, University of Buffalo, 1928–45; War Manpower Commission, 1942; education program for naval personnel; trimester college program; teacher quality and qualifications; US Commissioner of Education, 1949–53.
145 pp. *Closed until January 1, 1975.* 1963.

CARNEGIE CORPORATION

Relations with the Carnegie Corporation, 1933–67; University of Buffalo; American Council on Education, 1938; University of Kansas City, 1953–56; Institute for Higher Education, TC, 1956–67: selection of staff, fiscal problems, research programs, study of Negro colleges. Impressions of John Gardner and other Corporation officials.
107 pp. *Permission required.* 1967.

McGRAW, Donald C. (1897–   ) *See* McGraw-Hill.

McGRAW, Mrs. Donald C. (1900–   ) *See* McGraw-Hill.

McGRAW, Harold Whittlesey, Jr. (1918–   ) *See* McGraw-Hill.

McGRAW, James A. (1886–   ) *See* McGraw-Hill.

McGRAW-HILL

The development of McGraw-Hill, Inc. and its part in educational, industrial, and technical development in the US and abroad, 1886–1964, are traced in a series of interviews beginning with the lives of James H. McGraw (1860–1948) and John A. Hill (1858–1912). Associates recall the career of each as a publisher of trade and technical magazines. Others deal with the merger of the book publishing activities

REFER TO "NOTES ON USE" IN INTRODUCTION

of the two companies as the McGraw-Hill Book Co., 1909, and the purchase of the Hill interest in trade magazines by McGraw to form the McGraw-Hill Publishing Company in 1916. Interviews continue the story of the company's expansion through the acquisition of the F. W. Dodge Corporation, 1961, which brought the firm into the field of information services, the purchase of such periodicals as *House & Home* and *Modern Packaging*, and the acquisition of the Webster Publishing Co.

Editors of McGraw-Hill trade, educational, and business publications discuss editorial and circulation policy, standards of responsibility in dealing with readers and advertisers, and new functions and fields for the company's publications and instructional materials. The construction of the McGraw-Hill building (1931) is described, together with data on production operations.

Special phases include: changes in the writing and publishing of college textbooks, textbooks for courses in vocational education; elementary and high school materials, visual education aids, programmed books, and text films; Whittlesey House and trade book publishing, paperback books, technical writing, training manuals for the US armed forces, and international aspects of book publishing such as translation, licensing, and international editions of textbooks. Interviewees give background on such McGraw publications as the *Catholic Encyclopedia*, the *Encyclopedia of World Art*, and *Science and Technology*.

Participants and pages: Fred Annett, 65; Russell Anderson, 47; Edward C. Aswell, 49; Moses Baker, 23; Walter Bara, 23; Robert Beard, 38; William K. Beard, 35; Curtis G. Benjamin, 78; James Blackburn, 33; C. Presby Bliss, 43; Robert F. Boger, 23; Nelson Bond, 26; Edward Booher, 84; Waldo Bowman, 35; Harold Veatch Bozell, 56; Mason Britton, 56; Emerson Brown, 17; Herbert Buhrow, 32; John P. Burke, 27; William Buxman, 70; John Callaham, 43; Lillian Charlton, 25; Willard Townshend Chevalier, 129; Maud Clark, 27; Carl Coash, 51; Fred Herbert Colvin, 21; Robert Craig, 24; John Crossman, 29; Walter Crowder, 59; Basil Dandison, 35; Frank Dickman, 29; Frank Egner, 68; Frederick Morris Feiker, 45; Burnham Finney, 23; Edwin Shelton Fisher, 45; Helene Frye, 24;

Woodrow Wilson Garey, 84; William Gartner, 35; James L. Gilbert, 39; Elizabeth Gile, 26; Thomas Grogan, 39; Virgil B. Guthrie, 41; Hugh Handsfield, 28; Albert Hauptli, 103; Keith Henney, 22; S.T. Henry, 61; Robert Hotz, 42; Dexter Keezer, 19; Hugh Kelly, 27; Hugh Joseph Kelly, 62; Sidney Dale Kirkpatrick, 31; Alvin Knoerr, 100; Edgar Kobak, 120; Alice E. Kraft, 45; Kenneth Kramer, 30; Henry Gardner Lord, 71; Jerome

Luntz, 41; Donald C. McGraw, 27; Mrs. D.C. McGraw, 34; Harold W. McGraw, Jr., 29; James A. McGraw, 47; Alice McMullin, 52; George Mac-Murray, 23; Howard Mateer, 51; Edward J. Mehren, 53; Paul Montgomery, 25; Arch Morris, 36; L.C. Morrow, 75; Malcolm Muir, 25; Matthew Murphy, 43;

Carl Nagel, 29; Bela Reiter, 46; Margaret Richards, 32; A.J. Rosenberg, 36; Richard Rowden, 31; Louis Rowley, 74; George Sears, 15; H.W. Shaw, 14; Willard T. Shoener, 39; Robert Slaughter, 39; Ralph Smith, 24; John C. Spurr, 32; Alfred W. Staehle, 101; Philip William Swaine, 32; John Taylor, 27; George Clinton Tenney, 41; James Stacy Thompson, 80; Angelo Venezian, 58; William Weidig, 33; John E. Welle, 32; Joseph Vandenburg Wight, 58; John Wilhelm, 89; Lawrence Wray, 40; Norman Wynkoop, 45.

4,170 pp. *Permission required.* 1956.

Paul Abbott, 20; Curtis O. Benjamin, 51; Edward E. Booher, 57; Edwin Shelton Fisher, 69; Lawrence Keith Goodrich, 22; Hugh J. Kelly, 29; Donald C. McGraw, 7; Harold W. McGraw, Jr., 39; Wallace Traendly, 30; Harry Waddell, 30; John Wilhelm, 66.

420 pp. *Permission required.* 1964.
Underwritten by McGraw-Hill, Inc.

MacGREGOR, Frank (1897–1971) Publisher.

Family background and education, Nova Scotia and New England; Harvard; head of college department at Harper & Bros. from 1924; reminiscences of authors and publishers.

374 pp. *Open.* 1966.

McGREGOR, James Murray.

Impressions of Tracy McGregor.
86 pp. *Open.* 1954.

McGUIRE, Edward Perkins (1904–   ) *See* Eisenhower Administration.

MACHADO, Luis (1899–   ) Diplomat.

WORLD BANK

Bretton Woods; early years of Bank; loan policies; Latin American relations.
35 pp. *Permission required to cite or quote.* 1961.

REFER TO "NOTES ON USE" IN INTRODUCTION

McHARG, Ormsby (1871–   ) Lawyer, politician.

Frontier life in Dakota Territory; North Dakota politics, 1899–1900; Congressional personalities, 1900–12; New Mexico land fraud litigation, 1907–08; Republican national politics, 1908–12.
126 pp. *Permission required to cite or quote.* 1951. NYT (Part I).

McHUGH, James F. (1894–   ) *See* Popular Arts.

McINTOSH, Millicent Carey (1898–   ) Educator.

Family, youth, and education; Bryn Mawr School; Bryn Mawr College; Newnham College, Cambridge; career at Brearley School; changes in curriculum and methodology; trends in progressive education; comments on women's education; graduate school, Johns Hopkins, 1926–30; Barnard College, president; development of religion and education programs at Barnard; attitudes toward advanced placement; social work and community activities; reflections on changes in manners and morals and the generation gap; impressions of prominent educators.
695 pp. *Permission required.* 1966.

MacIVER, Robert Morrison (1882–1970) Sociologist.

Education in Scotland and at Oxford; teaching political science and sociology at Aberdeen University, 1907–11; University of Toronto, 1915–27; Barnard College, 1927–36; Columbia University, 1929–50; Russell Sage Foundation; "The Inquiry."
99 pp. *Permission required.* 1962.

MACK, Walter Staunton, Jr. (1895–   ) Executive.

Republican politics in NYC, 15th Assembly District; state senatorial campaign, 1932; election fraud investigation, 1933; Fusion Committee for election of Fiorello LaGuardia.

74 pp. *Permission required to cite or quote.* 1950. NYT (Part I).

McKEAN, Josephine. *See* Occupation of Japan.

McKELDIN, Theodore Roosevelt (1900–   ) Government official.

EISENHOWER ADMINISTRATION

Nominating speech for Eisenhower, 1952 convention; correspondence with Eisenhower; Mayor of Baltimore; Governor of Maryland.
78 pp. *Permission required to cite or quote.* 1968.

MacKENNA, Kenneth (1899–   ) *See* Popular Arts.

MacKENZIE, Donald. *See* Forest History Society.

McKINNEY, Ernest Rice (1886–   ) Organizer.

Development of the National Unemployed League, Depression days; organizing steel workers for CIO, and as a member of the Workers' Socialist Party; upgrading Negroes in industry; Working Men's Welfare Committees; Workers Party of the United States (Trotsykist Group) and its relationship to Communist and Socialist Parties; resignation from Workers Party.
116 pp. *Open.* 1961.

McKITTRICK, Thomas Harrington (1889–1970) Banker.

Childhood and education, Hackley School, Tarrytown, and Harvard; impressions of friends and teachers.
43 pp. *Permission required to cite or quote.* 1952.

McLAUGHLIN, Frederick Charles (1905–   ) Educator.

Part I: Childhood and education in Midwest; TC; US Army Air Force; Superintendent of Schools, NYC, hiring problems; Queens College case; Junior Red Cross Director; student volunteer workers in city hospitals; head of Public Education Association: activities, relationship with Board of Education and other organizations, public events. Impressions of Mayors William O'Dwyer, Vincent Impellitteri, and Robert F. Wagner; and Superintendents William Jansen, John Theobald, and Calvin Gross; comments on desegregation, busing, community relations in school issues.

531 pp. *Permission required to cite or quote.* 1964. NYT (Part II).

Part II: Young Plan to establish state university; Sviridoff Human Relations Study; issue of minimum days for school attendance; School 201 incident; Griffith Study; More Effective Schools program; Bundy report on decentralization; Ocean Hill-Brownsville project; teachers strike; impressions of personalities connected with NYC public education.

630 pp. *Permission required to cite or quote.* 1966. NYT (Part II).

McLAURIN, Benjamin. Labor organizer.

Childhood and education, Florida; Edward Water College; labor school at University of Wisconsin, Brookwood Labor College; Pullman Company, organization of Brotherhood of Sleeping Car Porters; Railway Labor Act amendment; A. Philip Randolph; salaries, tips and pensions; FEPC; American Negro Labor Council; Negro conditions in NYC; International Ladies Auxiliary; company unions, AFL-CIO relationships; American Labor Party; Morris Hillquit; Urban League, NAACP; organizing in the South; March on Washington, 1941.

353 pp. *Permission required to cite or quote.* 1960. NYT (Part I).

McLOUGHLIN, Donald. *See* Mining Engineers.

MacMAHON, Aline (1899–   ) *See* Popular Arts.

McMATH, Sidney Sanders (1912–   ) *See* Eisenhower Administration.

McMILLAN, Edwin Mattison (1907–   ) *See* Nobel Laureates.

McMULLIN, Alice (1902–   ) *See* McGraw-Hill.

MacMURRAY, George (1881–1961) *See* McGraw-Hill.

McNAIR, W. K. *See* Weyerhaeuser Timber Company.

McNERNEY, Walter James (1925–   ) *See* Social Security.

McPHEE, Henry Roemer, Jr. (1925–   ) *See* Eisenhower Administration.

McQUAID, Kay. *See* Adlai E. Stevenson Project.

McQUEEN, John Crawford (1899–   ) *See* Marine Corps.

MACREADY, John A. *See* Aviation.

McREYNOLDS, David. *See* Socialist Movement.

McWILLIAMS, Carey (1905–   ) *See* La Follette Civil Liberties Committee.

MACY, Helen (Mrs. George).

The career of her late husband, George Macy (1900–1956), the founder of the Limited Editions Club.
In process.

MADDEN, Joseph Warren (1890–1972) Judge.

Family and rural life; Freeport years; education and teach-

ing; NLRB; Roscoe Pound and the administrative process; US Court of Claims; legal division of the military government of Germany.
170 pp. *Permission required.* 1957.

MADIGAN, Michael J. (1894–   ) *See* Robert P. Patterson Project.

MAGGI, Juan. *See* Argentina in the 1930's.

MAGINNIS, Harry. *See* Robert A. Taft Project.

MAGNUSON, Paul Budd (1884–1970) (with Mrs. Magnuson) *See* Adlai E. Stevenson Project.

MAHLER, Margaret. *See* Psychoanalytic Movement.

MAHONEY, Jeremiah T. (1878–1970) Lawyer.

Education; NYC and State affairs: Board of Education, Banking Commission, Commission of Accounts, Democratic Party, Court of General Sessions of the Supreme Court; impressions of prominent NY politicians.
198 pp. *Permission required to cite or quote.* 1949.

MAHONEY, Margaret. *See* Carnegie Corporation.

MALACCORTO, Ernesto. *See* Argentina in the 1930's.

MALHERBE, Ernst G. *See* Carnegie Corporation.

MALKAMES, Don. *See* Popular Arts.

MALLORY, Leslie. *See* Weyerhaeuser Timber Company.

MALONE, Dumas (1892–   ) Historian.

Editing the *DAB*; impressions of Allen Johnson and others.

46 pp. *Permission required to cite or quote.* 1954. NYT (Part I).

MAMOULIAN, Rouben (1897–   ) Stage and motion picture director.

POPULAR ARTS

Director in London, 1919; directing opera in Rochester, NY; interviews with George Eastman; Theatre Guild in NYC; films: *Applause, Queen Christina, Becky Sharp;* stage productions of *Porgy and Bess* and *Carousel;* move from major studios to more individualized production units; impressions of Eugene O'Neill, Greta Garbo. 115 pp. *Closed during lifetime.* 1958.

MANATOS, Mike N. *See* Social Security.

MANHEIM, Sylvan (1897–   ) *See* Mt. Sinai Hospital.

MANKIEWICZ, Joseph Leo (1909–   ) *See* Popular Arts.

MANN, Delbert (1920–   ) *See* Popular Arts.

MANN, Thomas Clifton (1912–   ) Government official.

EISENHOWER ADMINISTRATION

Diplomatic service: Greece, 1953; Guatemala, 1955; El Salvador, 1955–57; Mexico, 1961–63; Assistant Secretary of State for economic affairs, 1957–60; Latin American affairs during Eisenhower administration; foreign aid; Fidel Castro; impressions of President Eisenhower. 60 pp. *Permission required.* 1968.

MANNES, Marya (1904–   ) *See* Journalism Lectures.

MANNING, Helen Herron Taft (1891–   ) *See* Robert A. Taft Project.

MANNING, Stanley Rutter (1891–   ) *See* Radio Pioneers.

REFER TO "NOTES ON USE" IN INTRODUCTION

MANSHIP, Paul (1885–1966) Sculptor.

Family background and youth; art education; study in Europe; professional career.
71 pp. *Open.* 1956.

MARBURY, William Luke (1901–   ) *See* Robert P. Patterson Project.

MARCANTONIO, Vito (1902–1954) *See* New York Political Studies.

MARCUS, Morris M.

Iran oil leases, 1952–53 and negotiations with Mohammed Mossadegh.
43 pp. *Closed during lifetime.* 1953.

MARGOLIES, Joseph A. Bookseller.

Rhine School; career at Brentano's, 1913–51; anecdotes of NYC publishers and bookstores.
38 pp. *Permission required to cite or quote.* 1971.

MARINE CORPS

This series of memoirs by retired Marines, begun in 1966, is a continuing program of the Historical Branch of the US Marine Corps. Together the interviews provide a picture of the development of the Marine Corps in the twentieth century. Personal experiences and anecdotes highlight events of WWI, duty in China and the Caribbean, the development of amphibious warfare in WWII, Marine aviation, the postwar unification struggle, and Korea. An example of material of special interest is the series of interviews with Marine Navajo code talkers conducted in 1971 in Window Rock, Arizona.

Participants and pages: Chester R. Allen, 383; Charles L. Banks, 51 *(permission required);* Robert O. Bare, 141 *(open);* William P. Battell, 101 *(permission required);* Fred D. Beans, 119; Sidney Bedoni, 13 *(permission*

The Oral History Collection

required); John Benally, 32 *(permission required);* James P. Berkeley, 481; Ion M. Bethel, 115; Wilfred Billey, 13 *(permission required);* Robert Blake, 117; Paul Blatchford, 27 *(permission required);* Thomas E. Bourke, 44 *(open);* Alpha Lyons Bowser, 393; William O. Brice, 98 *(permission required);* Wilburt S. Brown, 314; William Walter Buchanan, 86 *(open);*

Joseph C. Burger, 357; Clifton B. Cates, 254; George H. Cloud, 115 *(permission required);* John Pomeroy Condon, 147 *(permission required);* O. T. Cox, 99 *(permission required);* Edward Arthur Craig, 199; Donald Curtis, 117; Thomas Jackson Cushman, 31 *(open);* Marion L. Dawson, 140 *(open);* Karl S. Day, 86 *(permission required);* Harold O. Deakin, 101; Pedro del Valle, 245; James P.S. Devereux, 208; Edward Colston Dyer, 293; Thomas G. Ennis, 141 *(permission required);* Graves B. Erskine, 573; Louis J. Fields, 267; George F. Good, Jr., 141 *(permission required);* Carl Gorman, 3 *(permission required);* Samuel Griffith, 205; John Neely Hart, 192 *(open);* Charles Harold Hayes, 239; Leo David Hermle, 94 *(open);* Robert E. Hogaboom, 357; B.T. Holcomb, 86 *(permission required);*

Samuel S. Jack, 80 *(permission required);* Louis R. Jones, 164 *(open);* Russell N. Jordahl, 202; Jimmy King, Sr., 36 *(permission required);* Victor H. Krulak, 227; Melvin L. Krulewitch, 125 *(permission required);* Wood B. Kyle, 226; August Larson, 225; Alva B. Lasswell, 62 *(permission required to cite or quote);* Francis B. Loomis, Jr., 149 *(permission required);* Robert B. Luckey, 228; John C. McQueen, 161 *(open);* John H. Masters, 208; Vernon E. Megee, 377; Ivan W. Miller, 69 *(open);* Ralph J. Mitchell, 29 *(open);* Francis P. Mulcahy, 169 *(open);* John C. Munn, 115 *(permission required);* David R. Nimmer, 199; Alfred H. Noble, 111; Henry Reid Paige, 128 *(open);* DeWitt Peck, 169; Omar Titus Pfeiffer, 461; Carson A. Roberts, 82 *(open);* Ray Albert Robinson, 136; Ford O. Rogers, 108 *(open, except for certain pages);* William W. Rogers, 99 *(open);* George A. Roll, 196; Christian F. Schilt, 136; Alan Shapley, 161 *(permission required);*

Samuel R. Shaw, 373; Lemuel C. Shepherd, 500; Merwin H. Silverthorn, 479; Julian C. Smith, 354; Oliver P. Smith, 337; Edward W. Snedeker, 122 *(open);* Joseph L. Stewart, 112 *(open);* Gerald C. Thomas, 989; Daniel W. Torrey, 81 *(open);* James L. Underhill, 204; William J. Wallace, 127 *(open);* Alex Williams, 21 *(permission required);* Dean Wilson, 20 *(permission required);* Louis E. Woods, 354; Thomas A. Wornham, 127; William A. Worton, 328.

16,585 pp. *Consult individual entries for restriction where none is given in this listing.* 1966– .

In process: H.W. Buse, Albert D. Cooley, Walter G. Farrell, Ronald D. Salmon, L.H.M. Sanderson, Donald Weller, Frederick L. Wieseman.

Contributed by the Oral History Program, Historical Branch, USMC. Also available at the US Naval Institute, Annapolis, Maryland.

MARION, Frances. *See* Popular Arts.

REFER TO "NOTES ON USE" IN INTRODUCTION

MARKEL, Lester (1894-   ) *See* Journalism Lectures.

MARKS, Herbert Hilliard (1913–1960) *See* Popular Arts.

MARKS, Leonard Harold (1916–   ) *See* James Lawrence Fly Project.

MARQUAND, John Phillips (1893–1960) *See* Book-of-the-Month Club.

MARSH, Mae. *See* Popular Arts.

MARSHALL, Mrs. E. C. *See* James B. Duke Project.

MARSHALL, S. L. A. (1900–   ) *See* Air Force Academy.

MARSHALL PLAN

This group of memoirs gathers together material on the genesis and development of the Marshall Plan in the Department of State, and describes in particular the role played by Will Clayton.

Participants and pages: Dean Acheson, 5; Will Clayton, 32; Emilio G. Collado, 14; Lewis W. Douglas, 2; Livingston Merchant, 3; Norman Ness, 5; Paul Nitze, 8; Arthur Stevens, 4; James Stillwell, 5; Leroy Stinebower, 6; Ivan White, 19.

103 pp. *Permission required to cite or quote.* 1947–61. *Contributed by Ellen Garwood, Austin, Texas.*

MARTIN, C. S. *See* Weyerhaeuser Timber Company.

MARTIN, George. *See* World Bank.

MARTIN, Grier. *See* James B. Duke Project.

MARVEL, William. Educator.

CARNEGIE CORPORATION

Changes in focus of the Corporation; area studies versus

comparative studies; relationship of the government and foundations; Council on Higher Education in the American Republics; University Service Center, Hong Kong. 278 pp. *Permission required.* 1967.

MARVIN, Langdon Parker (1876–1957) Lawyer.

Alaska Boundary Tribunal; Leonard Wood; Franklin D. Roosevelt as a friend and law partner.
80 pp. *Permission required to cite or quote.* 1949. Papers. NYT (Part I).

MASON, L. Randolph. *See* Robert A. Taft Project.

MASSEE, May (1889–1966) Editor.

Early library work; Wisconsin Library School, Armour Institute, and Buffalo Library; organizer and editor of children's book department at Doubleday; impressions of publishers, including Frank Doubleday.
96 pp. *Permission required to cite or quote.* 1966. NYT (Part I).

MASTERS, Ellen Coyne (Mrs. Edgar Lee) (1899–   )

Anecdotes of Edgar Lee Masters' early life; courtship and marriage, NYC, 1920's; husband's personality and creative approach; discussion of specific works, especially *Spoon River Anthology* and *Domesday Book;* girlhood in Kansas City, Panama, and Missouri Ozarks; University of Chicago; Abbey Theatre, 1924; recollections of literary figures such as Theodore Dreiser, Vachel Lindsay, and H. L. Mencken.
208 pp. *Permission required.* 1971.

MASTERS, John H. (1913–   ) Marine Corps officer.

Education; early training and assignments; North Atlantic convoy duty; Sino-American Cooperative Organization in China, 1942–44; Gen. Tai Li and Commander Milton Miles; Gens. Clifton Cates and Alexander Vandegrift; Legislative

Assistant, 1960–62; USMC relationships with Congress. 208 pp. *Permission required.* 1971.

MASTERS, Robert. *See* Columbia Crisis of 1968.

MASTERSON, Charles Francis (1917–   ) *See* Howard Pyle.

MASUR, Jack (1908–   ) *See* Health Science.

MATEER, Howard (1894–   ) *See* McGraw-Hill.

MATTHEWS, Geoffrey (1917–   ) Educator.

Experiences as director, Nuffield project in mathematics teaching: choice of staff and pilot areas, curriculum, design of books and films, collaboration with Jean Piaget; Madison Project.
116 pp. *Permission required to cite or quote.* 1968.

MATTHEWS, Thomas Stanley (1901–   ) Editor.

Early career and associates on the *New Republic*, 1925–29; association with *Time*, as books editor, managing editor, and editor, including discussion of *Time*'s development, staff and the projected *Time-in-Britain;* Henry R. Luce.
136 pp. *Permission required.* 1959.
See also Adlai E. Stevenson Project.

MAUBORGNE, Joseph O. *See* Air Force Academy.

MAVERICK, Maury, Jr. (1895–   ) *See* Adlai E. Stevenson Project.

MAX, Pearl (Mrs. Louis W.) (1904–   ) Educator.

Administration of NYC Board of Higher Education, 1938–1961; relationships between city administrations and city colleges; Russell case; Rapp-Coudert Committee; Strayer

Committee; policies and personalities in NYC higher education; impressions of Mayors Fiorello LaGuardia, Vincent Impellitteri, and Robert F. Wagner.
185 pp. *Permission required to cite or quote.* 1961. NYT
(Part I).

MAXWELL, William L. Auditor, controller.
WEYERHAEUSER TIMBER COMPANY

Potlatch Lumber Company from 1906: excise tax law re-
quiring separate accounting for land and timber values,
Potlatch Village, 1910 forest fires at Elk River, IWW, eight-
hour day, blister rust, group insurance plan for Potlatch
employees. Impressions of William Deary, Allison W.
Laird, Andrew Bloom, Frederick and Charles A. Weyerhaeuser.
112 pp. *Permission required.* 1956.

MAY, Ernest Richard (1928–   ) *See* American Historians.

MAY, Herbert Louis (1877–1966) Lawyer, diplomat.

International narcotics control, 1926–51; League of Nations
and UN.
92 pp. *Permission required to cite or quote.* 1951. NYT
(Part I).

MAYER, Arthur Loeb (1886–   ) *See* Popular Arts.

MAYER, Maria Goeppert (1906–1972) *See* Nobel Laureates.

MAYER, Robert. *See* James B. Duke Project.

MAYES, Herbert Raymond (1900–   ) *See* Journalism Lectures.

MAYO, Leonard W. (1899–   ) *See* Association for the Aid
of Crippled Children *and* Health Science.

REFER TO "NOTES ON USE" IN INTRODUCTION

MAZO, Earl (1919–   ) *See* Eisenhower Administration.

MAZUR, Paul Myer (1892–   ) *See* Federated Department Stores.

MEAD, Margaret (1901–   ) *See* Journalism Lectures.

MEADE, Edward. *See* Children's Television Workshop.

MEANY, George (1894–   ) *See* Herbert H. Lehman Project.

MEGEE, Vernon Edgar (1900–   ) Marine Corps officer.

Education, Oklahoma, George Washington University; USMC service from 1919: early training, motor transport, Officer Candidates School, aviation experience, service in Haiti and China, amphibious and carrier group tactics; WWII: Iwo Jima, Okinawa, Western Caroline operations; Assistant Director Marine Corps Aviation, 1949; 1st Marine Aircraft Wing, Korea, 1953; Assistant Commandant USMC and Chief of Staff, 1956; CG, Marine Forces, Pacific, 1957–59; retirement. Impressions of many military figures.
377 pp. *Open.* 1967.

MEHREN, Edward J. (1884–1963) *See* McGraw-Hill.

MEIN, William Wallace (1873–1964) *See* Mining Engineers.

MELLOR, William. *See* Popular Arts.

MELMAN, Seymour. *See* Columbia Crisis of 1968.

MENCKEN, August (1889–1967) Engineer, author.

H. L. Mencken: a brother's reminiscence, including parents, trust in doctors, relationship with various friends, daily routine, wife's death, disposition of unpublished work; Mencken Room in Enoch Pratt Library, Baltimore. 150 pp. *Permission required.* 1958.

MENDELS, Morton M. (1908–   ) Lawyer.
WORLD BANK

Appointment to World Bank; organization, procedure for loan applications; International Monetary Fund; functions of executive directors; early loans, bond issues; Polish loan proposal; comparison of board functions in Fund and in Bank; weighted voting system.
76 pp. *Permission required to cite or quote.* 1961.

MERCHANDISING. *See* Federated Department Stores.

MERCHANT, Livingston Tallmadge (1903–   ) Government official.
EISENHOWER ADMINISTRATION

Career in State Department; Japan Peace Treaty, Assistant Secretary for European Affairs, 1953, organization and procedures; Bermuda Conference and EDC, Berlin Conference, 1954; presidential speech writers; press conferences. Impressions of President Eisenhower, Sir Winston Churchill, John Foster Dulles, Anthony Eden, Vyacheslav Molotov, and others.
86 pp. *Permission required to cite or quote.* 1967. *See also* Marshall Plan.

MERKLE, Edward Arrol (1909–   ) Financial executive.

Stock Exchange in the 1920's; financial structures, Europe and India; mutual funds, growth funds; SEC.
106 pp. *Permission required.* 1968.

MERRIAM, Robert Edward (1918–   ) Business executive.
EISENHOWER ADMINISTRATION

Early political career in Chicago, Washington; WWII: combat historian, 1944, Battle of the Bulge; early relationship with Gen. Eisenhower; postwar housing in Chicago; Alder-

man, Chicago, 1947; Eisenhower administration; Adlai E. Stevenson; White House experiences; HOPE, People to People program; workings of Presidential office; Bureau of the Budget; deputy assistant to President for intergovernmental relations; Ad Hoc Committee on Metropolitan Area problems; advisory committee on intergovernmental relations.
209 pp. *Permission required.* 1969.

MERRICK, Mr. and Mrs. E. R. *See* James B. Duke Project.

MERWIN, Loring Chase (1906–1972) *See* Adlai E. Stevenson Project.

MESERVE, Frederick Hill (1865–1962) Lincoln collector.

Early life and education; collecting historical photographs of the Civil War period; autobiographical comments.
96 pp. *Open.* 1953. Papers.

MESSERSCHMITT, Willy (1898–   ) *See* Aviation.

METZGER, Walter. *See* Columbia Crisis of 1968 *and* Richard Hofstadter Project.

MEYER, Eugene (1875–1959) Financier, newspaper executive.

Childhood and education; early financial operations; farm credit during the 1920's; Federal Farm Loan Bureau; RFC and the Federal Reserve System during the banking crisis, 1933; *Washington Post,* 1933–53; World Bank and International Monetary Fund; impressions of Presidents Warren Harding, Calvin Coolidge, Herbert Hoover, and Franklin D. Roosevelt, and many other political and financial figures.
938 pp. *Permission required.* 1953.

MEYER, Joseph. *See* Popular Arts.

MEYNER, Robert Baumle (1908–   ) Governor.

Background; Lafayette College, Columbia Law School; New Jersey Democratic Party; Frank Hague, J. Parnell Thomas; minority leader, State Senate; court reform; Arthur T. Vanderbilt; gubernatorial campaign, 1953; governorship, 1954–61.
    157 pp. *Closed during lifetime.* 1962.

MICKELSON, Sig (1913–   ) Journalist, broadcasting executive.

Childhood and education; School of Journalism, University of Minnesota; teaching; radio news work, WCCO, Minneapolis, 1943; documentaries; CBS, 1950; television coverage, special news events; news on film; *Time,* 1961.
    122 pp. *Permission required.* 1961.
    See also Journalism Lectures.

MILLER, Arthur (1915–   ) *See* Popular Arts.

MILLER, Dorothy Canning. *See* Holger Cahill.

MILLER, Henry L. (1912–   ) *See* Eisenhower Administration.

MILLER, Ivan W. (1898–   ) *See* Marine Corps.

MILLER, Leslie A. (1886–   )
                                    JACKSON HOLE PRESERVE
Experience in politics; early contact with Jackson Hole: purchase of land, forest-park feud, Congressional delegation, monument proclamation, local press; member of Board of Jackson Hole Preserve. Impressions of the Rockefeller family.
    122 pp. *Permission required.* 1966.

MILLER, Mitchell William (1911–   ) *See* Popular Arts.

MILLER, Morton David (1915–   ) *See* Social Security.

MILLER, Neville (1894–   ) *See* James Lawrence Fly Project.

MILLER, Robert. *See* Popular Arts.

MILLIKEN, Carl Elias (1877–1961) Governor.

Maine politics, 1905–27; Hays Office, 1927–47.
142 pp. *Permission required to cite or quote.* 1950. NYT (Part I).

MILLING, Thomas D. (–1960) *See* Henry H. Arnold Project.

MINING ENGINEERS

Brief interviews with notable mining engineers on salient phases of their careers. Consultants and executives of companies in widely scattered areas from Alaska to South Africa, they also provide information on the discovery and exploration of new mines.

Participants and pages: Robert Annan, 24; John Baragwanath, 30; Alan Bateman, 15; Arthur Bunker, 47; Henry Carlisle, 34; Louis Cates, 15; Cleveland Dodge, 25; John Gustafson, 40; David Irwin, 20; Ira B. Joralemon, 18; James Knapp, 27; Robert Koenig, 26; Lewis Levensaler, 12; Jaffet Lindberg, 35; Donald McLoughlin, 19; W. W. Mein, 18; Reno Sales, 28; Henry DeWitt Smith, 22; Comar Wilson, 21; William E. Wrather, 42.

518 pp. *Permission required to cite or quote.* 1961. *Contributed by Henry C. Carlisle, San Francisco.*

MINKOFF, Nathaniel. *See* Socialist Movement.

MINNICH, Lawrence Arthur (1918–   ) Government official.

EISENHOWER ADMINISTRATION

Assistant White House Staff Secretary, 1953–60; preparing *The Public Papers of the President.*
34 pp. *Permission required to cite or quote.* 1968.

MINOW, Newton Norman (1926–   ) Lawyer.
ADLAI E. STEVENSON PROJECT

Education; Stevenson campaign, 1948; Stevenson staff, 1952; 1952 campaign; legal practice with Stevenson, 1954; 1956 campaign; Eisenhower's heart attack; Lyndon Johnson; relations with the Kennedys; 1960 campaign; Stevenson in the UN; Bay of Pigs; ambitions in 1964. Impressions of William McCormick Blair, Willard Wirtz, Arthur Schlesinger, Jr., and other Stevenson aides.
122 pp. *Permission required.* 1969.

MINSTER, Leonard. *See* Federated Department Stores.

MINTENER, James Bradshaw (1902–   ) Lawyer.
EISENHOWER ADMINISTRATION

Youth; education, Yale and Oxford; first meetings with Gen. Eisenhower; Minnesota "write-in" primary, 1952.
65 pp. *Closed during lifetime.* 1968.

MITCHELL, Broadus (1892–   ) Economic historian.
SOUTHERN INTELLECTUAL LEADERS

Childhood and education; career of Samuel Chiles Mitchell, University of Richmond and University of South Carolina; graduate work and teaching, Johns Hopkins University; Socialist Party in Maryland; research on cotton textile industry; Baltimore Urban League; *Alexander Hamilton;* impressions of Elizabeth Gilman, Jacob Hollander, Douglas Southall Freeman, George S. Mitchell, Morris Mitchell, and Josiah Morse.
165 pp. *Closed pending publication of a study.* 1972.

MITCHELL, George Wilder (1904–   ) *See* Adlai E. Stevenson Project.

MITCHELL, Harry Leland (1906–   ) Union official.

Formation of the Southern Tenant Farmers Union; its eventual affiliation with the CIO; resistance to the Communist Party; reorganization with the AFL as the National Agricultural Workers Union; conditions among tenants and sharecroppers in Arkansas, Missouri, Oklahoma, and Mississippi.

191 pp. *Permission required to cite or quote.* 1957. NYT (Part I).

MITCHELL, Lucy Sprague (1878–   ) Educator.

Dean of Women at University of California, 1906; marriage to Dr. Wesley Clair Mitchell and move to NY, 1912; interest in experimental education, founding of Bank Street School; teaching and writing for children.

167 pp. *Permission required to cite or quote.* 1960. *Conducted by Regional Oral History Office, University of California, Berkeley; contributed by Bank Street School of New York City.*

MITCHELL, Ralph Johnson (1891–1970) *See* Marine Corps.

MITCHELL, Stephen Arnold (1903–   ) Lawyer.

ADLAI E. STEVENSON PROJECT

Family background; education; law practice in Chicago; activities in Democratic Party; WWII; Stevenson campaign, 1948; Stevenson's attitude towards politics; Ellen Borden Stevenson; pressures of public office; Chairman Democratic National Committee, 1952–55; 1952 campaign: Harry Truman, party unity; 1956 campaign: civil rights plank, the Kennedys; impressions of various political figures.

173 pp. *Permission required.* 1967.

MITCHELL, William Lloyd (1900–   ) *See* Social Security *and* Eisenhower Administration.

MOCK, Richard M. (1905–   ) *See* Aviation.

MOISANT, Mathilde (–1964) *See* Aviation.

275

MOLEY, Raymond (1886–　) *See* Social Security.

MOLINAS, Luciano F. *See* Argentina in the 1930's.

MONRONEY, Almer Stillwell Mike (1902–　) Senator.
ADLAI E. STEVENSON PROJECT

First impressions of Stevenson; Speakers Bureau; whistle-stop speeches; 1956 battle over the vice presidential candidate; "draft Stevenson" movement, 1960; John F. Kennedy; 1960 Democratic Convention; Stevenson's influence on younger politicians and the party.
128 pp. *Permission required.* 1969.

MONRONEY, Michael (1927–　) *See* Adlai E. Stevenson Project.

MONTGOMERY, Douglass (1912–　) *See* Popular Arts.

MONTGOMERY, Paul (1892–　) *See* McGraw-Hill.

MOON, S. G. and C. D. Moon. *See* Weyerhaeuser Timber Company.

MOORE, Arthur. *See* Adlai E. Stevenson Project.

MOORE, Charles J. (1889–　) Naval officer.

Family and early life; Naval Academy, early cruises; WWI convoys; Naval Overseas Transportation Service; teaching at Naval Academy, Navigation Department; Yorktown Sesquicentennial; Naval War College duty; Pacific Fleet: Gilberts campaign, attacks on Kwajalein, Truk, Saipan; diversion of forces to the Marianas, Philippine Sea Battle; impressions of Adms. Chester Nimitz, Edward Kalbfuss, H. Kent Hewitt, Raymond Spruance, and others.
1,244 pp. *Permission required.* 1967.

REFER TO "NOTES ON USE" IN INTRODUCTION

MOORMAN, Thomas Samuel (1910–   ) Air Force officer.

AIR FORCE ACADEMY

Experiences as USAF Academy Superintendent, 1965–70: curriculum reform, athletics, honor code, 4th class system, recruitment among minorities, White Committee investigation and cadet morale, library, programs in military training and airmanship.

134 pp. *Restriction pending.* 1971.

MOOS, Malcolm Charles (1916–   ) Author, educator. *See* Eisenhower Administration.

MORELLO, Alberto. *See* Argentina in the 1930's.

MORGAN, Cary (–1960) *See* Popular Arts.

MORGAN, Edward P. (1910–   ) Writer, broadcaster.

EISENHOWER ADMINISTRATION

1952 and 1960 campaigns; Eisenhower's news conferences; impressions of Dwight Eisenhower and Richard Nixon; "Kitchen Debate."

53 pp. *Closed during lifetime.* 1967.

MORGAN, Gerald Demuth (1908–   ) Lawyer.

EISENHOWER ADMINISTRATION

Harvard Law School; legislative drafting, Legislative Counsel Office to 1945; legislative liaison staff, 1953; administrative assistant to President Eisenhower, 1955–58.

133 pp. *Closed during lifetime.* 1968.

MORGAN, Howard Waldron (1902–   ) *See* Weyerhaeuser Timber Company.

MORGAN, Jack. *See* Weyerhaeuser Timber Company.

The Oral History Collection

MORGAN, Shepard Ashman (1884–1968) Banker.

Early life in Rochester, NY; Williams College; NY *Sun.*
63 pp. *Permission required to cite or quote.* 1950.

MORGENTHAU, Henry, Jr. (1891–1967) *See* Herbert H. Lehman Project.

MORLEY, James W. *See* Columbia Television Lectures.

MORRILL, Chester (1885–   ) Lawyer, Administrator.

Childhood and education; Department of Agriculture, 1914–25: various activities in the agricultural fields of marketing and distribution, including the Grain Futures and the Packers and Stockyards Administrations; WFC, 1925–31; Federal Farm Loan Bureau, 1927–31; Federal Reserve System, 1931–50; RFC, 1931–33; banking in Nationalist China, 1951.
311 pp. *Closed until 5 years after death.* 1952.

MORRIS, Arch (1889–1964) *See* McGraw-Hill.

MORRIS, Chester (1901–   ) *See* Popular Arts.

MORRIS, Newbold (1902–1966) Lawyer.

NYC politics, 1934–49; Fiorello H. LaGuardia.
94 pp. *Open.* 1950.
See also New York Political Studies.

MORRIS, Richard Brandon (1904–   ) *See* American Historians.

MORRISETT, Lloyd N. (1929–   ) Foundation executive.
CARNEGIE CORPORATION

First association with the Carnegie Corporation, 1957; experiences as staff member, later vice president of Corpora-

tion, 1958–67: staff members; program areas; cognitive research; Educational Testing Service; daily routine. Impressions of Corporation officers and trustees.
214 pp. *Permission required.* 1967. *See also* Children's Television Workshop.

MORRISSEY, Muriel E. *See* Aviation.

MORROW, Everett Frederic (1909–   ) Government official.

EISENHOWER ADMINISTRATION

Eisenhower campaign train, 1952; administrative officer, Special Projects, 1955–61; Eisenhower and civil rights; impressions of Sherman Adams, Martin Luther King, Jr., and others; field secretary, NAACP; CBS; staff advisor on race relations to Eisenhower administration.
175 pp. *Permission required to cite or quote.* 1968.

MORROW, L. C. (1888–1971) *See* McGraw-Hill.

MORSE, Carlton Errol (1901–   ) *See* Radio Pioneers.

MORSE, David A. (1907–   ) Lawyer.

Parents' experiences as immigrants, London and NYC; boyhood, Somerville, New Jersey; faculty and students, Rutgers College and Harvard Law School; New Deal lawyers; Petroleum Labor Policy Board, 1934–35; Enid, Oklahoma strike; impressions of Paul Robeson, Felix Frankfurter, Herbert Marks, Paul Freund.
127 pp. *Permission required.* 1971.

MORSE, True Delbert (1896–   ) Agricultural official.

EISENHOWER ADMINISTRATION

Department of Agriculture during his years as Under Secretary, 1953–61: programs, relations with President and Congress, Rural Development Program; impressions of Eisenhower and others in the administration.
144 pp. *Permission required.* 1967.

MORSE, Wayne Lyman (1900–   ) *See* Herbert H. Lehman Project.

MOSCOW, Warren (1908–   ) Journalist.

NY politics, 1940–50; William O'Dwyer; Thomas E. Dewey; Democratic National Convention, 1952.
83 pp. *Permission required to cite or quote.* 1953. NYT (Part I).

MOSSBAUER, Rudolf Ludwig (1929–   ) *See* Nobel Laureates.

MOTION PICTURES. *See* Popular Arts.

MT. SINAI HOSPITAL

A history of Mt. Sinai Hospital, NYC, with emphasis on staff contributions to medical knowledge, growth and development of specialized departments within the hospital, and comparison of modern medical training with earlier practices; brief description of establishment of Mt. Sinai Medical School. Transcripts of certain faculty meetings, investitures, and seminars are included.

Participants and pages: George Baehr, 36; Bryan Brooke, 46; Ralph Colp, 22; B.B. Crohn, 11; John Gerster, 21; Leon Ginzberg, 31; Abraham Hyman, 33; George James, 37; Hillard Jason, 49; Samuel Klein, 44; Percy Klingenstein, 29; Sylvan Manheim, 50; Hans Popper, 34; Coleman Rabin, 20; Martin Steinberg, 80; Joseph Turner, 37; Peter Vogel, 17; Harry Wessler, 15; Ashe Winkelstein, 23.

Faculty Meetings, 269; Investitures: Morris P. Bender, 24; Kurt Hirschhorn, 24; George James, 26; Alan Eugene Kark, 14; Ralph Kaufman, 29; Hans Popper, 28; Memorial Dr. Garlock, 15; Seminars, 148.

1,212 pp. *Permission required.* 1965–69. *Contributed by Dr. Albert S. Lyons, Mt. Sinai Hospital, New York City.*

MUDGE, Isadore Gilbert (1875–1957) *See* Columbiana.

MUIR, Malcolm (1885–   ) *See* McGraw-Hill.

REFER TO "NOTES ON USE" IN INTRODUCTION

MULCAHY, Francis Patrick (1894–   ) *See* Marine Corps.

MULHEARN, Henry (1912–   ) Police officer.

Childhood in Brooklyn; teacher training; social work; NYC Police Department, 1936; Police Academy; Lower East Side, Chinatown; Brooklyn gang warfare, 1945–48; Juvenile Aid Bureau, 1949; Youth Board; Precinct Captain, 1956.
122 pp. *Permission required to cite or quote.* 1960. *Contributed by John K. Kelly, Newark, Delaware.*

MULLER, Hermann Joseph (1890–   ) *See* Nobel Laureates.

MULLINER, Maurine

SOCIAL SECURITY

Personal secretary to Senator Robert F. Wagner, 1932; technical adviser to Social Security Board, 1936; impressions of Abe Epstein, Arthur Altmeyer, John Winant, John Carson, Frances Perkins, Ellen Woodward, Vincent Miles.
303 pp. *Open.* 1967.

MUNN, John Calvin (1906–   ) *See* Marine Corps.

MURKLAND, Lois. *See* Carnegie Corporation.

MURO DE NADAL, Francisco (1908–   ) Businessman.

ARGENTINA IN THE 1930'S

Production and sale of men's clothing; shift from importing materials to local production; use of credit, seasonal demand, piecework; sources of capital, tariff protection; labor relations; effects of Depression, WWII, economic controls; ILO; business philosophy.
59 pp. *Open.* 1971.

MURPHY, Charles Springs (1909–   ) *See* James Lawrence Fly Project.

MURPHY, Donald Ridgway (1895–   ) *See* Farm Holiday Association.

MURPHY, Jay. *See* Civil Rights in Alabama.

MURPHY, Katherine Prentis (1882–1969) Art collector.

Random reflections by a collector of early American furnishings.
50 pp. *Open.* 1957.

MURPHY, Matthew J. (1920–   ) *See* McGraw-Hill.

MURPHY, Robert Daniel (1894–   ) *See* Eisenhower Administration.

MURPHY, William Parry (1892–   ) *See* Nobel Laureates.

MURRAY, James P. (1892–   ) *See* Aviation.

MURRAY, Mae (–1965) *See* Popular Arts.

MURRAY, Robert K. *See* American Historians.

MURTAUGH, Joseph Stuart (1912–   ) *See* Health Science.

MUSSER, Charles Riley (1911–   ) *See* Weyerhaeuser Timber Company.

MUSTE, A. J. (1885–1967) Clergyman.

Childhood in Michigan; first contact with AFL; New Brunswick Theological Seminary; experiences, Lower East Side, NYC; pastorates, NYC and Massachusetts; Socialist Party; Social Gospel Movement; WWI: pacifism, conscientious objectors; 1919 Lawrence strike; Amalgamated Textile Workers Union; Brookwood Labor College.

REFER TO "NOTES ON USE" IN INTRODUCTION

470 pp. *Permission required to cite or quote.* NYT (Part I). *See also* Socialist Movement.

MUZZEY, David Saville (1870–1965) Historian.

Early life and education; Columbia University; Ethical Culture Society; writing American history.
44 pp. *Open.* 1956.

MYERS, Henry. Writer.

POPULAR ARTS

Early life, Columbia University; Larry Hart; early playwriting; press agent for Shuberts; Dmitri Tiomkin; first reactions to Hollywood; Clara Bow; "Writers Building," Paramount; *Million Dollar Legs;* writing for Columbia, Universal, MGM; comedy writing for films; *Destry Rides Again;* departure from Hollywood, 1950.
123 pp. *Open.* 1959.

MYERS, Robert Julius (1912–   ) Actuary.

SOCIAL SECURITY

Actuarial cost estimates for Social Security and allied legislation; Social Security Administration actuarial office; sources of data for cost estimates: American Hospital Association, Blue Cross, AFL-CIO, private insurance companies; legislative history of Medicare and the preceding insurance and assistance programs, 1900–67.
94 pp. *Permission required to cite or quote.* 1967.

MYERS, Robin. *See* Socialist Movement.

MYERS, Theodore. *See* Adlai E. Stevenson Project.

MYGATT, Tracy (1885–   ) *See* Frances Witherspoon.

MYRDAL, Gunnar Karl (1898–   ) Economist.

CARNEGIE CORPORATION

Origin of studies which resulted in *An American Dilemma:*

the Negro Problem and Modern Democracy, 1944; impressions of Frederick Keppel, Charles Dollard, Arnold Rose, Ralph Bunche, Richard Sterner.
122 pp. *Permission required.* 1968.

NAGEL, Carl (1920–   ) *See* McGraw-Hill.

NAGEL, Conrad (1897–   ) *See* Popular Arts.

NALDI, Nita (1902–1961) *See* Popular Arts.

NARASIMHAN, Chakravarthi V. (1915–   ) *See* Dag Hammarskjold Project.

NASAW, Barbara (Mrs. David). *See* Columbia Crisis of 1968.

NASAW, David. *See* Columbia Crisis of 1968.

NASH, Ogden (1902–1971) *See* Friends of the Columbia Libraries.

NAVAL HISTORY

This project, conducted with the cooperation of the Director of Naval History (Navy Department), covers many phases of modern naval history, among them training, procurement, logistics, ordnance, naval aviation, submarines, scientific development, salvage, and intelligence.

Operational strategy and tactics during WWI and in particular WWII are analyzed in detail; there is material also on Korea. Many political and military figures, American and foreign, appear, *passim,* along with fresh material on major battles.

Unification of the armed services and relationships in the Department of Defense are discussed.

Participants and pages: Walter S. Anderson, 290; John Jennings Ballentine, 758; Richard B. Black, 89; Robert B. Carney, 768; Joseph J. Clark, 840; Richard L. Conolly, 411; Benjamin S. Custer, 1,022; Walter S. Diehl, 93; Donald Duncan, 981; William M. Fechteler, 266; James Fife, 617; Paul

F. Foster, 373; John L. Hall, Jr., 338; Thomas C. Hart, 284; H. Kent Hewitt, 478; Harry W. Hill, 955; James L. Holloway, Jr., 187; John H. Hoover, 432; George F. Hussey, Jr., 582;

Royal E. Ingersoll, 126; Alfred W. Johnson, 88; Thomas C. Kinkaid, 450; Alan G. Kirk, 386; Emory S. Land, 227; Charles A. Lockwood, 720; Charles J. Moore, 1,244; Chester W. Nimitz, 89; Ralph C. Parker, 146; William A. Read, 739; Samuel M. Robinson, 56; Felix B. Stump, 364; William A. Sullivan, 1,784; William Tarrant, 53; Harold C. Train, 451; Henry Williams, 251; Eugene E. Wilson, 974.

17,912 pp. *Individual restrictions apply.* 1960–69. *Copies of the memoirs are also available at the Division of Naval History, Washington, D.C.*

NEAL, Alfred. *See* Federated Department Stores.

NEAL, Robert R. *See* Social Security.

NEALE, Robert. *See* Flying Tigers.

NEF, John Ulric (1899–   ) *See* Adlai E. Stevenson Project.

NEGULESCO, Jean (1900–   ) *See* Popular Arts.

NEILSON, Isabelle. *See* Carnegie Corporation.

NELSEN, Ancher (1904–   ) Congressman.
EISENHOWER ADMINISTRATION
REA under President Eisenhower.
34 pp. *Permission required to cite or quote.* 1970.

NELSON, Richard. *See* Adlai E. Stevenson Project.

NESS, Norman Theodore (1903–   ) *See* Marshall Plan.

NESTINGEN, Ivan Arnold (1921–   ) Government official.
SOCIAL SECURITY
John F. Kennedy campaign in Wisconsin, 1960; Under

Secretary, HEW: budgets and administration, Medicare legislation.
109 pp. *Open.* 1965.

NEUMANN, Henry (1882–1966) Educator.

Founding of Ethical Culture Society; Dr. Felix Adler.
89 pp. *Permission required to cite or quote.* 1965. NYT (Part I).

NEUSTADT, Richard Elliott (1919–   ) Political scientist.

Experiences as adviser to John F. Kennedy, 1960–61.
77 pp. *Permission required.* 1961.

NEVINS, Allan (1890–1971) Author, historian.

Illinois farm life in the 1890's; family and neighbors; education, formal and informal: reading, the University of Illinois; Stuart Pratt Sherman; NYC and editorial work for the *Nation* and *Evening Post,* 1913–18: editorial conferences, Oswald Garrison Villard, Rollo Ogden, Simeon Strunsky; social and intellectual activities: the Strunsky circle; the *Literary Review,* book reviewing, Christopher Morley; sale of the *Post,* 1923; NY *Herald* and NY *Sun:* Frank Munsey; NY *World,* 1923–31: Walter Lippmann, Claude Bowers, Herbert B. Swope; Cornell, 1927: Carl Becker; early books and the legacy of journalism experience; Columbia, 1928–58: teaching; biographies of Cleveland and Fish; Oxford, 1940–41; for OWI to Australia and New Zealand, 1942; chief public affairs officer, London, for Department of State, 1946–47; founding of Oral History Research Office, 1948–49; *American Heritage,* 1950; business history: Hewitt, Rockefeller, Ford, and Weyerhaeuser studies; *Ordeal of the Union;* to California, 1958.
375 pp. *Closed until March 5, 1976.* 1963.
See also Allan Nevins Project.

NEVINS, Arthur (1891–   ) Army officer.
EISENHOWER ADMINISTRATION

Early Army days; early recollections of Dwight D. Eisenhower; WWII; War Department; Eisenhower farm at Gettysburg.
87 pp. *Permission required to cite or quote.* 1970.
See also Allan Nevins Project.

NEVINS, Mary Fleming (Mrs. Allan) (1894–   ) *See* Allan Nevins Project.

ALLAN NEVINS PROJECT

Associates of Allan Nevins during his long career at Columbia (1928–58) and later at the Huntington Library recall the historian and the man as they knew him. Many of the first interviews, contributed by Mort Lewis, a California friend, deal largely with his last years. Subsequent interviews will cover the Columbia years and other phases of the historian's life.

Participants and pages: Lillian Bean, 47; Ray Allen Billington, 40; William Cullen Bryant II, 21; Carl Haverlin, 25; Mort Lewis, 173; E. B. Long, 29; Allan Nevins, 61; Arthur Nevins, 17; Mary Nevins, 81; John Niven (with Hal Bridges and Leonard W. Levy), 43; Irving Stone, 37; Jean Stone, 11; James Thorpe, 3; Justin Turner, 11.

599 pp. *Closed until March 5, 1976.* Papers.

NEW SCHOOL LECTURES

Two lectures from the Wisdom of Life series delivered at the New School, dealing primarily with the management of human resources.

Participants and pages: Lillian M. Gilbreth, 34; Alvin Johnson, 24.

58 pp. *Open.* 1959.

NEW YORK POLITICAL STUDIES

From earliest days the Oral History Research Office has

maintained an interest in gathering the recollections of those intimately connected with political developments in New York City and State. More than one hundred memoirs in this catalogue attest to this objective; they illuminate varied aspects and events of NYC political life extending back to the Draft Riots of 1863. A host of civic and political figures live again in their pages, ranging from mayors, district attorneys, judges, and reformers to precinct politicians, social workers, criminals, and members of street gangs.

In addition, the three special projects described below focus directly upon particular aspects of the New York political scene.

A. BROOKLYN POLITICS, 1930–50

Selected individuals recount their experiences in the Brooklyn political arena during these two decades. Journalists, lawyers and politicians describe the problems and achievements of the borough and its relationship to the Mayor and the city and state administrations. The office of the district attorney receives special attention, centering on William O'Dwyer and his incumbency. Mayors James Walker and Fiorello LaGuardia, John McCooey, Frank Kelly, John Cashmore, Rudolph Halley and other local leaders appear in these pages. Accounts of police procedure, political club practices, and court room incidents abound.

Participants and pages: Oscar Bernstien, 79; Paul Crowell, 40; Clarence de la Chapelle, 56; Henry P. Dolan, 76; Clifford Evans, 141; George J. Joyce, 45; Solomon Klein, 160; John J. Lynch, 98; Paul O'Dwyer, 245; William O'Dwyer, 1,783.

2,723 pp. *Permission required. 1960–62. Contributed by John K. Kelly of Newark, Delaware.*

B. CITIZENS BUDGET COMMISSION

Ten years after the establishment in NYC of the office of Deputy Mayor, a group of civic organizations undertook to sponsor a scholarly study of this office in its first decade. Participating organizations included the Citizens Budget Commission, the Citizens Union, the New York Chamber of Commerce, the Women's City Club, and the Commerce

REFER TO "NOTES ON USE" IN INTRODUCTION

and Industry Association. Transcripts of these interviews became a basis for the report, *New York City's Deputy Mayor, City Administrator—Accomplishments, Problems and Potentialities* by Professor Demetrios Caraley.

Participants and pages: Demetrios Caraley, 41; Henry Cohen, 36; John V. Connorton, 34; Julius C. Edelstein, 24; Lyle C. Fitch, 28; Luther Gulick, 28; Meyer Kailo, 25; Maxwell Lehman, 33; Charles F. Preusse, 28; Mathias L. Spiegel, 67 *(closed until January 1, 1975);* Charles H. Tenney, 6; Robert F. Wagner, 29.

379 pp. *Permission required except as noted. 1966. Contributed by the Citizens Budget Commission.*

C. NEW YORK ELECTION OF 1949

A series of interviews and speeches on the New York City and State elections of 1949 in an attempt to record history as it transpired and to cover all candidates and parties. Discussion of the issues of the campaign, including federal aid to education, Communism, municipal corruption, and minority problems is combined with analyses of political organization and techniques, voting of religious and nationality groups, and the effect of labor union support and newspaper coverage upon the election.

Participants and pages: Alger Baldwin Chapman, 14; George Hamilton Combs, 21; John Foster Dulles, 13; Hiram Selig Gans, 68; Julius Isaacs, 8; Marie M. (Mrs. Fiorello H.) LaGuardia and Newbold Morris, 8; Reuben Avis Lazarus, 23; Herbert H. Lehman, 12; Vito Marcantonio, 7; Newbold Morris, 16; William Louis Pfeiffer, 9; Paul L. Ross, 35; David Sher, 4; Jane H. Todd, 23; Harry Uviller, 7; John A. Wells, 16; Abraham Zeitz, 7.

292 pp. *Permission required to cite or quote. 1949.*

NEWBY, Ray. *See* Radio Pioneers.

NEWLIN, Thomas J. *See* Benedum and the Oil Industry.

NEWMAN, Paul (1925–   ) *See* Popular Arts.

NEWMAN, Pauline. *See* Socialist Movement.

NEWSOM, Herschel D. (1905–1970) *See* Eisenhower Administration.

NICHOLS, Kenneth David (1907–)
EISENHOWER ADMINISTRATION

Deputy Director of Guided Missiles; Chief of Armed Forces Special Weapons Projects; General Manager AEC; Robert Oppenheimer case.
100 pp. *Closed during lifetime.* 1967.

NICHOLS, Roy Franklin (1896–1973) *See* American Historians.

NICHOLS, Ruth Rowland (1901–1960) *See* Aviation.

NIEBUHR, Reinhold (1892–1971) Theologian.

Early life and education; Yale Divinity School; Christianity in an industrial setting in Detroit; writings and views on religious thought.
95 pp. *Permission required to cite or quote.* 1953. NYT (Part I).

NIESS, Oliver K. *See* Air Force Academy.

NIMITZ, Chester W. (1885–1966) Naval officer.

Early life in Texas; family background; career at Naval Academy; early commands; reorganization of Pearl Harbor after Japanese attack.
89 pp. *Permission required.* 1965. Papers.

NIMMER, David Rowan (1894–) Marine Corps officer.

Early assignments; occupation duty in France and Germany, 1918–19; *Mississippi*, 1925–27; China, 1929; Russian language student; American Embassy, Moscow, 1934–35; missions to Warsaw, Helsingfors, Leningrad, Sevastopol; Quantico, 1939–42; Guadalcanal and South Pacific, 1942–43, Okinawa, 1945.
199 pp. *Permission required.* 1970.

REFER TO "NOTES ON USE" IN INTRODUCTION

NITZE, Paul Henry (1907–   ) *See* Marshall Plan.

NIVEN, John. *See* Allan Nevins Project.

NOBEL LAUREATES ON SCIENTIFIC RESEARCH

An intensive study of Nobel laureates in science with particular emphasis on their relations with co-workers. The interviews include information on their associations with Nobel prize winners and other eminent scientists who have played important roles in the discoveries for which they were awarded the prize. Each laureate was asked to describe the sequence of events leading to his discovery, and the parts played by others in this process. This project was supported by the National Science Foundation.

Participants and pages: Carl D. Anderson, 46; John Bardeen, 43; George Beadle, 46; Felix Bloch, 24; Walter H. Brattain, 54; Melvin Calvin, 12; Owen Chamberlain, 44; Carl Cori, 52; André Cournand, 54; E. A. Doisy, 30; Vincent du Vigneaud, 33; Joseph Erlanger, 30; Robert L. Hofstadter, 32; Edward C. Kendall, 62; Arthur Kornberg, 24; Polykarp Kusch, 49; T. D. Lee, 23; Rudolf F. Libby, 58; Fritz Lipmann, 41;

Edwin N. McMillan, 49; Maria Goeppert Mayer, 51; Rudolf L. Mossbauer, 38; Hermann J. Muller, 57; William Parry Murphy, 37; Linus Pauling, 51; Edward Mills Purcell, 35; Isidor Isaac Rabi, 44; Dickinson W. Richards, 20; Frederick C. Robbins, 37; Glenn T. Seaborg, 20; Emilio Segre, 50; William Shockley, 51; Wendell Stanley, 36; Albert Szent-Gyorgyi, 49; Edward Lawrie Tatum, 32; Max Theiler, 42; Harold Urey, 44; Eugene P. Wigner, 60; Chen Ning Yang, 67.

1,525 pp. *Permission required. 1964.*
Contributed by Harriet Zuckerman, New York.

NOBILE, Umberto. *See* Aviation.

NOBLE, Alfred Houston (1894–   ) Marine Corps officer.

Education; WWI service; amphibious warfare concepts; duty in Haiti; 5th Marines, 1939–41; WWII: Bougainville, Guam; 1st Marine Division, China, 1946; CG, Department of the Pacific, 1951–52; Head, Military Assistance Advisory Group, The Hague, 1952–54; CG, Camp Le-

jeune, 1954–55; CG, Fleet Marine Force, Atlantic, 1955–56.
111 pp. *Open.* 1968.

NORTON, John Kelley (1893–   ) Educator.

Education, Palo Alto and Stanford University; athletics; 1920 Olympics; early experiences in teaching and educational administration; NEA, 1922–30; Columbia University, 1930–58; Educational Policies Commission; India, 1958–60; analysis of problems, policies, and progress at TC. Impressions of Elwood Cubberley, Lewis Terman, John Dewey, W. H. Kilpatrick, George Strayer, William Carr, and James B. Conant.
270 pp. *Permission required until March 1, 1975.* 1963.

NORTON, William John (1883–   ) Social worker.

Goodrich House, Cleveland, 1915; social work movements in Cincinnati, Detroit; Community Union and Tracy McGregor.
67 pp. *Open.* 1954.

NOVAK, Robert. *See* Social Security.

NOYES, Blanche. *See* Aviation.

NUCLEAR ENERGY

A joint lecture by Professor Menelaos D. Hassialis and Dean John G. Palfrey.
38 pp. *Open.* 1958.

NUGENT, Elliott (1900–   ) *See* Popular Arts.

NURICK, Lester. *See* World Bank.

NYE, Russell B. (1913–   ) *See* American Historians.

REFER TO "NOTES ON USE" IN INTRODUCTION

NYGAARD, Leonard H. *See* Weyerhaeuser Timber Company.

OAKES, John Bertram (1913–   ) Newspaper editor.

Journalistic experiences at school and Princeton; Rhodes Scholar, Oxford University; British press; Russia, 1936; Trenton-Times papers; Washington *Post*, 1937–41; US Army, 1941; officers training; intelligence work.
177 pp. *Permission required.* 1964.

OATES, James Franklin, Jr. (1899–   ) *See* Adlai E. Stevenson Project.

O'BRIAN, John Lord (1874–   ) Lawyer.

Early childhood and education; Harvard; public activities in Buffalo; law practice, 1900; Crapsey case; NY Assemblyman, 1907; NY State politics, 1898–1915; NY Constitutional Convention, 1915; election of 1916; US Attorney; Theodore Roosevelt-William Barnes libel suit; WWI: Von Rintelen conspiracy case, 1917; War Emergency Division, Department of Justice, 1917–19; German espionage, First Amendment cases before the Supreme Court; "Red Raids" and A. Mitchell Palmer; Zimmermann Note, 1917; election of 1920, head of Anti-Trust Division, 1929–32; TVA; law practice in Washington; Republican National Convention, 1940; OPM; SPAB; WPB; impressions of Theodore Roosevelt, Elihu Root, Henry L. Stimson, Alfred E. Smith, Supreme Court Justices Louis Brandeis, Oliver W. Holmes, and Benjamin Cardozo.
611 pp. *Permission required to cite or quote.* 1952. NYT (Part I).
See also James Lawrence Fly Project.

O'BRIEN, James Cuff. Labor official.

SOCIAL SECURITY

Volunteer labor organizer, 1948; full time labor organizer, 1952; *Senior Steelworker;* 1960 Senior Citizens for Kennedy-Johnson campaign; executive board of the National

Council of Aging, NYC; National Council of Senior Citizens; impressions of Nelson Cruikshank, Blue Carstenson, Ray Henry.
220 pp. *Open.* 1966.

O'BRIEN, Robert Lincoln (1865–1955) Publisher.

Early life; Boston *Evening Transcript* and *Herald,* 1895–1928; Tariff Commission, 1928–37; Sacco-Vanzetti case; political observations.
177 pp. *Permission required to cite or quote.* 1951. NYT (Part I).

OCCUPATION OF JAPAN

This project embraces the memoirs of various participants in the occupation of Japan and in the formulation of its Constitution. Within the overall discussions of occupation programs and policies are specific accounts of social, economic, agricultural, educational, and cultural developments, together with material on the purges and problems of civil rights. There are vivid descriptions of the drafting of the new Constitution and steps leading to the change in the role of the Emperor of Japan. Leading figures of SCAP and the Far Eastern Commission are portrayed in action, notably Gens. Douglas MacArthur, Courtney Whitney, Charles Willoughby, and Colonels Charles Kades and Richard Nugent.

Participants and pages: Lauren V. Ackerman, 28; Roger Nash Baldwin, 116; Joseph Ballantine, 271; Faubion Bowers, 56; Burton Crane, 74; Esther Crane, 58; Joseph Gordon, 31; Alvin Grauer, 139; John Harold, 54; Harold Henderson, 61; Lulu Holmes, 54; Charles Kades, 78; Mme. Ai Kume, 59; Josephine McKean, 79; Douglas Overton, 51; Cyrus H. Peake, 55; Harlan Youel, 53.

1,317 pp. *Permission required to cite or quote.* 1960–61.

O'CONNELL, Joseph J. (1892–) *See* Weyerhaeuser Timber Company.

O'CONNOR, Roderick Ladew (1921–) *See* Eisenhower Administration.

REFER TO "NOTES ON USE" IN INTRODUCTION

ODELL, Charles

SOCIAL SECURITY

Syracuse University, 1937; intern, National Institute for Public Affairs; unemployment security; White House Conference on Aging, 1950; UAW, 1957; health insurance for the aged; National Council of Senior Citizens: John F. Kennedy and the Council, the aged as a political factor, Medicare; staff, rallies; 1964 election. Impressions of James O'Brien, George McLain, Blue Carstenson, Wilbur Cohen, and others.
117 pp. *Open.* 1966.

ODOM, Will E. *See* Benedum and the Oil Industry.

O'DONNELL, Emmett, Jr. (1906–1971) Air Force officer.

AIR FORCE ACADEMY

West Point; WWII and Korea; use of B-29's; SAC in a limited war environment.
48 pp. *Permission required.*

O'DONNELL, Phillip Kenneth (1924–   ) *See* Social Security.

O'DWYER, Paul (1907–   ) Lawyer, politician.

NEW YORK POLITICAL STUDIES

Childhood in Ireland, coming to US; early jobs, Fordham Law School; NY waterfront practice; NYC politics; William O'Dwyer and the District Attorney's Office; American Labor Party, impressions of Fiorello LaGuardia, Robert Moses, Vito Marcantonio.
245 pp. *Permission required.* 1962.
Contributed by John K. Kelly, Newark, Delaware.

O'DWYER, William (1890–1964) City official.

NEW YORK POLITICAL STUDIES

Early experiences and education in Ireland and Spain; Brooklyn, informal education, 1910; Brooklyn policeman, lawyer, magistrate; district attorney, 1940–42; Prohibition and organized crime; Murder, Inc.; WWII, investigating government contracts for Air Force; War Refugee Board, Italy, 1944; Mayor of NYC, 1945–50; establishment of UN headquarters; Idlewild, transportation, housing, schools, gambling; illness, appointment as Ambassador to Mexico, 1950–52; reflections on NYC power structure, politics, the office of the mayor, judicial appointments, court reform, charter revisions, Tammany Hall, the American dream and opportunity, attitudes toward the law and democracy, metropolitan press; impressions of John B. Johnson, Edward Flynn, Fiorello LaGuardia, Robert Moses, William Reed, Michael Quill, Newbold Morris, Maximilian Moss.

1,783 pp. *Permission required.* 1962. Papers: Typescript copies of personal records, newspaper articles; partial transcripts of court testimony and of Estes Kefauver hearings, with some commentary.

Contributed by John K. Kelly, Newark, Delaware.

OGDEN, Michael (1911–   ) *See* Journalism Lectures.

OGG, Oscar (1909–1971) *See* Book-of-the-Month Club.

OGLE, Harold H. *See* Weyerhaeuser Timber Company.

O'HARE, John (1881–   ) Labor unionist.

Unionism in the automobile industry in the 1920's; organizing the Tobacco Workers' International Union; attempts to organize Reynolds' plant.

108 pp. *Permission required to cite or quote.* 1957. NYT (Part I).

OLDER, Charles. *See* Flying Tigers.

OLIPHANT, Paul. *See* Radio Pioneers.

OLIVER, Maria Rosa (1904–   ) Author.

ARGENTINA IN THE 1930's

Literary climate of Argentina from 1925; influential European and US writers; *Sur.*

57 pp. *Open.* 1971.

REFER TO "NOTES ON USE" IN INTRODUCTION

OLIVER, Ruth Law (1891–1970) *See* Aviation.

OLIVEY, Alexander P. (1866–   ) *See* Benedum and the Oil Industry.

OLMAN, Adolph. *See* Popular Arts.

O'MAHONEY, Joseph Christopher (1884–1962) Senator.

Boyhood in Massachusetts and NY; education at Columbia; work as journalist in Colorado and Wyoming; Wyoming politics; impressions of Senator John B. Kendrick and James A. Farley: the 1932 Presidential campaign.
57 pp. *Open.* 1958.

O'NEAL, Edward Asbury (1875–1958) Agriculturist.

Early years, farming in Alabama, 1899–1919; the Farm Bureau; Muscle Shoals; McNary-Haugen movement, 1919–32; AAA; TVA, 1932–52.
136 pp. *Permission required to cite or quote.* 1952. NYT (Part I).

O'NEILL, Maggie Orr. *See* Forest History Society.

O'NEILL, Michael. *See* Social Security.

ORDE, Alan Campbell. *See* Aviation.

O'ROURKE, Dennis (1914–   ) Corporation executive.
EISENHOWER ADMINISTRATION

Vice president and general counsel, Holly Sugar Co.; sugar legislation during Eisenhower administration.
41 pp. *Permission required to cite or quote.* 1967.

O'RYAN, John F. (1874–1961) Lawyer.

Education; military training; officer in Mexico, 1916; NYC

Transit Commissioner, 1922–26; Police Commissioner, 1934.
136 pp. *Permission required to cite or quote.* 1950. NYT (Part I).

OSBORN, Frederick (1889–   ) Corporation executive.
CARNEGIE CORPORATION

Trustee of Carnegie Corporation from 1936; impressions of other board members; role of the Corporation; WWII service; postwar foreign affairs programs; area studies; Alger Hiss; Congressional investigations; impressions of Russell Leffingwell, Morris Hadley, Charles Dollard, and others.
140 pp. *Permission required.* 1967.

OSBORNE, Lithgow (1892–   ) Diplomat.

Childhood and education; diplomatic service in Germany and Denmark, 1915–19; Treaty of Versailles; NY State Conservation Commissioner, 1933–42; Ambassador to Norway, 1944–46; OFRRO and UNRRA; impressions of prominent NY politicians.
228 pp. *Permission required to cite or quote.* 1953. NYT (Part I).

OSTROFF, Isidor. *See* Independence Park.

OVERTON, Douglas. *See* Occupation of Japan.

OWENS, J. Hamilton (1888–1967) Editor.

Family background; early career in NY and Baltimore journalism; editor-in-chief, Baltimore *Sun* papers; colleague and friend of H. L. Mencken.
70 pp. *Open.* 1958.

OWINGS, Dorsey. *See* Radio Pioneers.

PAARLBERG, Don (1911–   ) Educator.
EISENHOWER ADMINISTRATION

Economic Advisor, later Assistant Secretary, Department of Agriculture, 1953–58: agricultural legislation; Department's relations with Congress, farm organizations, other departments, and the President; Special Assistant to the President and coordinator of Food-for-Peace, 1958–61; Rural Development Program; Sugar Act; Cabinet meetings. Impressions of Ezra Taft Benson, Dwight Eisenhower, and others.
164 pp. *Permission required.* 1968.

PAEPCKE, Elizabeth (Mrs. Walter) *See* Adlai E. Stevenson Project.

PAGE, Arthur Wilson (1883–1960) Business consultant.

Editing *World's Work,* 1913–27; Walter Hines Page and Woodrow Wilson; War Department in WWII; Doubleday, Page & Company.
77 pp. *Permission required to cite or quote.* 1956. NYT (Part I).

PAGE, Geraldine (1924–   ) *See* Popular Arts.

PAIGE, Henry Reid (1904–   ) *See* Marine Corps.

PAIN, Evelyn. *See* Popular Arts.

PALEY, William S. (1901–   ) Broadcasting executive.

Childhood and education in Chicago; cigar factory, Philadelphia; Wharton School; advertising manager, Congress Cigar Company; use of radio in advertising; CBS, 1928 on; programing, stations, financing; Don Lee, Paramount Pictures; Adolph Zukor; Columbia Artists, Community Concerts.
67 pp. *Closed during lifetime.* 1960. Papers.

PALFREY, John G. (1919–   ) *See* Nuclear Energy.

PALMER, Frederic. *See* American Association of Physics Teachers.

PANTELL, Kate. *See* Joseph M. Proskauer Project.

PAPANEK, D. Ernst. *See* Socialist Movement.

PAPANEK, Jan (1896–   ) Diplomat.

Czech legions in Italy, 1916–19; independence of Czechoslovakia; study in Paris; Czech Ministry of Foreign Affairs; secretary to Eduard Benes; UN Conference in San Francisco, 1945; permanent representative to the UN, 1946–48; comments on Czech affairs, international politics, Czech-Soviet relations; National Committee of a Free Czechoslovakia.
374 pp. *Closed during lifetime.* 1951.

PARADO, Alan. *See* Popular Arts.

PARISIUS, Herbert W. (1895–   ) Government official.

Youth and education; ministry and teaching; FSA; Assistant Secretary of Agriculture; head of Food Production Board under Claude Wickard; in North Africa with UNRRA; Foreign Economic Administration; Department of Commerce.
226 pp. *Closed until 5 years after death.* 1954. Papers.

PARKER, Dorothy Rothschild (1893–1967) *See* Popular Arts.

PARKER, Ralph Chandler (1883–   ) Naval officer.

Education at Naval Academy and early cruises; destroyer duty, WWI convoys; Naval War College 1921–22; War Plans Division, 1929; cruiser duty; Command of Alaska Sector, 1941; Japanese attack on the Aleutians, 1942; training school

at Princeton; Adm. Chester Nimitz's staff at Pearl Harbor. Impressions of Adm. Husband Kimmel and Samuel E. Morison.
146 pp. *Open.* 1963.

PARKIN, George Raleigh (1896–   ) Business executive.
CARNEGIE CORPORATION
Carnegie grants to Canada; Seigniory Club meeting in 1938; programs for libraries, museums, adult education, and travel grants; impressions of Frederick Keppel, John Russell, Stephen Stackpole, and Whitney Shepardson.
152 pp. *Permission required.* 1968.

PARRAN, Thomas (1892–1968) *See* Health Science.

PARRIOTT, Foster Brooks (1878–1957) *See* Benedum and the Oil Industry.

PARSONS, Geoffrey (1879–1956) Journalist, lawyer.

Woodrow Wilson and the League of Nations; NY politics.
26 pp. *Open.* 1949.

PARSONS, Louella O. (1893–1972) *See* Popular Arts.

PARSONS, Talcott (1902–   ) *See* Carnegie Corporation.

PARTON, James (1912–   ) Publisher, editor.

Time; American Heritage; editorial staff, NY *Herald Tribune.*
24 pp. *Open.* 1959.

PATT, John Francis (1905–1971) *See* Radio Pioneers.

PATTBERG, Emil (1910–   ) (with George Martin) *See* World Bank.

PATTERSON, Bradley. *See* Eisenhower Administration.

PATTERSON, Hugh Baskin, Jr. (1915–   ) *See* Eisenhower Administration.

PATTERSON, John Sutton (1902–   ) Government official.
EISENHOWER ADMINISTRATION

Veterans Administration, 1953–57; Office of Civil and Defense Mobilization, 1958–61; impressions of President Eisenhower.
54 pp. *Permission required to cite or quote.* 1970.

ROBERT P. PATTERSON PROJECT

Interviews on the life of Judge Robert Porter Patterson (1891–1952) as related by his associates covering his career as a lawyer, US District and Circuit judge, Assistant Secretary of War, Under Secretary of War, and Secretary of War.

Participants and pages: Bernard Baruch, 19; Chauncey Belknap, 51; Robert R. Bowie, 30; Grenville Clark, 35; Ferdinand Eberstadt, 27; Peter Finucane, 21; Herbert Freidlich, 30; Edward S. Greenbaum, 56; Leslie A. Groves, 51; Richard H. McCann, 11; Michael Madigan, 47; William Marbury, 40; Howard Petersen, 25; Auguste Richard, 23; Elihu Root, Jr., 15; David Sarnoff, 9; Bayard Schieffelin, 22; Austin Scott, 3; George Spiegelberg, 20; Raymond Wilkins, 50.

585 pp. *Closed until Jan. 1, 1980.* 1960–61.
Underwritten by a gift of a Friend of the University.

PAUL, John R. (1893–   ) *See* Health Science.

PAULEY, Edwin Wendell (1903–   ) Political leader.

Allan Nevins's account of his interview with Mr. Pauley regarding the Vice Presidential nomination on the Democratic ticket in 1944. Efforts to prevent the renomination of Henry Wallace; how Harry Truman was chosen.
11 pp. *Permission required.* 1957.

PAULING, Linus Carl (1901–   ) *See* Nobel Laureates.

REFER TO "NOTES ON USE" IN INTRODUCTION

PEAKE, Cyrus Henderson (1900–   ) *See* Occupation of Japan.

PECK, DeWitt (1894–   ) Marine Corps officer.

Development of Marine Officers Training Schools; tactics of Marine operations; WWII in the Pacific; impressions of William Halsey, Richmond Turner, Robert Ghormley. 169 pp. *Open.* 1967.

PECK, Hoyt. *See* World Bank.

PECORA, Ferdinand (1881–1971) Judge.

Family background, boyhood in NYC, primary and high school education; New York Law School, 1903–05; legal experience; Progressive Party, NYC, 1912, convention, 1916; Counsel to Register of NY County; Assistant District Attorney, NY County, 1918–30; detailed description of District Attorney's office and relationship to other branches of government; NY County Democratic politics, 1919–30; law practice, 1930–33; Counsel for Senate Banking and Currency Committee, 1933; detailed description of "Pecora investigation." Impressions of prominent figures in NYC politics, including Charles Murphy and Mayors John Hylan and James Walker. 1,570 pp. *Permission required.* 1962.

PELL, Herbert Claiborne (1884–1961) Congressman.

Early life, education; Tuxedo Park; Spanish-American War; Progressive era; European travel; election of 1912; Congressman from NY, 1919–21; NY State Democratic chairman, 1921–26; Syracuse convention, 1922; the Ruhr; Charles F. Murphy and the Democratic Convention of 1924; Italy and Fascism; Germany and Hitler's Reich; minister to Portugal, 1937–41; coming of WWII; refugees; minister to Hungary, 1941; Hitler's timetable; returning home, 1942; UN Commission for Investigation of War Crimes; wartime London; reflections on corruption, education,

intelligence, and progress; hopes for the future.
658 pp. *Open.* 1951. NYT (Part I).

PENA, Jose Luis (1892–   ) Politician.
ARGENTINA IN THE 1930's

Socialist Party from 1912: Dr. Repetto, party organization
and leaders, Dr. Agustin Justo, political factionalism; National Chamber of Deputies, 1924–28, 1932–36: budget,
railroads, banking, and finance; revolution of 1930; Roca-Runciman Treaty.
74 pp. *Open.* 1971.

PEPPER, Claude Denson (1900–   ) *See* Social Security.

PERCY, Charles Harting (1919–   ) Senator.
EISENHOWER ADMINISTRATION

First contact with Dwight Eisenhower; entrance into
Republican politics; Commission on National Goals; Committee on Programs and Progress; party platforms; recession; Sputnik; National Defense Education Act.
33 pp. *Permission required to cite or quote.* 1970.

PEREZ LEIROS, Francisco (1895–1971) Labor leader, politician.
ARGENTINA IN THE 1930's

Labor movement in Argentina from 1916: political affiliations of various unions, labor associations, leaders, General
Confederation of Workers, international labor meetings;
political career as Socialist: member of National Chamber
of Deputies, 1930 revolution and labor movement, analysis
of pre-Peron and Peron era; labor and political philosophy.
180 pp. *Permission required to cite or quote.* 1971.

PERKINS, Frances (1882–1965) Government official.

An extended memoir dealing in particular with the following: Mt. Holyoke College; social work in Chicago and Philadelphia; NY: Consumers' League, 54-hour bill, Triangle
fire, Factory Investigation Commission, 1909–10; woman's

REFER TO "NOTES ON USE" IN INTRODUCTION

suffrage, 1905–10; NY State Legislature, 1910–13; Mayor John P. Mitchel's administration, 1913–17; art and literature; Committee on Safety; WWI; NY Industrial Commission; Democratic National Convention, 1920; Merchants Association; Spargo Wire Company strike; Alfred E. Smith as Governor; Democratic National Convention, 1924; Mayor James Walker and Tammany Hall; workmen's compensation, 1922–28; NY election of 1926; labor unions and labor legislation; election of 1928; Alfred E. Smith and Franklin D. Roosevelt; NY Labor Department; unemployment, 1929–32; NY election of 1930; Samuel Seabury Investigation; election of 1932; women and careers; Secretary of Labor, 1933–45; inauguration, 1933; the cabinet; reorganizing the Department of Labor; press and congressional relations; Gen. Pelham Glassford and migrant labor; Black bill; relief; FERA, CCC, WPA; Russian recognition; NY election of 1934; background of NRA; Title II; NRA administrative committees; Section 7(a) and textile code; coal and steel codes; Atlanta speech; NLRB; Avondale strike; automobile workers; Toledo strike; Akron sit-down strike; General Motors strike, 1937; steel strike; San Francisco longshoremen's strike; election of 1936; Walsh-Healy Act; Schechter case; Supreme Court fight; Communist Party; outbreak of WWII; third term issue; election of 1940; cabinet reorganization; Department of Labor preparing for war; Advisory Commission to the Council for National Defense; Lend-Lease; Cabinet Propaganda Committee; Pearl Harbor; labor and manpower in wartime; President Harry Truman; Civil Service Commission; ILO.

5,566 pp. *Closed until May 14, 1975.* 1955. Papers.

PERKINS, James Alfred (1911–   ) *See* Carnegie Corporation.

PERKINS, Jorge Walter. *See* Argentina in the 1930's.

PERKINS, Roswell Burchard (1926–   ) Lawyer, government official.

SOCIAL SECURITY

Education; consultant with HEW, 1953; analysis of Social

Security laws; Assistant Secretary, HEW, 1954; President Dwight Eisenhower on social security; politics behind legislation; dealing with the aged; evaluation of AMA; insurance companies' position; Forand Medicare bill; advising Governor Nelson Rockefeller on health legislation; impressions of Oveta Culp Hobby, Wilbur Cohen, others. 143 pp. *Open.* 1968.

PERKINS, Thomas Lee (1905–   ) Lawyer.
JAMES B. DUKE PROJECT

Family background; William Perkins as James B. Duke's private counsel and principal aide in drafting indenture for the Duke Endowment; own education and legal career: counsel for Duke family, trustee of Duke Endowment from 1948; impressions of Doris Duke and fellow trustees. 126 pp. *Permission required.* 1964.

PERLBERG, William (1899–   ) *See* Popular Arts.

PERRIN, Robert. *See* Social Security.

PERROTT, George St. John (1893–   ) *See* Health Science.

PERRY, Rufus P. *See* James B. Duke Project.

PERSONS, Wilton B. *See* Eisenhower Administration.

PETERSEN, Howard Charles (1910–   ) *See* Eisenhower Administration, Robert P. Patterson Project, *and* Adlai E. Stevenson Project.

PETERSEN, Ray. *See* Aviation.

PETERSON, A.C. *See* Henry H. Arnold Project.

PETERSON, Charles Emil (1906–   ) *See* Independence Park.

PETERSON, Houston (1897–   ) Educator.

Account of lecture programs at Cooper Union Forum, 1938–46, with vignettes of speakers and analysis of audience reaction; brief history of Cooper Union; experiences as writer and teacher.
398 pp. *Permission required.* 1967.

PETRIE, Daniel. *See* Radio Pioneers.

PFAEHLER, Richard. *See* James B. Duke Project.

PFEIFFER, Louis. *See* John Robert Gregg Project.

PFEIFFER, Omar Titus (1895–   ) Marine Corps officer.

WWI service; Santo Domingo, 1919–21; duties as legal officer; China, 1926–27; Quantico, 1937–41; attack on Pearl Harbor; WWII: USMC Pacific operations and Navy strategy; 7th Fleet, 1947; Fleet Marine Force, Western Pacific, 1947; rise of Chinese Communists; Camp Pendleton, 1948–50. Impressions of Adms. Husband Kimmel, Chester Nimitz, Ernest King, and Jesse Cooke; and Presidents Franklin D. Roosevelt and Harry Truman.
461 pp. *Open.* 1968.

PFEIFFER, William Louis (1907–   ) *See* New York Political Studies.

PHILLIPS, Kathryn Sisson (1879–1968) Educator.

Childhood in Kansas and Nebraska; Ohio Wesleyan; YWCA Secretary; early experiences as Dean of Women; formation of National Association of Deans of Women; educational opinions and theories; Phillips Foundation.
98 pp. *Permission required to cite or quote.* 1962. NYT (Part I).

The Oral History Collection

PHILLIPS, William (1878–1968) Diplomat.

Youth and education; diplomatic career in China and Britain; Minister: Holland, Luxembourg, Canada; Ambassador: Belgium, 1924, Italy, 1936–41; wartime assignments; OSS, London; ambassadorial mission, India; Palestine; Assistant Secretary of State, 1914–20; Under Secretary of State, 1922–24, 1933–36.
165 pp. *Permission required to cite or quote.* 1951. NYT (Part I).

PICKFORD, Mary (Mrs. Buddy Rogers) (1894–   ) *See* Popular Arts.

PIFER, Alan (1921–   ) Foundation executive.
CARNEGIE CORPORATION
Introduction to the Carnegie Corporation; Commonwealth Program: Ashley Commission, travels, especially in Africa; vice president, 1963–67: relationships with board members and staff, decision-making, programs and ideas, Negro education, the disadvantaged, educational television; role of foundations; presidency; sketches of officers, particularly John Gardner, James Perkins, Stephen Stackpole.
273 pp. *Permission required.* 1967.

PIKE, James Albert (1913–1969) *See* Radio Pioneers.

PINEDO, Federico (1895–1971) Lawyer, economist, Cabinet Minister.
ARGENTINA IN THE 1930's
Member Socialist Party; election to Chamber of Deputies, 1920; founder of Independent Socialist Party, 1927; economic and political conditions leading to revolution of 1930; Minister of Treasury, 1933 and 1940: banking reforms, problems of credit, inflation, devaluation; political alliances during 1930's and 40's; foreign trade and domestic economy, effect of WWII.
84 pp. *Permission required to cite or quote.* 1971.

REFER TO "NOTES ON USE" IN INTRODUCTION

PINK, Louis Heaton (1882–1955) Lawyer, government official.

Social work in NYC; Mayor John P. Mitchel and the Committee of 107; NY State Housing Board; urban redevelopment; rent control; NY State Insurance Department, 1932–42: Depression and mortgages, industrial insurance, hospital and medical insurance, rewriting the Insurance Law; the Philippines after the war.
233 pp. *Permission required to cite or quote.* 1949. NYT (Part I).

PISTARINI, Pedro. Union official.

ARGENTINA IN THE 1930's

Officer, railway union from 1926; political activities of unions, 1930's and 1940's; salary levels, working conditions, local union's differences with national headquarters; formation of General Confederation of Workers; labor divisions during WWII; 1951 railway strike.
46 pp. *Open.* 1971.

PITTENGER, Richard.

EISENHOWER ADMINISTRATION

Houston National Governors Conference, 1952; Republican Convention and campaign, 1952; anecdotes of the Eisenhower administration.
40 pp. *Permission required to cite or quote.* 1967.

PLANT, ELTON M. (1903–   ) *See* Radio Pioneers.

PLATT, Alexander B. *See* Columbia Crisis of 1968.

PLIMPTON, Francis Taylor Pearsons (1900–   ) *See* Adlai E. Stevenson Project.

PLOTKIN, Harry. *See* James Lawrence Fly Project.

PLYLER, John Laney (1894–   ) *See* James B. Duke Project.

POETS ON THEIR POETRY

Discussions with modern American poets on the nature, technique, and qualities of their work.

Participants and pages: Gregory N. Corso, 131; James Dickey, 42; James Wright, 29.

202 pp. *Permission required. 1972. Contributed by Michael Andre, New York.*

POLETTI, Charles (1903–   ) *See* Herbert H. Lehman Project.

POLLACK, Jerome. *See* Social Security.

POLLOCK, William (1899–   ) Union official.

Origins and early development of the Textile Worker's Union; autobiographical details.
74 pp. *Permission required to cite or quote.* 1957. NYT (Part I).

POND, M. Allen. *See* Social Security.

PONTING, Herbert (1881–   ) *See* Radio Pioneers.

PONTON DE ARCE, Leroy. *See* Aviation.

POOL, Ithiel de Sola (1917–   ) *See* International Negotiations.

POOLE, DeWitt Clinton (1885–1952) Diplomat.

Early life and education; journalism; vice consul in Berlin, 1911–14; Paris; detailed account of Russia during the Revolution, 1917–18; Archangel, 1919; division of Russian Affairs, Department of State.
490 pp. *Permission required to cite or quote.* 1952. NYT (Part I).

REFER TO "NOTES ON USE" IN INTRODUCTION

POPPER, Hans (1903–   ) *See* Mt. Sinai Hospital.

POPULAR ARTS PROJECT

Material on the development of the performing arts in this century is provided here through interviews with producers, directors, writers, playwrights, scenarists, composers, lyricists, orchestra conductors, designers, cinematographers, film cutters, actors, dancers, advertising and promotion men, distributors, music publishers, song "pluggers," journalists, columnists, critics, and "fan" magazine editors.

The development of the motion picture is described from early nickelodeon days to the present: accounts of the early studios and equipment in New York and New Jersey and acting, directing, and distributing techniques; the Hollywood mythology from the time the industry moved to California until the coming of sound; recollections of the emergence of slapstick comedy, the Mack Sennett Studios and others; the beginnings of many Hollywood careers; scandals and provocative films; state censorship; pressure groups and the origin of the Motion Picture Code; analyses of artistic problems created by the Code, of European influences and of the appeal of the silent film; the effects of the introduction of sound; mechanical and technical innovations; the making of *The Jazz Singer;* new ideas in acting, writing and producing; the casualties of sound.

The Hollywood of the 1930's is portrayed in comments on its social structure, life on the lot, and the life of a child actor, as well as in reflections on the intellectual, social, and political climate of the New Deal era, the California election of 1934, artistic problems, the economics of the industry, and block booking. Problems of the postwar period, in particular the impact of television and of charges of Communism upon the entertainment industry, are detailed together with other major changes: the arrival of new faces with training in other media, influence of the Motion Picture Code in the 1950's, and the decline of the studios with the rise of independent producers and agencies. Some of the films discussed are: *The Great Train Robbery, Intolerance, Sunrise, Safety Last, The Jazz Singer, A Day at the Races, San Francisco, Gone with the Wind, How Green*

The Oral History Collection

Was My Valley, The Southerner, The Best Years of Our Lives, Marty, Twelve Angry Men, Mr. Roberts, and *The Three Faces of Eve.* Personalities discussed include D. W. Griffith, Douglas Fairbanks, Sr., John Gilbert, Rudolph Valentino, Carl Laemmle, Irving Thalberg, Louis B. Mayer, Frederic Murnau, Ernst Lubitsch, Harry Langdon, and W. C. Fields.

Interviews in the field of popular music cover Tin Pan Alley and the vaudeville circuits, techniques of publicizing songs, styles in popular songs, effects of the player piano, phonograph and radio, music and the movies, the era of the big bands, and more recent trends in popular music.

Interviews on the stage cover the theater of Victor Herbert, Jerome Kern and George Gershwin, the stock company as training ground, the road, the Group Theatre, the Stanislavsky method, new methods of acting and directing, Actors' Studio, changes in business methods, the role of the legitimate theater in contemporary life, artistic freedom, comparisons of stage with screen techniques, concentration of theater in NYC.

Participants and pages: Walter C. Abel, 41; Jean and Julius Aberbach, 33; Edward Albee (with Alan Schneider), 86 *(permission required);* Willard Alexander, 34; G. M. Anderson, 35; Dana Andrews, 50; George K. Arthur, 22; Abel Baer, 23; Richard Barthelmess, 45; Ralph Bellamy, 31; Louis Bernstein, 22; Walter Bishop, 39; Sidney Blackmer, 50; Louis A. Bonn, 33; Richard A. Boone, 36; Charles Brackett, 25; Harry Brandt, 67; Irving Caesar, 32; James Cagney, 56; Frank Capra, 73; Morris Carnovsky, 55 *(permission required);* John Cassavetes, 28; Betty Comden and Adolph Green, 59; Chester Conklin, 22; Marcus Cook Connelly, 43; Jackie Cooper, 86; Katharine Cornell, 106 *(permission required);* John Cromwell, 45; Bosley Crowther, 32;

Morton DaCosta, 43; Delmer Daves, 66; Alfred Delacorte, 57; William Demarest, 62; Cecil B. de Mille, 24; Reginald Denham, 64; Reginald Leigh Denny, 34; Edward Dmytryk, 78; Melvyn Douglas, 29; Glenda Farrell, 61; Jose Ferrer, 70 *(permission required);* Betty Field, 49; Dorothy Fields, 40; Gracie Fields, 49; Henry Fonda, 62; Carl Foreman, 44; Arthur Freed, 16; Milton Gabler, 69; Lee Garmes, 64; Janet Gaynor, 28; Louis Wolfe Gilbert, 19; Benny Goodman, 16; Jay Gorney, 42; Sheilah Graham, 21; Bonita Granville, 38;

Albert Hackett, 37; Oscar Hammerstein II, 34; Earle Woolbridge Hammons, 19; Otto Harbach, 48; Julie Harris, 31; Sessue Hayakawa, 95; George Francis Hayes, 60; Ben Hecht, 64; Ray Henderson, 19; Joe Higgins, 43; Pat Hingle, 74; Celeste Holm, 96; Arthur Hornblow, Jr., 49; Albert Howson, 42; Nunnally Johnson, 52; Eric Johnston, 23; Dave Kapp, 31; Boris Kauf-

REFER TO "NOTES ON USE" IN INTRODUCTION

Columbia University

man, 33; Buster Keaton, 39; Gene Kelly, 22; Burton Lane, 35; Paul N. Lazarus, Jr., 41; Lila Lee, 46; Jack Lemmon, 55; Edgar Leslie, 13; Katherine Handy (Mrs. Homer) Lewis, 27; Robert Lewis, 61; Anatole Litvak, 23; Harold Lloyd, 76;

Anita Loos, 37; Myrna Loy, 57; Sidney Lumet, 54; Joel McCrea, 30; Jeanette MacDonald, 61; Roddy McDowall, 58; James Francis McHugh, 82; Kenneth MacKenna, 44; Aline MacMahon, 28; Don Malkames, 23; Rouben Mamoulian, 115 *(closed during lifetime);* Joseph Mankiewicz, 47; Delbert Mann, 61; Frances Marion, 29; Herbert Marks, 35; Mae Marsh, 40; Arthur L. Mayer, 43; William Mellor, 43; Joseph Meyer, 25; Arthur Miller, 44; Mitch Miller, 86; Robert Miller, 18; Douglass Montgomery, 98; Cary Morgan, 21; Chester Morris, 34; Mae Murray, 28; Henry Myers, 123;

Conrad Nagel, 59; Nita Naldi, 22; Jean Negulesco, 21; Paul Newman, 66; Elliott Nugent, 85; Adolph Olman, 29; Geraldine Page, 97; Evelyn Pain, 37; Alan Parado, 30; Dorothy Parker, 20; Louella O. Parsons, 35; William Perlberg, 33; Mary Pickford, 94; Otto Preminger, 37; Martin Joseph Quigley, 26; Richard Quine, 35; Tony Randall, 63; Samson Raphaelson, 123 *(closed during lifetime);* Basil Rathbone, 49; Gottfried Reinhardt, 39; Jean Renoir, 23; Blanche Ring, 18; Leo Rosten, 116; Harry Ruby, 39; Charles Ruggles, 42;

Dore Schary, 87 *(closed during lifetime);* Arthur Schwartz, 20; Zachary Scott, 39; George Seaton, 46; David O. Selznick, 21; Sigmund Spaeth, 52; Samuel and Bella Loebel Spewack, 49; Kim Stanley, 41; Maureen Stapleton, 79 *(permission required);* Rod Steiger, 87; Albert E. Sutherland, 188; Gloria Swanson, 50; Akim Tamiroff, 55; King Wallis Vidor, 49; Rocco Vocco, 31; Tommy Volando, 12; Jerry Wald, 66; Eli Wallach, 22; Hal Wallis, 40; Bert Wheeler, 36; Meredith Willson, 42; Carey Wilson, 90; Julius Witmark, 23; Joanne Woodward, 74; Teresa Wright, 47; Jack Yellen, 40; Max Youngstein, 52; Adolph Zukor, 37.

7, 819 pp. *Open except as noted.* 1958–60. *Contributed mainly by Mr. and Mrs. Robert C. Franklin of New York and Professor Arthur B. Friedman of the University of California.* See also: Sol Lesser *and* Richard Rodgers.

PORTER, Homa Jackson (1896–   ) Republican National Committeeman.

EISENHOWER ADMINISTRATION

Eisenhower movement in Texas, 1952; Republican Party and politics in Texas.

47 pp. *Closed during lifetime.* 1969.

PORTER, Paul Aldermandt (1904–   ) *See* James Lawrence Fly Project.

PORTAS, Jose Luis. Union official.

ARGENTINA IN THE 1930's

Transport and printers' unions in Buenos Aires, 1930's and '40's: political affiliations, strikes, job security, salary levels, dues, seniority, contracts.

47 pp. *Open.* 1971.

POST, Marjorie Merriweather (1887–   ) Businesswoman, philanthropist.

Family background, early life, Springfield, Illinois, Battle Creek, Michigan; education; C. W. Post; Post Cereal Co.; early travels.

34 pp. *Closed during lifetime.* 1964.

POTOFSKY, Jacob Samuel (1894–   ) Union official.

Family background and education in Russia; emigration to US, Chicago; first job in Hart, Schaffner and Marx; 1910 Chicago clothing worker strike; United Garment Workers; Sidney Hillman; arbitration agreements; formation of Amalgamated Clothing Workers of America; industrial unionism; union banking; experiments with unemployment insurance; cooperative housing; the Depression; the New Deal.

883 pp. *Permission required to cite or quote.* 1965.

POTTER, David Morris (1910–   ) *See* American Historians.

POTTS, Ramsay. *See* Aviation.

POWELL, Terrell. *See* Eisenhower Administration.

POWER, Thomas S. (1905–   ) *See* Aviation.

PRATT, Robert L. *See* Radio Pioneers.

PREMINGER, Otto (1906–   ) *See* Popular Arts.

REFER TO "NOTES ON USE" IN INTRODUCTION

PRENDERGAST, William Ambrose (1867–1954) Banker, politician.

Childhood on the East Side, NYC; business and finance; National Association of Credit Men, 1899–1905; national bankruptcy act, 1906; interest in politics, lecturing; NYC finances; the Office of Comptroller, 1909; NY State and City politics; Board of Estimate and Apportionment; Gaynor Charter; Progressive Party; 1912 Republican National Convention; new subway system, 1913; Mayor William Gaynor and NYC finances; Municipal Reference Library; NY State Constitutional Convention, 1915; Gary plan, 1915; legislative investigations, 1915–16; WWI; West Side improvement plan; "land deals," 1917; retrospections; impressions of prominent New Yorkers, including Theodore Roosevelt, Bainbridge Colby, Herbert Parsons, Henry L. Stimson.
995 pp. *Permission required to cite or quote.* 1951. NYT (Part I). Papers. Memoir was written by Mr. Prendergast for the Oral History Research Office.

PRENTICE, Ezra Parmalee (1863–1955) *See* Theodore Roosevelt Association.

PRENTIS, Edmund Astley (1883–1969) Engineer, collector.

Columbia University School of Mines; mining experiences, Mexico and Peru; Spencer, White & Prentis; military construction; White House repairs; King's College Room, Columbia, furnishings and acquisitions; comments on antique collecting.
232 pp. *Permission required to cite or quote.* 1962.

PRESCOTT, Robert (1913–   ) *See* Flying Tigers.

PRESSMAN, Lee (1906–1969) Lawyer.

Education, Harvard; assistant general counsel AAA; RA; general counsel WPA, 1935–1936: general counsel CIO, 1936; sit down strikes; General Motors Detroit strike, 1936, U. S. Steel, 1937, Chrysler strike, Fansteel strike, 1938;

power struggle and leadership in the UAW; Communist influence on CIO; cases before NLRB; portal to portal; anti-trust act, Clayton Act; power struggle in CIO: 1940 CIO convention, John L. Lewis' speech supporting Wendell Willkie; World Trade Union movement; CIO struggle for recognition and competition with AFL; impressions of John L. Lewis, Philip Murray, Sidney Hillman, Walter Reuther, James B. Carey and others.

475 pp. *Permission required to cite or quote.* 1958. NYT (Part II).

PREUSSE, Charles F. (1902–   ) *See* New York Political Studies.

PRIAULX, Arthur. *See* Weyerhaeuser Timber Company.

PRICE, David E. *See* Health Science.

PRINZ, Leroy. *See* Aviation.

PROSKAUER, Joseph M. (1877–1971) Judge.

JOSEPH M. PROSKAUER PROJECT

Family background; influence of James Harvey Robinson, George Woodberry, teachers at Columbia; Columbia Law School; law practice; bench; NY State Crime Commission; Citizens Union; "Happy Warrior" speech; St. Lawrence water power; Liberty League; Charter Commission; American Jewish Committee; human rights and UN Conference at San Francisco; impressions of Alfred E. Smith, Franklin Delano Roosevelt, Charles Michelson, Robert Moses, Stephen Wise, Louis Marshall, Chaim Weizmann, Wendell Willkie.

141 pp. *Permission required.* 1961.

JOSEPH M. PROSKAUER PROJECT

Anecdotes and recollections from family, friends, and associates have been added to Judge Proskauer's own reminiscences, with a view to preparing a biography.

REFER TO "NOTES ON USE" IN INTRODUCTION

Participants and pages: Albert Fiorello, 20; Jacob Goldberg, 26; Kate Pantell, 32; Joseph M. Proskauer, 141; James N. Rosenberg, 32; Abram S. Sacher, 21; Ruth Proskauer Smith, 27.

299 pp. *Permission required.* 1966.
Contributed by friends of Judge Joseph M. Proskauer.

PRUDEN, Wesley. *See* Eisenhower Administration.

PRUSS, Max (–1960) *See* Aviation.

PSYCHOANALYTIC MOVEMENT

The early history of psychoanalysis and its subsequent ramifications, as discussed by psychoanalysts and others closely associated with the movement. The series includes interviews, in this country and abroad, with associates of Sigmund Freud and leading representatives of major schools of psychoanalytic theory. The project aims to provide anecdotal, subjective material that will shed new light on the pioneers of the psychoanalytic movement and its influence on contemporary society.

Participants and pages: Michael Balint, 78; Edward Glover, 108; Heinz Hartmann, 145; Willi Hoffer, 116; Abram Kardiner, 712; Rudolf Loewenstein, 149; Sandor Rado, 317; Raymond de Saussure, 73; René Spitz, 104.

1,802 pp. *Individual restrictions apply.* 1963–66.
In process: Margaret Mahler, Joseph Sandler. *Underwritten by the New-Land Foundation of New York City.* *See also* Theodor Reik.

PULITZER, Joseph, Jr. (1885–1955) Editor.

Relations with his father; education at Harvard; early training on the NY *World* and the St. Louis *Post-Dispatch;* philosophy of journalism; publishing the *Post-Dispatch.*
193 pp. *Permission required.* 1954.

PURCELL, Edward Mills (1912–   ) *See* Nobel Laureates.

317

PURDY, Lawson (1863–1959) Lawyer, civic worker.

NYC and State social work, taxation and housing, 1900–30. 47 pp. *Open.* 1948.

PYE, Lucien (1921–) *See* International Negotiations.

PYLE, Howard (1906–) Government official.

EISENHOWER ADMINISTRATION

National Safety Council; early career; contacts with Dwight Eisenhower; fact papers; impressions of White House staff; political career in Arizona; Citizens for Eisenhower; Interstate Defense Highway legislation; Bricker amendment; workings within the administration. A joint interview with Charles Masterson. 134 pp. *Closed during lifetime.* 1967.

QUALEY, Carlton Chester (1904–) Historian, educator.

Relations between Bard College and Columbia University during the 1930's. 9 pp. *Permission required.* 1968. *Contributed by Lila Johnson, Minnesota Historical Society.*

QUESADA, Elwood Richard (1904–) *See* Henry H. Arnold Project, Aviation, *and* Eisenhower Administration.

QUIGG, Murray T. (–1956) *See* Theodore Roosevelt Association.

QUIGLEY, Martin Joseph (1890–) *See* Popular Arts.

QUINE, Richard (1920–) *See* Popular Arts.

RABB, Maxwell M. (1910–) *See* Eisenhower Administration.

RABI, Isidor Isaac (1898–   ) Physicist.

Childhood and education, NYC; early interest and experiments in physical sciences; Cornell and first awareness of physics; return to NYC; Brooklyn Study Circle and intellectual ferment of the 1920's; dissertation, early papers; Europe 1927–29, especially Copenhagen and Hamburg; Columbia 1929 on; activity in theoretical and experimental physics; quantum theory, complementarity; students. Impressions of many scientists, including Niels Bohr, Wolfgang Pauli, Robert Oppenheimer.
In process.
See also Nobel Laureates.

RABIN, Coleman Berley (1900–   ) *See* Mt. Sinai Hospital.

RABINOFF, Max (1876–1966) Impresario.

Introduction of Russian ballet to US, 1909–1911; touring with Boston National Opera and Ballet Russe until 1917; opera production, Mexico, 1910; beginning of Chicago Opera Company; American Institute of Operatic and Allied Arts, 1925.
48 pp. *Open.* 1963.

RABINOWITZ, Louis (1887–1957) Manufacturer, philanthropist.

Early life and immigration to the US; hook-and-eye industry; philanthropy and its problems.
42 pp. *Permission required to cite or quote.* 1957. NYT (Part I).

RADIO LIBERTY

In anticipation of the 50th anniversary of the Russian Revolution, Radio Liberty and the Institute for the Study of the Union of the Soviet Socialist Republics in Munich collected memoirs of participants in the events of 1917. The material presents a broad political, social, economic, and cultural panorama of Russia at that time. The 75 interviews, conducted in Europe in 1964–65, are in Russian; a list is available on request.

824 pp. *Permission required.* 1965.
Contributed by Radio Liberty Committee, New York.

RADIO PIONEERS

A comprehensive record of the early history of radio contributed by engineers, station and network executives, government officials, writers, directors, and performers.

Scientific matters discussed include types of sending apparatus, early experiments with wireless, radio antennas, wireless and radio transmitters, the Alexanderson alternator, early experiments with television, transmitters for radio stations, mobile radio units, problems of engineering in network broadcasts, manufacturers' laboratory research, and the effects of WWII on radio engineering.

The growth of the radio business from the days of amateurs is described in accounts of manufacturing apparatus for the radio market (Westinghouse Electric Company, General Electric Corporation, and the Radio Corporation of America), wireless telegraphy and telephony on the Great Lakes, operating methods in early radio stations, establishing and financing a radio station in the 1920's, persuading advertisers to buy radio time, responses of and to the radio audience, broadcast ethics, and the impact of television with its new business and performing methods.

The growth of networks and network competition with local stations is detailed in accounts of the development of NBC, the Red and Blue networks and the outgrowth of the American Broadcasting Company from them, CBS, Mutual Broadcasting System, American Telephone & Telegraph Company, and the stations of General Electric and Westinghouse.

Radio's relations with government are dealt with in accounts of the Washington Conference assigning international wavelengths, 1927; Federal Radio Commission; FCC, radio law and legislation; government regulation and comparisons of radio in the US, Great Britain, and Canada; the British Broadcasting Corporation; patent-licensing and the

Columbia University

Department of Justice, 1932; US censorship in WWII; postwar problems.

The problems of programing and the evolution of types of radio programs are described, particularly musical programs, the use of music on the radio, early radio acting, talent scouting, audience participation programs, children's programs, and information and public service programs. News reporting, as a type of program, is discussed, including matters such as news analysis, sports reporting, rivalry between the press and radio, radio columns and columnists, Association of Radio News Analysts, and an account of reporting the Spanish Civil War by H. V. Kaltenborn.

Specific details are provided on the history of Stations WWJ, Detroit, and WBEN, Buffalo, the development of a classical music station (WQXR, NY) and a municipal station (WNYC, NY), and on such programs as "Amos n' Andy," "Information Please," "Town Meeting of the Air," and "The Voice of Firestone." Impressions are given of Walter Damrosch, David Sarnoff, Bertha Brainerd, Frank Conrad, Al Jolson, Owen D. Young, Henry Ford, Fred Waring, William S. Paley, George F. McClelland, Merlin H. Aylesworth, and others. Erik Barnouw, Professor of Film at Columbia University, has added to the original series a number of interviews conducted in connection with his three-volume history of broadcasting in the US.

Participants and pages: Ernest Frederick Werner Alexanderson, 61; Ed Allen, 7; Frank Atkinson Arnold, 101; Walter Ransom Gail Baker, 20; Harry Ray Bannister, 62; Howard Barlow, 213; Patrick Henry Barnes, 35; Joseph M. Barnett, 30; Gustave A. Bosler, 21; Everett L. Bragdon, 20; Harry P. Breitenbach, 10; William Wilbur Brown, 28; Lyman Lloyd Bryson, 254; Orestes Hampton Caldwell, 28; Joseph D. Cappa, 22; Phillips Carlin, 27; Abram Chasins, 89; Thomas Edward Clark, 38; Norman Corwin, 100; Louis Cowan, 225 *(permission required to cite or quote)*; Thomas H. Cowan, 119; Roderick Cupp, 12; Lee DeForest, 9; Richard K. Doan, 26; Glen Dolberg, 8;

Lloyd Espenschied, 48; Walter Chew Evans, 65; Edgar Felix, 55; John Earl Fetzer, 115; Fred Friendly, 50; Robert Fuller, 13; Wayland Fullington, 24; John Gambling, 39; George Gingell, 14; Harry Goodman, 8; Dorothy Gordon, 168; Ben Grauer, 65; Gordon Gray, 2; Gordon Greb, 29; Rosaline Greene, 42; Wilton Gunzendorfer, 10; Raymond Frederick Guy, 78; Joseph Anthony Haeffner, 30; Kolin Hager, 36; Richard F. Hanser, 32; William E. Harkness, 99; Herschell Hart, 21; Laurence Ashley Hawkins,

28; William Saxby Hedges, 123; John E. Hill, 8; Lawrence LaMotte Holland, 25; Herbert Clark Hoover, 21; Albert Wallace Hull, 31; E.P.H. James, 17; Eddie Janis, 25; Arthur Judson, 25; William J. Kaland, 7; H.V. Kaltenborn, 248; Ken Kennedy, 7; Alfred Henry Kirchhofer, 21; Kirk Knight, 34; Chester Henry Lang, 29; Leon Lichtenfeld, 22; Donald G. Little, 101; Edgar J. Love, 15; Ruth Lyons, 7; Stanley Rutter Manning, 16; Carlton Morse and Michael Rafetto, 18; Ray Newby, 38; Paul Oliphant and F.C. Sowell, 32; Dorsey Owings, 16; John F. Patt, 73; Daniel Petrie, 48; James A. Pike, 18; Elton M. Plant, 45; Herbert Ponting, 10; Robert L. Pratt, 7; Harry Rasky, 42; Philip H. Reisman, 60 *(permission required to cite or quote);* Lord John Reith, 25; Bruce Robertson, 15; Otis E. Robinson, 17; William N. Robson, 41; Manuel Rosenberg, 8; Abel Alan Schechter, 33; William Edmund Scripps, 33; Robert L. Shayon, 41; John L. Slaton, 7; Robert Smiley, 18; Ira D. Smith and Fred J. Hart, 82; Sigmund Spaeth, 121; Jeff Sparks, 60; Davidson Taylor, 82; Sybil True, 23; Edwin Lloyd Tyson, 32; Clyde D. Wagoner, 34; James Truman Ward, 10; Gene Waters, 8; Irving Reid Weir, 31; Grover A. Whalen, 27; Rex G. White, 19; William Cummings White, 20; Mark Woods, 120; William R. Yates, 50.

4,789 pp. *Open except as noted.* 1950– *Sponsored jointly by the Twenty Year Club (now Broadcast Pioneers) and the Oral History Research Office and underwritten by gifts of the Twenty Year Club and members of the radio industry.*
See also: James Lawrence Fly Project, Dan Golenpaul, Carl Haverlin, William Paley, *and* Frank Stanton.

RADO, Sandor (1890–1972) Psychoanalyst.
PSYCHOANALYTIC MOVEMENT

Early education, Hungary; M.D., 1915; education as a psychoanalyst; work with Sigmund Freud and Sandor Ferenczi; faculty member of Berlin Psychoanalytic Institute, 1923–31; Karl Abraham; managing editor, *Internationale Zeitschrift fuer Psychoanalyse* and *Imago;* the US and organization of a psychoanalytic institute on the Berlin model; educational director, NY Psychoanalytic Institute, 1931–41; comments on the evolution of psychoanalytic theory and technique.

317 pp. *Permission required to cite or quote.* 1965.

RAFETTO, Michael (with Carlton Morse) *See* Radio Pioneers.

RAMICONE, Luis (1901–   ) Union official.

ARGENTINA IN THE 1930's

Printers' union official, 1918–38: working conditions, wage scales, six-hour day, technological improvements, 1930–45, internal organization; General Confederation of Workers Congress, 1936; National Chamber of Deputies, 1934–38. 43 pp. *Open.* 1971.

RAMSEY, Norman (1915–   ) Physicist.

Education, Columbia; Depression; Cambridge University, England; research with I. I. Rabi, Enrico Fermi; NDRC radiation laboratory, MIT; England, 1941; security problems; radar; Manhattan Project, 1943; Los Alamos; discussions on use of bomb and possible targets; Trinity test; Tinian; estimates of damage, Hiroshima; Brookhaven; Harvard; Congressional investigations; Harold Velde and Joseph McCarthy hearings; area rule; appearance on "Meet the Press," subsequent meeting with Senator McCarthy; contempt citations; Kamen trial; Robert Oppenheimer case; Gray Board; science adviser, NATO; impressions of Gen. Leslie Groves, Adm. Lewis L. Strauss, Edward Teller. 358 pp. *Permission required.* 1960.

RANDALL, Tony. *See* Popular Arts.

RANDOLPH, Asa Philip (1889–   ) Labor leader.

Boyhood, Jacksonville, Florida: family, education; first experiences in NYC: west side, CCNY; Socialist and pacifist opposition to WWI; Eugene Debs; postwar Harlem: Lafayette Theater, the *Messenger;* Chandler Owen, Marcus Garvey, Madame C.J. Walker; early union work. *In process.* *Underwritten by the Center for War/Peace Studies, New York.*

RANDOLPH, Jennings (1902–   ) *See* Social Security.

RANKIN, Grady (with Norman A. Cocke) *See* James B. Duke Project.

RANKIN, Watson Smith (1879–) *See* James B. Duke Project.

RANSOM, Harry Huntt (1908–) University chancellor.
AMERICAN CULTURAL LEADERS
Boyhood and early education, Texas and Tennessee; University of Texas, 1935–67; campus activism and academic freedom; educational administration in US.
87 pp. *Closed pending publication of a study.* 1967.

RANUM, Orest. *See* Columbia Crisis of 1968.

RAPER, Arthur Franklin (1899–) Sociologist.
SOUTHERN INTELLECTUAL LEADERS
Boyhood; education, University of North Carolina and Vanderbilt; Commission on Interracial Cooperation, research and field secretary, 1926–42; Southern Commission on the Study of Lynching; Southern Conference for Human Welfare; Carnegie Corporation study of the American Negro, 1939–40; Department of State and AID, 1952–62; agricultural development work in Japan, the Middle East, and Taiwan; East Pakistan; impressions of Will Alexander, Frank P. Graham, Gunnar Myrdal, and others.
161 pp. *Closed pending publication of a study.* 1971.

RAPHAELSON, Samson (1896–) Author.
POPULAR ARTS
Lower East Side NYC and Chicago; stage and film versions of *The Jazz Singer; Young Love;* move to Hollywood, 1929; scriptwriter; life in Hollywood; major motion picture studios; relations with producers, agents, directors, actors; censorship; impressions of Al Jolson, George Jessel, Harry Cohn, Ernst Lubitsch, Myron Selznick, Billy Wilder, Frank Capra, and others.
123 pp. *Closed during lifetime.* 1959.

REFER TO "NOTES ON USE" IN INTRODUCTION

RASKY, Harry. *See* Radio Pioneers.

RATHBONE, Basil (1892–1967) *See* Popular Arts.

RAUGHT, Al. *See* Weyerhaeuser Timber Company.

RAUH, Joseph L. (1911–   ) *See* James Lawrence Fly Project.

RAUP, R. Bruce (1888–   ) Educator.

Education and early teaching experiences in the Middle
West; TC, 1920–54; *Social Frontiers;* social and philosoph-
ical foundations of education; relationship of TC and Columbia University. Impressions of John Dewey, W. H. Kilpatrick, E. L. Thorndike, James Russell and William Russell,
Harold Rugg, and others.
230 pp. *Permission required to cite or quote.* 1963. NYT
(Part I).

RAUSHENBUSH, Paul and Elizabeth (Mrs. Paul).
SOCIAL SECURITY

Personal backgrounds; teaching at University of Wisconsin
from early 1920's; Wisconsin's Unemployment Act and the
AFL; Louis Brandeis' work in unemployment; Wagner-
Lewis bill, 1933–34; administration of Wisconsin's State
Unemployment Compensation; development of Social
Security and federal unemployment bills; other work in
unemployment and Social Security; recollections of Harold
Groves, John R. Commons, Frances Perkins, Arthur Alt-
meyer, and others.
297 pp. *Permission required to cite or quote.* 1966.

RAVDIN, Isidor Schwaner (1894–1972) Surgeon.

B.A. Indiana University; M.D. University of Pennsylvania;
academic surgery; specific procedures in gastrointestinal
surgery in early 1930's; impact of WWII; 20th General Hospital in the CBI; academic surgery at Pennsylvania after
WWII.

555 pp. *Permission required to cite or quote.* 1962. NYT (Part II).

RAY, Gordon Norton (1915–   ) *See* American Cultural Leaders.

RAYMOND, Arthur Emmons (1899–   ) *See* Henry H. Arnold Project.

READ, William Augustus, Jr. (1895–   ) Naval officer.

Harvard, National Guard Service; naval aviation; WWI, Pensacola; banking career, Dillon, Read; Hanover Bank; Naval Reserve from 1939; special assistant to Adm. John Towers, 1942; experiences with fast carrier task forces as Staff Officer to Adm. Marc Mitscher: logistics, morale, air-sea rescue, buildup; death of Adm. Isoroku Yamamoto; operations in New Caledonia, Gilberts, Marshalls, Marianas, Saipan, Philippines, Formosa, Leyte Gulf; plans for Iwo Jima, Okinawa; kamikaze attacks; postwar naval activities; impressions of Adm. Ernest King.
739 pp. *Permission required.* 1964.

REARDY, Viola. *See* Adlai E. Stevenson Project.

REED, Alice Clara (1890–   ) *See* China Missionaries.

REED, Charles S. *See* James B. Duke Project.

REED, Richard. *See* Adlai E. Stevenson Project.

REED, Stanley Forman (1884–   ) Supreme Court Justice.

Boyhood in Kentucky; education in US and abroad; Kentucky legislature; the farm problem in the Hoover administration; appointment as Solicitor General in the early New Deal; presenting cases before the Supreme Court; appointment to the Supreme Court; impressions of other members of the Court and members of the bar; cases presented before the Court; the role of the Court in the New Deal; impressions of men and events of the Roosevelt administration. The memoir includes brief contributions by Harold Leventhal and John Sapienza.

350 pp. *Closed during lifetime.* 1959.

REESE, Benjamin Harrison (1888–   ) Journalist.

Childhood; early years in journalism in Joplin, Missouri; St. Louis *Post-Dispatch,*1913–51: impressions of associates, notable public service campaigns and news beats, the Pulitzer trust; American Press Institute, Columbia University; seminars, reflections on journalism.

200 pp. *Permission required to cite or quote.* 1954. NYT (Part I).

REEVE, Robert. *See* Aviation.

REICH, Joseph. *See* Air Force Academy.

REID, Ogden Rogers (1925–   ) Congressman.
                      EISENHOWER ADMINISTRATION

Ambassador to Israel, 1959–1961.

22 pp. *Permission required to cite or quote.* 1967.

REID, Ralph Waldo Emerson (1915–   ) *See* Eisenhower Adminstration.

REIDY, William.
                                        SOCIAL SECURITY

University of Wisconsin, 1934; FSA, California, 1940; health programs, group health contracts; health insurance adviser to Senator James Murray, 1945; health reforms during the Truman administration; AMA position on compulsory health insurance; Wagner-Murray bill; National Council of Senior Citizens; cooperation with Robert McNamara; impressions of Isidore Falk, Wilbur Cohen, and others.

101 pp. *Open.* 1966.

REIK, Theodor (1888–1969) Psychoanalyst.

Protegé and friend of Sigmund Freud; recollections of Otto Rank and Hans Sachs; analysis with Dr. Karl Abraham; founding of National Association for Allied Psychoanalysts. 99 pp. *Permission required to cite or quote.* 1965. NYT (Part I).

REINHARDT, Gottfried. *See* Popular Arts.

REISMAN, Philip H.

RADIO PIONEERS

Education; early experiences in radio, Pathé News; combat photography; producing programs and script materials; script editor, William Esty agency. 60 pp. *Permission required to cite or quote.* 1968.

REITER, Bela Z. (1890–1957) *See* McGraw-Hill.

REITH, Lord John (–1971) *See* Radio Pioneers.

REITSCH, Hanna. *See* Aviation.

RENOIR, Jean (1894–   ) *See* Popular Arts.

RESTON, James Barrett (1909–   ) *See* Journalism Lectures.

REYNOLDS, Jackson E. (1873–1958) Lawyer, banker.

Columbia University Law School, 1896–99; founding of the Bank for International Settlements; Bank Holiday, 1933; Herbert C. Hoover. 179 pp. *Permission required to cite or quote.* 1949. NYT (Part I). Papers: 148 letters and newspaper clippings about the Bank for International Settlements.

REYNOLDS, William. *See* Social Security.

REFER TO "NOTES ON USE" IN INTRODUCTION

RHIND, Flora Macdonald (1904–   ) Foundation officer.

Background and education; experience with General Education Board and Rockefeller Foundation, 1933–64: requests received, limitations on grants, procedures in handling, program meetings, docket conferences, trustee meetings, evaluation of programs; responsibilities of Secretary's office, relation with counsel; social science program; fellowships and grants-in-aid; evolution of general education program; Laura Spelman Rockefeller Memorial, Education Policies Commission, American Council on Education, American Youth Commission; development of southern program: Southern Fellowships Fund, Southern Regional Education Board, Southern Education Fund, George Peabody College, state agents for rural schools; European program; congressional investigations, travel in connection with programs; Villa Serbelloni; retirement. Impressions of Raymond Fosdick, John D. Rockefeller, Jr., John D. Rockefeller 3rd, Beardsley Ruml, George Vincent, Edwin E. Day, Dean Rusk, John Foster Dulles, J. George Harrar, many others.
1,520 pp. *Permission required.* 1969.
Underwritten by the Rockefeller Foundation, New York.

RICCIO, Vincent (1919–   ) Youth worker.

Work with NYC Youth Board among juveniles in Brooklyn; gang warfare, customs, dress, and talk.
290 pp. *Permission required.* 1961.
Contributed by John K. Kelly, Newark, Delaware.

RICHARD, Auguste (1890–   ) *See* Robert P. Patterson Project.

RICHARDS, Bernard G. (1877–1971) Jewish leader.

American Jewish community during 20th century; Zionist and Territorialist organizations; Peace Conference, 1919; impressions of Dr. Judah Magnes, Dr. Stephen S. Wise, Louis Marshall, Louis Brandeis, Israel Zangwill.

360 pp. *Permission required to cite or quote.* 1960. NYT (Part II).

RICHARDS, Dickinson W. (1895–   ) *See* Nobel Laureates.

RICHARDS, Homer C. *See* Jackson Hole Preserve.

RICHARDS, Margaret (1900–   ) *See* McGraw-Hill.

RICHARDSON, Doc. *See* Flying Tigers.

RICHARDSON, Elliot Lee (1920–   ) *See* Social Security.

RICHARDSON, Holden C. (–1960) *See* Aviation.

RICHARDSON, Stephen A. (with Herbert Birch) *See* Association for the Aid of Crippled Children.

RICKENBACKER, Edward Vernon (1890–   ) *See* Air Force Academy *and* Aviation.

RIESMAN, David (1909–   ) *See* Carnegie Corporation.

RILEY, Edward. *See* Independence Park.

RING, Blanche (1872–1961) *See* Popular Arts.

RIPMAN, Hugh. *See* World Bank.

RIST, Leonard Bernstein (1905–   ) Banker, economist.
                                    WORLD BANK

\ Early organization of Bank and International Monetary Fund; economic department; evolution of credit standards; studies of internal fiscal policies of borrowing countries; commodity studies; Meyer, McCloy, and Black presidencies; reconstruction loans and development loans;

REFER TO "NOTES ON USE" IN INTRODUCTION

loans for imports, education, and public health programs. 62 pp. *Open.* 1961.

ROBB, Andrew Donaldson. *See* Benedum and the Oil Industry.

ROBBINS, Frederick Chapman (1916–   ) *See* Nobel Laureates.

ROBERTS, Carson A. (1905–   ) *See* Marine Corps.

ROBERTS, Chalmers McGeagh (1910–   ) Journalist.
EISENHOWER ADMINISTRATION
Covering State Department and foreign affairs during the Eisenhower administration; John Foster Dulles.
36 pp. *Permission required to cite or quote.* 1967.

ROBERTS, Charles Wesley (1916–   ) Journalist. *See* Eisenhower Administration.

ROBERTS, Clifford (1904–   ) Business executive.
EISENHOWER ADMINISTRATION
Recollections of Dwight Eisenhower from 1948: hobbies, Presidency of Columbia University, NATO, 1952 and 1956 campaigns; Eisenhower's personal financial arrangements; Republican politics; impressions of Eisenhower's friends, family, aides, Cabinet; Eisenhower Citizens Committee; heart attack and ileitis operation; Augusta National Golf Club; impressions of W.A. (Pete) Jones, and others.
878 pp. *Closed until 20 years after death.* 1972. Papers.

ROBERTSON, Bruce. *See* Radio Pioneers.

ROBERTSON, Walter Spencer (1893–1970) Diplomat.
EISENHOWER ADMINISTRATION
Experiences as Far Eastern affairs expert in State Department; China with Gens. Patrick Hurley and George Mar-

331

shall, 1945–6; Assistant Secretary of State for Far East, 1953–59; policies in South East Asia; SEATO; Korea; impressions of John Foster Dulles, President Eisenhower, Mao Tse-tung, Chou En-lai, Jawaharlal Nehru, Syngman Rhee.
194 pp. *Permission required.* 1967.

ROBINSON, Beverley Randolph (1876–1951) Lawyer.

Education at Harvard and Columbia Law School; Republican political scene in NYC, 1897–1906; NY legislature, 1907–09; impressions of Theodore Roosevelt, Chauncey DePew, and others; 1916 Republican convention and campaign.
95 pp. *Permission required to cite or quote.* 1949.

ROBINSON, Helen R. Roosevelt. *See* Theodore Roosevelt Association.

ROBINSON, Otis E. *See* Radio Pioneers.

ROBINSON, Ovid Daniel (1885–   ) *See* Benedum and the Oil Industry.

ROBINSON, Ray Albert (1896–   ) Marine Corps officer.

Education; duty in France, 1917; China, 1927–29; Marine Corps Schools, 1935–39; North China, 1939; WWII, Director, Division of Plans and Policies, HQMC, 1941–44; Guam and Iwo Jima; occupation of Japan; reorganization of USMC forces in the Pacific; USMC Inspector General, 1949–50; CG, Camp LeJeune, 1950–52, mobilization for Korean War; CG, Department of the Pacific, 1952–54; Chief, Military Assistance Advisory Group, The Hague, 1954–56; CG, Fleet Marine Force, Atlantic.
136 pp. *Open.* 1968.

ROBINSON, Samuel Murray (1882–1972) Naval officer.

Naval engineering, electric ship propulsion; Puget Sound

Navy Yard, 1927–31; Chief of Bureau Engineering, 1931; development of high speed diesel engine; Chief of Bureau of Ships, 1940; Chief of Procurement and Material, 1942–46; Webb Institute of Naval Architecture, 1946–51.
56 pp. *Permission required to cite or quote.* 1963.

ROBINSON, William Smith O'B., Jr. (1885–   ) *See* James B. Duke Project.

ROBSON, William N. *See* Radio Pioneers.

ROCKEFELLER, John Davison 3rd (1906–   ) Philanthropist.

Part I: Concept and development of Lincoln Center for the Performing Arts: private and public financing, city and state authorities and NY World's Fair, relationship with Metropolitan Opera, Philharmonic, Juilliard, NY Public Library, City Center. Interest in Asia: International House (Japan), Population Council, agricultural economics, Council on Economic and Cultural Affairs, Japan Society, Asia Society.
334 pp. *Permission required.* 1963.

Part II: The evolution and execution of Lincoln Center for the Performing Arts.
69 pp. *Permission required.* 1967.

ROCKEFELLER, Laurance S. (1910–   ) *See* Jackson Hole Preserve.

ROCKEFELLER, Nelson Aldrich (1908–   ) Government official.

Travel abroad, 1930–39; Creole Petroleum Corporation; entering government service, 1937–39; Office of the Coordinator of Inter-American Affairs; wartime economic cooperation in the Americas; anti-Axis measures; programs for economic development, 1940–44; Institute for Inter-American Affairs; politics in Washington: Congress, Department of State, BEW, information programs; wartime relations with Argentina; developing a Latin American policy and the Mexico City Conference; recognition of Argentina and relations between Argentina and the UN; Russia and San Francisco Conference, 1945; retirement from State Department; Latin American political, economic, and social prospects and hopes.

730 pp. *Closed until 1997 or death, whichever is later.* 1952.

EISENHOWER ADMINISTRATION

President's committee for Government Organization; Special Assistant to the President on International Affairs; Geneva Conference; relations with President Eisenhower and Vice President Richard Nixon; the "Fourteen Points."

40 pp. *Closed until 1997 or death, whichever is later.* 1967.

ROCKEFELLER FOUNDATION

The memoirs in this series, each of which was obtained quite independently of the others across the years, nonetheless have this much in common: all are about significant careers—in public health, plant pathology, foundation administration, and other areas—with the Rockefeller Foundation. Beyond this, the memoirs vary widely in subject, scope, and style, and there are comparatively few inter-connections, each memoirist having been invited to respond in his own way. *See:* J. Curtis Dixon, John Grant, Alan Gregg, J. George Harrar, Flora Rhind, E.C. Stakman, Benjamin Washburn, Robert Briggs Watson, and Warren Weaver.

Copies are on deposit also at the Rockefeller Foundation Archives.

RODGERS, Cleveland (1885–1956) Editor.

Childhood; experience as linotype operator; NYC theaters; city planning movement, 1916; Brooklyn *Eagle*, 1906–37:

REFER TO "NOTES ON USE" IN INTRODUCTION

and personalities covered; NYC Board of Education, 1919–23; NYC Planning Commission, 1938–50; interest in Walt Whitman.
288 pp. *Open.* 1950. Papers.

RODGERS, Richard (1902–   ) Composer.

Childhood; start in theater; role of Dramatists Guild in securing rights of playwrights; beginnings of the Music Theater of Lincoln Center; association with Lorenz Hart and Oscar Hammerstein II; impressions of George Balanchine, Gertrude Lawrence, Florenz Ziegfeld, Billy Rose, and others.
392 pp. *Permission required to cite or quote; certain pages closed during lifetime.* 1968.

RODRIGUEZ, Juan (1903–   ) Union and government official.
ARGENTINA IN THE 1930'S

Railroad union funds, 1930 revolution, British management, work stoppages, organizing white collar workers; ILO, Geneva, 1945; candidacy for Secretary General of General Confederation of Workers, 1946; impressions of Juan D. Peron, Jose Domenech, Antonio Tramonti, and others.
70 pp. *Open.* 1971.

RODRIGUEZ, Luis Maria. Railroad union official.
ARGENTINA IN THE 1930'S

Union official from 1927; vice president of railroad union, 1930–36; salary and work reduction, 1932; General Confederation of Workers.
21 pp. *Open.* 1970.

ROGERS, Ford O. (1894–   ) *See* Marine Corps.

ROGERS, Lindsay (1891–1970) Political scientist.

Part I: Nicholas Murray Butler; mediation commission for

335

the garment industry in the 1920's; Democratic conventions of 1928 and 1932.
106 pp. *Open.* 1958.

Part II: Experiences as assistant director, ILO, Montreal; UN conference in San Francisco.
21 pp. *Open.* 1965.

ROGERS, T.Y. *See* Civil Rights in Alabama.

ROGERS, William P. (1913–   ) Government official.
EISENHOWER ADMINISTRATION
Counsel for Senate Investigating Subcommittee; contested delegate cases, 1952 Republican convention; campaigning with Richard Nixon, 1952; Nixon Fund; Deputy Attorney General.
51 pp. *Closed until 1977.* 1968.

ROGERS, William Walter (1893–   ) *See* Marine Corps.

ROLL, George Arthur (1913–   ) Marine Corps officer.

Education: instructor, Quantico, 1941–44; officer training in early WWII; Iwo Jima operation; China, 1946; Inspector-Instructor, 1946–49; Parris Island, 1949–51; Office of Manpower Management, Office of Secretary of Defense, 1954–57; Net Evaluation Subcommittee, NSC, 1959.
196 pp. *Open.* 1968.

ROMNEY, Vernon (1896–   ) *See* Robert A. Taft Project.

ROOSA, Robert Vincent (1918–   ) Banker. *See* Eisenhower Administration.

ROOSEVELT, Eleanor (Mrs. Franklin D.) (1884–1964) *See* Herbert H. Lehman Project.

THEODORE ROOSEVELT ASSOCIATION

Friends and associates reminisce about Theodore Roosevelt and the Roosevelt family and circle, with reappraisals of Theodore Roosevelt's impact upon American life. Some new light is thrown on the Bull Moose campaign.

Participants and pages: Karl Howell Behr, 19; William Merriam Chadbourne, 34; William Sheffield Cowles, 118; F. Trubee Davison, 7; Barclay H. Farr, 33; Stanley Meyer Isaacs, 28; Jesse Langdon, 67; Samuel McCune Lindsay, 49; Alice R. Longworth, 41; Ezra Parmelee Prentice, 5; Murray T. Quigg, 28; Helen R. Roosevelt Robinson, 35; William Savacool, 30; Henry R. Stern, 21.

515 pp. *Permission required to cite or quote.*

ROOT, Elihu, Jr. (1881–1967) *See* Robert P. Patterson Project.

ROSENBERG, A.J. (1909–   ) *See* McGraw-Hill.

ROSENBERG, Anna M. (Mrs. Paul Hoffman) (1902–   ) *See* Herbert H. Lehman Project.

ROSENBERG, James N. *See* Joseph M. Proskauer Project.

ROSENBERG, Manuel (–1967) *See* Radio Pioneers.

ROSENMAN, Samuel Irving (1896–   ) Judge.

NYC and State politics in the 1920's; speech-writing for Franklin D. Roosevelt; Washington personalities in the New Deal; administrative work; reorganization of the executive branch during WWII.
233 pp. *Closed until 5 years after death.* 1959.
See also Herbert H. Lehman Project.

ROSENSTEIN-RODAN, Paul. *See* World Bank.

ROSENSTOCK-HUESSY, Eugen. *See* Danforth Lectures.

ROSENTHAL, Morris Sigmund (1897–1958) Foreign trade consultant.

Family, youth and education; experience with Stein-Hall, Inc., importers; government service during the New Deal and after, especially BEW, 1941–43; views on liberalism in business and government; PAC of the CIO; ADA; Progressive Party; North African campaign; Milo Perkins and Henry A. Wallace.
484 pp. *Permission required to cite or quote.* 1953.

ROSIN, Axel G. (1907–   ) *See* Book-of-the-Month Club.

ROSS, Mrs. Jesse Evans. *See* Federated Department Stores.

ROSS, Paul L. Lawyer.

NYC politics; mayoralty election of 1949; "Peekskill Riots," 1949; American Labor Party; election of 1948; federal war agencies, WWII.
135 pp. *Permission required to cite or quote.* 1950.
See also New York Political Studies.

ROSTEN, Leo Calvin (1908–   ) *See* Journalism Lectures *and* Popular Arts.

ROTHMAN, David. *See* Columbia Crisis of 1968.

ROUNDS, Frank W., Jr. (1915–1970) Journalist, author.

Childhood and education; Princeton, 1934–38; Harvard, 1947–50; White House correspondent, 1938–41; chief, China Bureau, 1946–47; WWII: press officer for Adm. William Halsey, South Pacific, 1941–46; attaché, US Embassy, Moscow, 1951–52; travels in China, India, Africa; impressions of Ambassadors Alan Kirk and George Kennan, Mao Tse-tung, Mohandas Gandhi.
222 pp. *Permission required to cite or quote.* 1963. NYT (Part II).
See also James B. Duke Project.

REFER TO "NOTES ON USE" IN INTRODUCTION

ROVERE, Richard Halworth (1915–   ) Writer, editor.
EISENHOWER ADMINISTRATION
Impressions of President Eisenhower and his administration; Eisenhower's relations with the press.
44 pp. *Permission required to cite or quote.* 1968.

ROWDEN, Richard (1905–   ) *See* McGraw-Hill.

ROWE, James Henry, Jr. (1909–   ) *See* James Lawrence Fly Project.

ROWE, Stanley (with Mrs. Rowe) *See* Robert A. Taft Project.

ROWLEY, Louis Napoleon, Jr. (1909–   ) *See* McGraw-Hill.

ROYALL, Kenneth Claiborne (1894–1971) Public official.

Education; Harvard Law School and *Law Review;* German saboteurs case, 1942; head legal department, Fiscal Division of Army Service Forces, 1942–43; Special Assistant to Secretary of War, 1944–45; postwar congressional relations and investigating committees; Under Secretary of War, Secretary of War, Secretary of Army, 1945–49; unification of armed forces; 1948 Democratic presidential nomination; postwar crises: Turkey, Greece, Berlin blockade, Korea, Japan and Douglas MacArthur; integration efforts in Army; rejection of suggested appointment, Nuremberg trials. Impressions of Presidents Harry Truman and Dwight Eisenhower, Gens. George Marshall and James Van Fleet, Secretaries James Forrestal and Stuart Symington, others.
347 pp. *Permission required.* 1963.

RUBIEN, Gerel. *See* Social Security.

RUBIN, Max Jacob (1906–   ) Lawyer.

Education, NYC; NYU Law School; law practice from 1927; Board of Education, Great Neck, NY, 1948–52; salary scales; Board of Regents; Board of Education, NYC, 1961.

260 pp. *Permission required to cite or quote.* 1967. NYT (Part I).

RUBLEE, George (1868–1957) Lawyer.

Early life and law career; Ballinger-Pinchot controversy; election of 1912; FTC; WWI government work; Dwight Morrow and US relations with Mexico, 1928–30; election of 1928; London Naval Conference, 1930; adviser to the Colombian government, 1930–32; Leticia dispute between Peru and Colombia, 1932; coal arbitrator, 1933; war debts; German refugee relief, 1938.
307 pp. *Permission required to cite or quote.* 1951. NYT (Part I).

RUBOTTOM, Roy Richard, Jr. (1912–   ) Diplomat.
EISENHOWER ADMINISTRATION

Assistant Secretary of State for Inter-American Affairs under President Eisenhower; relations with Cuba and other Latin American nations.
95 pp. *Closed during lifetime.* 1969.

RUBY, Harry (1895–   ) *See* Popular Arts.

RUDZINSKI, Aleksander Witold. Diplomat.

Motives for his resignation from the Polish Foreign Service; structure and function of diplomatic service in Poland; accounts of Polish Consulate General in NYC and Polish UN delegation, 1949–50.
221 pp. *Permission required.*

RUGGLES, Charles (1892–1971) Actor.
POPULAR ARTS

Early career; San Francisco earthquake, 1906; first acting experience in NYC; first movie; vaudeville; first talking film, 1929; impressions of early motion picture personalities; philosophy of the art of comedy; Ernst Lubitsch.
42 pp. *Open.* 1959.

REFER TO "NOTES ON USE" IN INTRODUCTION

RUMBOUGH, Stanley Maddox, Jr. (1920–) Industrialist.
EISENHOWER ADMINISTRATION

Formation of Citizens for Eisenhower, Citizens for Eisenhower-Nixon; Commerce Department; Executive Branch
Liaison Office.

43 pp. *Open.* 1967.

RUSHER, William Allen (1923–) *See* Journalism Lectures.

RUSSELL, James Sargent (1903–) *See* Aviation.

RUSSELL, John McFarlane (1903–) Foundation president.

CARNEGIE CORPORATION

Carnegie Corporation, 1930–39; journey to New Zealand, Australia, and South Africa, 1927; evaluation of
educational systems in Dominions; description of Corporation office, officers, and trustees; daily routine; recollections of grants and special programs; Myrdal Study;
Commonwealth Program; Harvard, 1940–42; Markle
Foundation from 1945. Impressions of Frederick Keppel,
Morse Cartwright, Charles Dollard, Florence Anderson,
and others.

290 pp. *Permission required.* 1967.

RUST, Lawrence (with Mrs. Rust) *See* Adlai E. Stevenson
Project.

RUTLEDGE, P. J. *See* Forest History Society.

RYAN, John Harold (1885–1961) *See* Radio Pioneers.

SABERSON, R.E. *See* Weyerhaeuser Timber Company.

SACHER, Abram. *See* Joseph M. Proskauer Project.

SACHS, Paul Joseph (1878–1965) Professor of fine arts.

Childhood, early career as banker and subsequent work in fine arts at Harvard until 1930; impressions of scholars of art and science; print collecting; collectors and their purveyors; patrons of art in the 20th century; Fogg Art Museum; Museum of Modern Art; Harvard Museum course; cooperation with Princeton Department of Art and Archaeology; Bliss Collection at Dumbarton Oaks; Roberts Fine Arts Commission, WWII; American museums after WWII with particular reference to activities of former students; a retrospective look at art critics, dealers, training, and the development of art in America. The memoir is drawn in large part from Mr. Sachs' correspondence.
1,395 pp. *Permission required.* 1958. Papers.

SACHS, Walter Edward (1884–   ) Banker.

Part I: Early life in NYC; study at Harvard and abroad; career with Goldman, Sachs & Co. since 1910.
124 pp. *Permission required to cite or quote.* 1956. NYT (Part I).

Part II: Description of the investment banking business in general and the operations of Goldman, Sachs in particular; anti-trust trial before Judge Harold Medina.
230 pp. *Permission required to cite or quote.* 1964. NYT (Part I).

SACKHEIM, Maxwell. *See* Book-of-the-Month Club.

SACKS, Herbert (1926–   ) Psychiatrist.

Account of Black Panthers rally, New Haven, Connecticut, May 1–3, 1970: Yale-community relations; roles of students, radical leaders Abby Hoffman and Jerry Rubin, faculty, police, National Guard.
59 pp. *Permission required to cite or quote.* 1970. NYT (Part II).

REFER TO "NOTES ON USE" IN INTRODUCTION

SACKS, Leon. *See* Independence Park.

SACKS, I. Milton (1919–   ) *See* International Negotiations.

SAFRAN, Frank. *See* Columbia Crisis of 1968.

SAILLE, Lewis. *See* Federated Department Stores.

SALADIN, Raymond (with Leon Bathiat) *See* Aviation.

SALES, Reno. *See* Mining Engineers.

SALISBURY, Harrison Evans (1908–   ) *See* Eisenhower Administration *and* Journalism Lectures.

SALMON, Ronald D. (1909–   ) *See* Marine Corps.

SALOMON, Irving. *See* Eisenhower Administration.

SALTONSTALL, Leverett (1892–   ) Senator.
EISENHOWER ADMINISTRATION
1952 pre-convention period and campaign; transition period; Senate Armed Services Committee; Appropriations Committee; White House legislative conferences; Republican politics, 1952–60.
151 pp. *Permission required to cite or quote.* 1967.

SAMUEL, Athanasius Yeshu (1907–   ) Archbishop.

Childhood in Syria; refugee, illness; orphanage and monastery care; St. Mark's monastery and seminary, Jerusalem; exploration of caves near Jericho and Jordan; Egypt; archaeological studies; St. Catherine's monastery at Mount Sinai; Archbishop and Metropolitan of Jerusalem, 1946; Dead Sea scrolls: discovery, problems of interpretation and authentication; US, 1949: lectures and exhibits; sale of scrolls, 1954; detailed description of scrolls, contents and significance.
183 pp. *Permission required.* 1961.

SAMUEL, Irene (Mrs. John) *See* Eisenhower Administration.

SANCERNI GIMENEZ, Julian. *See* Argentina in the 1930's.

SANDERS, Sol. *See* International Negotiations.

SANDERSON, L.H.M. *See* Marine Corps.

SANDLER, Joseph. Psychoanalyst.

PSYCHOANALYTIC MOVEMENT

Early interest in psychoanalysis; education; work at Hampstead Clinic; impressions of Anna Freud and others; views of psychoanalytic theories and child analysis.
In process.

SANSOM, Sir George (1883–1965) Diplomat, orientalist.

Education; British foreign service in Japan; Japanese cultural life; WWII; peace terms; East Asian Institute, Columbia.
96 pp. *Open.* 1957.

SANTANDER, Silvano (1895–1971) Politician.

ARGENTINA IN THE 1930'S

Postal workers' strike, 1917–18; provincial newspaperman, 1920–22; political disputes during Yrigoyen administration; imprisonment in Ushuaia, 1930–32; political agitation among the military; provincial legislature, 1935; National Chamber of Deputies, 1939–43; opposition to Nazi influence.
81 pp. *Open.* 1971.

SAPERSTEIN, Sydney.

SOCIAL SECURITY

Columbia University, 1939; Federal Security Agency, 1941; drafting health insurance legislation; Murray-Wagner-Dingell bill; Social Security; Ways and Means Committee; relations between politicians; American Hospital Association

and AMA positions on health legislation, 1960's; Medicare; impressions of Wilbur Mills, Irwin Wolkstein, Wilbur Cohen, and others.
122 pp. *Closed during lifetime.* 1967.

SAPIENZA, John. *See* Stanley Reed.

SARACHAGA, Dario (1901–   ) Lawyer, politician.
ARGENTINA IN THE 1930'S

Gen. Agustin P. Justo as soldier and statesman: Minister of War, 1922, modernizing army, developing national munitions industry, President, 1932–38, administrative and economic reform, Roca-Runciman Treaty, railroads.
21 pp. *Open.* 1971.

SARGEANT, Howland. *See* Eisenhower Administration.

SARNOFF, David (1891–1971) *See* Robert P. Patterson Project.

SAULNIER, Raymond J. (1908–   ) Economist.
EISENHOWER ADMINISTRATION

Council of Economic Advisors as organized under President Eisenhower: functions, operations, relations with President, Congress, and other agencies; Advisory Board on Economic Growth; economic policies under Eisenhower.
71 pp. *Open.* 1967.

SAUSSURE, Raymond de (–1971) Psychoanalyst.
PSYCHOANALYTIC MOVEMENT

Studies of psychoanalysis, Berlin, Vienna, Paris; theories of psychoanalysis; impressions of other analysts.
73 pp. *Permission required.* 1965.

SAVACOOL, William. *See* Theodore Roosevelt Association.

SAXE, Martin (1874–1967) Lawyer, politician.

Activities as NY State Senator; Republican Convention, 1915; law practice with Morris, Plante and Saxe; NYC and State politics, 1902–13.
40 pp. *Permission required to cite or quote.* 1949. NYT (Part I). Papers.

SAYRE, E. Berthol. *See* Columbiana.

SAYRE, Francis Bowes (1885–1972) Diplomat.

Early life; Williams College; work in Labrador with Dr. Wilfred Grenfell; Harvard Law School; Woodrow Wilson; Massachusetts State Commissioner of Correction; foreign affairs adviser to Thailand, 1933; observations on Thailand and the Far East.
127 pp. *Permission required.* 1952.

SAYRE, Wallace Stanley (1905–1972) *See* Journalism Lectures.

SCHAEFER, Walter Vincent (1904–   ) *See* Adlai E. Stevenson Project.

SCHAPER, Wilfred. *See* Flying Tigers.

SCHARY, Dore (1905–   ) *See* Popular Arts.

SCHEAF, Oral. *See* Federated Department Stores.

SCHECHTER, Abel Alan (1907–   ) *See* Radio Pioneers.

SCHEELE, Leonard Andrew (1907–   ) Physician.
                              EISENHOWER ADMINISTRATION

Surgeon-General, 1948–56; Salk vaccine; impressions of Oveta Culp Hobby and other members of the Eisenhower administration.

REFER TO "NOTES ON USE" IN INTRODUCTION

44 pp. *Permission required to cite or quote.* 1968.
See also Health Science.

SCHERER, Raymond Lewis (1919–   ) Journalist.

EISENHOWER ADMINISTRATION

President Eisenhower's news conferences; early use of television; relations with the press; impressions of Eisenhower and his administration.
54 pp. *Open.* 1968.

SCHERMAN, Harry (1887–1969) Book-club executive, author.

BOOK-OF-THE-MONTH-CLUB

Childhood in Philadelphia; journalism, advertising, NYC, 1907–16; formation of Little Leather Library Corporation, 1916; inception of Book-of-the-Month Club idea, 1926; selection committee and the book selection process; characteristics and tastes of the committee and of Club subscribers; book-dividend, gift book, and premium systems; structure and administration of Club; most notable and most popular books, 1928–54; art reproductions and records; pressure groups and Club; book-club movement in America; reflections on American culture.
367 pp. *Permission required to cite or quote.* 1955. NYT (Part I).

SCHIEFFELIN, Bayard (1903–   ) *See* Robert P. Patterson Project.

SCHIEFFELIN, William Jay (1866–1955) Businessman, civic worker.

Investigations of corruption in NYC during the 1890's; Committee of 70, 1894; reform movements, Mayor William Strong and William Travers Jerome; president of the Citizens Union, 1908–41; Council on African Affairs and Negro leaders. Impressions of J.P. Morgan, Alfred E. Smith, Nicholas Murray Butler.
126 pp. *Permission required to cite or quote.* 1949. NYT (Part I).

347

SCHILT, Christian Franklin (1895–   ) Marine Corps officer.

Family background and education; WWI service; pilot training; Haiti, 1920–21; Santo Domingo, 1921–22; early USMC aircraft; International Air Races, 1920's; Nicaragua, 1927–29; WWII, Guadalcanal operation; Commander, Marine Air Reserve Training, 1946–49; Korea, 1951–52; Director of Aviation, 1955–57.
136 pp. *Open.* 1969.
See also Aviation.

SCHINE, Gerard David (1927–   ) *See* Eisenhower Administration.

SCHLENCK, Hugo. *See* Weyerhaeuser Timber Company.

SCHLESINGER, Arthur Meier (1888–1965) Historian.

Early childhood; college experiences at Ohio State, 1909–13; graduate work, Columbia University; teaching at Ohio State during WWI; writing *Colonial Merchants and the American Revolution* and *New Viewpoints in American History;* liberal movement during WWI; University of Iowa, 1919–24; Harvard University from 1925, including Sacco-Vanzetti case, Harvard and academic freedom, graduate students; around the world trip, 1933; experiences at the University of Leiden, 1948; freedom of the press investigation, 1943–45; editing the "History of American Life" series and the *Harvard Guide to American History;* leading personalities in the American historical profession from about 1915. The material includes much correspondence.
1,266 pp. *Permission required.* 1959. Papers.

SCHLESINGER, Arthur Meier, Jr. (1917–   ) *See* American Historians, Richard Hofstadter Project, *and* Adlai E. Stevenson Project.

SCHLESS, Howard. *See* Columbia Crisis of 1968.

SCHLOSS, Ann Lazarus. *See* Federated Department Stores.

SCHLOSSBERG, Joseph (1901–   ) *See* Socialist Movement.

SCHMIDT, Orvis Adrian. *See* World Bank.

SCHNEIDER, Alan (with Edward Albee) *See* Popular Arts.

SCHOENBRUN, David F. (1915–   ) *See* Journalism Lectures.

SCHOENWERK, Otto C. *See* Weyerhaeuser Timber Company.

SCHORR, Lisbeth Bamberger.
SOCIAL SECURITY
Role of AFL-CIO in health insurance and social security programs from 1958; legislation in Eisenhower, Kennedy, and Johnson administrations; relationship with AMA.
105 pp. *Permission required to cite or quote.* 1967.

SCHOTTLAND, Charles Irwin (1906–   ) University dean.
SOCIAL SECURITY
Work with California State Relief Administration, Los Angeles Federation of Jewish Welfare Organizations, and US Children's Bureau, 1933–41; Gen. Dwight Eisenhower's staff, WWII; Director of Social Welfare, California, 1950; Commissioner of Social Security, 1952: relations with Children's Bureau, other agencies, executive and legislative branches; Medicare; "Thrift" speech, 1956; impressions of Katherine Lenroot, Martha Eliot, Oveta Culp Hobby, Marion Folsom, Loula Dunn, Nelson Rockefeller, Wilbur Cohen.
167 pp. *Open.* 1965.

SCHULZ, Robert L. (1907–   ) Army officer, presidential aide.

EISENHOWER ADMINISTRATION

Military transportation officer; military aide to President Eisenhower; details of Eisenhower's travels; personal recollections of the Eisenhowers.
293 pp. *Closed until 1993.* 1968.

SCHUSTER, Max Lincoln (1897–1970) Editor, publisher.

NYC childhood; copy boy, NY *Evening World,* 1913; Columbia School of Journalism, 1917; early literary and journalistic interests; intellectual ferment and radicalism; journalistic experience in Washington and NYC, 1917–24; formation of Simon and Schuster, 1924; crossword puzzle books; *Story of Philosophy.*
226 pp. *Permission required to cite or quote.* 1964.

SCHUYLER, George Samuel (1895–   ) Author, journalist.

Background, childhood, and education in Syracuse; job discrimination; enlistment US Army, 1912; military transports, commission, segregation within armed forces; Government civil service, 1919; Harlem; Marcus Garvey; *The Messenger; Pittsburgh Courier;* magazine supplement, Chicago; differences among Negro leaders; southern travels; Socialist Party activities; NAACP; *The Crisis;* Negroes in politics; housing; interracial marriage; Liberia; consumer cooperatives; Ethiopia; American Negroes in WWII; race relations in Latin America; Negro journalism; Negroes and Jews; Negroes and Communist Party; National Negro Congress; March on Washington; impressions of Benjamin Davis, A. Philip Randolph, Chandler Owen, James W. Ivy, James Weldon Johnson, Roy Wilkins, H. L. Mencken, Walter White.
723 pp. *Permission required to cite or quote.* 1960. NYT (Part I).

SCHWARTZ, Arthur (1900–   ) *See* Popular Arts.

REFER TO "NOTES ON USE" IN INTRODUCTION

SCIENTIST AS CITIZEN

The common denominator for these interviews is the experience of scientists whose work has thrust them into national and world affairs. Among the subjects discussed are: problems of communication with scientists in other fields and with nonscientists, civil rights and freedom of speech, relationships with government and industry, the changing role of the scientist, control and direction of research, influence of foundations. The memoirs reflect the education and background of 20th century scientists and the accelerated pace of scientific thought. There are evocations of some memorable moments in scientific research in such fields as nuclear physics, chemistry, plant pathology, meteorology, and genetics. *See:* Kenneth T. Bainbridge, Charles D. Coryell, Albert Crarey, Theodosius Dobzhansky, L.C. Dunn, J. George Harrar, Joseph Kaplan, James Killian, Polykarp Kusch, I.I. Rabi, Norman Ramsey, Elvin C. Stakman, Sir Robert Watson-Watt, Warren Weaver.
See also Nobel Laureates.

SCOTT, Austin Wakeman (1884–   ) *See* Robert P. Patterson Project.

SCOTT, Ernest Lyman (1878–1966) Scientist.

Insulin research.
11 pp. *Open.* 1964. Papers.

SCOTT, Hardy (1907–   ) *See* Independence Park.

SCOTT, Roderick (1885–   ) *See* China Missionaries.

SCOTT, Zachary (1914–1965) *See* Popular Arts.

SCRIBNER, Fred C., Jr. (1908–   ) Lawyer. *See* Eisenhower Administration.

SCRIPPS, William Edmund (1882–1952) *See* Radio Pioneers.

SEABORG, Glenn Theodore (1912–   ) *See* Nobel Laureates.

SEARS, George (1887–1960) *See* McGraw-Hill.

SEATON, George (1911–   ) *See* Popular Arts.

SEBRELL, William Henry, Jr. (1901–   ) Public health officer.

HEALTH SCIENCE

Background in medicine; US Public Health Service, 1925–55; quarantine stations; NIH; nutritional research; administrative personnel and policies; Institute of Nutrition Sciences, Columbia University, from 1957.
72 pp. *Permission required.* 1962.

SEGER, Gerhart Henry (1896–1967) Editor, author, lecturer.

Journalism in Germany and Europe, 1921–33; German Reichstag, 1930–33; concentration camp experiences and escape, 1933; immigration to the US; lecturing on international affairs.
154 pp. *Permission required to cite or quote.* 1950. NYT (Part I).

SEGRE, Emilio (1905–   ) *See* Nobel Laureates.

SELF, Sir Henry (1890–   ) *See* Henry H. Arnold Project.

SELZNICK, David Oliver (1902–1965) *See* Popular Arts.

SEMANS, Mary Duke Biddle Trent (Mrs. James H.) (1920–   ) *See* James B. Duke Project.

SENN, Milton (1902–   ) *See* Association for the Aid of Crippled Children.

REFER TO "NOTES ON USE" IN INTRODUCTION

SESSIONS, Roger Huntington (1896–   ) Composer.

New England background; early music lessons and first composition, 1909; Harvard *Musical Review*, 1913; Yale Music School, 1915–17: Horatio Parker; Smith College, 1919–21; teaching music theory, Roy Welch; Cleveland Conservatory, Ernest Bloch; fellowships and work abroad, 1925–33: Florence, Rome, Berlin; comments on his own compositions, as well as on techniques of composition, tonality, harmony, teaching young composers, and on many artists, especially Igor Stravinsky, Otto Klemperer.
309 pp. *Closed during lifetime.* 1962.

SEVAREID, Eric Arnold (1912–   ) *See* Journalism Lectures *and* Adlai E. Stevenson Project.

SEWARD, Ralph Theodore (1907–   ) *See* Ching, Cyrus.

SHACHTMAN, Max (1903–1972) Trotskyite.

Development of socialist and radical groups in the 1920's and '30's, particularly Communist Workers Party, Workers' Council, and Trotskyites; factional struggles; trips to Moscow, 1925, 1927; International Labor Defense group; publications and editorial work; expulsion from Communist Party; effects of international political events; Socialist Party; split over Nazi-Soviet alliance; visits to Leon Trotsky in Turkey, Norway, Paris, Mexico; Trotsky's assassination; Independent Socialist League, 1948–58. Impressions of Joseph Stalin, Norman Thomas, Eugene V. Debs, A.J. Muste, and many others.
522 pp. *Permission required to cite or quote.* 1963. NYT (Part I).
See also Socialist Movement.

SHADEGG, Stephen (1909–   ) Author.
EISENHOWER ADMINISTRATION
Campaigns of Dwight Eisenhower, Richard Nixon, Barry Goldwater; Charles Percy Committee.
30 pp. *Closed during lifetime.* 1967.

SHAHN, Ben (1898–1969) Artist.

Early life in Lithuania and Brooklyn; training in lithography; painting experiences with Diego Rivera; WPA art project.
136 pp. *Permission required to cite or quote.* 1960.

SHANNON, James A. (1904–   ) *See* Health Science.

SHAPLEY, Alan (1903–   ) *See* Marine Corps.

SHARON, John.
ADLAI E. STEVENSON PROJECT
Campaigns of 1952 and 1956; choosing the 1956 Democratic vice presidential nominee; draft-Stevenson movement, 1960; relationship of Stevenson with Harry Truman, Estes Kefauver, John F. Kennedy, and Lyndon Johnson; Stevenson at the UN.
148 pp. *Permission required.* 1969.

SHARP, Dudley Crawford (1905–   ) Government official.
EISENHOWER ADMINISTRATION
Assistant Secretary, later Secretary, of the USAF: missiles, Department of Defense, Joint Chiefs of Staff; U-2 incident; relations with President Eisenhower.
67 pp. *Permission required to cite or quote.* 1969.

SHATTUCK, Roger (with William Arrowsmith) *See* American Cultural Leaders.

SHAW, H. *See* Aviation.

SHAW, H.W. (1904–   ) *See* McGraw-Hill.

SHAW, Samuel Robert (1911–   ) Marine Corps officer.

US Naval Academy, 1930–34; early training and assignments; Pearl Harbor, 1940–43; Okinawa operation; occupa-

tion of Japan; unification fight; 1st Marine Division, Korea, 1953–54; Director, Policy Analysis Division, HQMC, 1955–58, legislative matters affecting USMC; Ribbon Creek affair; Staff Director, Senate Programs Preparedness Subcommittee.
373 pp. *Permission required.* 1970.

SHAYON, Robert Lewis (1912–   ) *See* Radio Pioneers.

SHEFFER, Eugene. *See* Columbiana.

SHEFFIELD, Frederick (1902–1971) *See* Carnegie Corporation.

SHELDON, A. O. *See* Weyerhaeuser Timber Company.

SHELDON, Bobby. *See* Alaskan Pioneers.

SHELDON, Joseph S.
EISENHOWER ADMINISTRATION
Republican Party in Texas; Taft-Eisenhower contest, 1952; impressions of Eisenhower and his administration.
28 pp. *Permission required to cite or quote.* 1969.

SHELLWORTH, H. C. *See* Weyerhaeuser Timber Company.

SHELTON, Robert. *See* Civil Rights in Alabama.

SHELTON, William T. *See* Eisenhower Administration.

SHENTON, James P. *See* Columbia Crisis of 1968.

SHEPARD, Frank B. (1888–   ) *See* Bendum and the Oil Industry.

SHEPHARD, W. P. *See* Health Science.

SHEPHERD, Lemuel Cornick, Jr. (1896–   ) Marine Corps officer.

Family background, education; WWI service, France; occupation of Germany; Aide to Gen. Lejeune, 1920–22; China, 1927–29; Haiti, 1930–34; Naval War College; WWII: Cape Gloucester, Guam, Okinawa operations; occupation of Tsing-tao; USMC Assistant Commandant, 1946–48; unification fight; Commandant, USMC schools, 1948–50; Korea: Inchon landing, Gen. Douglas MacArthur and the USMC; USMC Commandant, 1952–56: role in Joint Chiefs of Staff deliberations, outstanding developments during period; Chairman, Inter-American Defense Board, 1956–59.
500 pp. *Permission required.* 1967.

SHEPLEY, James Robinson (1917–   ) Journalist.
EISENHOWER ADMINISTRATION

Impressions of President Eisenhower, John Foster Dulles, Richard Nixon; Eisenhower's relations with the press.
39 pp. *Permission required to cite or quote.* 1967.

SHEPPARD, Harold.
SOCIAL SECURITY

Senate subcommittee on the problems of the aged, 1958; Patrick McNamara; relations with UAW; Kennedy administration and Social Security; senior citizens' groups; Senior Service Corps; impressions of Wilbur Cohen, Charles Odell, Sidney Spector, William Reidy.
104 pp. *Permission required to cite or quote.* 1967.

SHER, David (1908–   ) *See* New York Political Studies.

SHERROD, Robert Lee (1909–   ) *See* Eisenhower Administration.

SHERWIN, William R. *See* Alaskan Pioneers.

REFER TO "NOTES ON USE" IN INTRODUCTION

SHIELDS, Robert Hazen (1905–   ) Agriculturist.

Early life; University of Nebraska; Harvard Law School; AAA; peanut program, 1935 "purge," sugar program, 1938 Agricultural Adjustment Act; Office of Solicitor, Department of Agriculture: AAA and conservation, crop insurance, regional problems, Commodity Credit Corporation; Office of the Secretary of Agriculture: prices, ceilings, and production in wartime, OPA, FSA, private farm organizations, Steagall amendment to 1938 Agricultural Adjustment Act, 1941 "Omnibus Bill," relations with wartime agencies; personalities in the Agriculture Department during the New Deal and early war years.
572 pp. *Closed during lifetime.* 1954.

SHIMKIN, Leon (1907–   ) *See* Freeman Lewis.

SHIMKO, Margaret R. *See* John Robert Gregg Project.

SHISHKIN, Boris Basil (1906–   ) Economist.

Early life and education in Russia; WWI and the Russian Revolution; flight to Istanbul; Columbia University during the late 1920's; role of AFL in New Deal legislation; AFL conventions, 1933–36; impressions of William Green, John L. Lewis, Maurice Tobin, Matthew Woll, and other labor leaders.
872 pp. *Permission required.* 1957.

SHIVERS, Allan (1907–   ) Governor.
EISENHOWER ADMINISTRATION

Tidelands issue; meeting with Adlai Stevenson; 1952 election; relations with President Eisenhower; Texas politics and the Eisenhower administration.
58 pp. *Permission required to cite or quote.* 1969.

SHOCKLEY, William Bradford (1910–   ) *See* Nobel Laureates.

357

SHOENER, Willard T. *See* McGraw-Hill.

SHOTWELL, James Thompson (1874–1965) Historian.

Education in Canada; Columbia University, historical studies; 11th edition of *Encyclopaedia Britannica;* WWI; Creel Committee; "The Inquiry"; Paris Peace Conference; the "Big Four"; ILO; *Economic and Social History of the World War;* postwar problems; British Imperial Conference, 1921; Locarno Treaties.
230 pp. *Permission required to cite or quote.* NYT (Part I).
See also Columbiana.

SHOUP, David M. (1904–   ) *See* Eisenhower Administration.

SHROYER, Thomas. *See* Robert A. Taft Project.

SHUEBRUK, Pete. *See* James Lawrence Fly Project.

SICKLES, Trent. *See* Federated Department Stores.

SILBERT, Myron. *See* Federated Department Stores.

SILVERTHORN, Merwin Hancock (1896–   ) Marine Corps officer.

Family background and education; WWI duty in France; Haiti, 1923–26; Gen. Smedley Butler; Guam, 1930–32; Naval War College; Staff, Adm. Ernest King, Pacific Fleet, 1941–43; preparations for invasion of Japan, occupations of Japan and North China; demobilization; reorganization of Marine units in Pacific; mobilization of reserves for Korea; Assistant Commandant, USMC, 1949–50; Chief of Staff, HQMC, 1950–52, the Clifton Cates Commandancy.
479 pp. *Open.* 1969.

SINCLAIR, Upton (1878–1968) Author.

Background, youth and education; early experiments in writing; comments on friends; *The Jungle* and other muckraking books; life in experimental communities and colonies, Helicon Hall; Lanny Budd books; Socialist Party; strikes and arrests; EPIC and campaign for California governorship, 1934; *Dead Hand* series; *Oil;* movie industry; William Fox; *The Brass Check;* self help cooperative; child labor. Impressions of many American writers.
363 pp. *Permission required to cite or quote.* 1962. NYT (Part I).
Contributed by Ronald Gottesman, Highland Park, New Jersey.

SINCLAIRE, Reginald.
AIR FORCE ACADEMY
Lafayette Escadrille, training in France for WWI.
58 pp. *Open.* 1969.

SINGER, Arthur. Foundation official.
CARNEGIE CORPORATION
Introduction to Carnegie Corporation; nature of a foundation officer's work; automation, job-training, programs for the disadvantaged; Commission on Public Television; Center for Urban Education; Alfred P. Sloan Foundation. Impressions of John Gardner, Alan Pifer, and others.
138 pp. *Permission required.* 1969.

SINGER, Herman. *See* Socialist Movement.

SINGSEN, Anton Gerhardt (1915–   ) *See* Social Security.

SLATER, Ellis Dwinnell (1895–   ) *See* Eisenhower Administration.

SLATER, Ilene.
EISENHOWER ADMINISTRATION
Secretary for Citizens for Eisenhower; secretary to Sher-
ˉman Adams in the White House.
58 pp. *Permission required.* 1968.

SLATER, Robert James (1923–   ) *See* Association for the
Aid of Crippled Children.

SLATON, John L. *See* Radio Pioneers.

SLAUGHTER, Robert (1910–   ) *See* McGraw-Hill.

SLESSOR, Sir John Cotesworth (1897–   ) *See* Henry H.
Arnold Project.

SLICK, Thomas Baker (1916–1962) *See* Benedum and the Oil
Industry.

SLOANE, Madeleine Edison (Mrs. John Eyre) *See* Thomas A.
Edison Project.

SMILEY, Robert. *See* Radio Pioneers.

SMILLIE, Wilson George (1886–   ) *See* Health Science.

SMITH, Bromley. *See* Eisenhower Administration.

SMITH, Bruce. *See* Columbia Crisis of 1968.

SMITH, Charles (1842–   ) Black cowboy.

Reminiscences of his boyhood in Africa, abduction by a
slavetrader, and sale in a New Orleans slave market; experiences as a slave and free man on the ranch of Charles
Smith near Galveston, Texas.

52 pp. *Open.* 1963.
Contributed by Holland A. Kelley, Bartow, Florida.

SMITH, Cyrus Rowlett (1899–   ) *See* Aviation.

SMITH, Dean. *See* Aviation.

SMITH, H. Alexander (1880–1966) Senator.

Boyhood in NYC; Princeton, Columbia Law School; Colorado practice, 1905; US Food Administration, Herbert Hoover, WWI; executive secretary, Princeton, 1920–30; Chairman, Republican Party, New Jersey, member Republican National Committee, 1939; US Senate career, 1944–58: primaries and campaigns, labor reform legislation, party reorganization, refugee problems, Taft-Hartley Act, Voice of America, Smith-Mundt Act; extensive travel in Europe and Far East; Republican Policy Committee, 1951; Douglas MacArthur hearings; Japan Peace Treaty; Senate Labor Committee; SEATO, 1954; health legislation; civil rights; impressions of many political figures.
595 pp. *Permission required to cite or quote.* 1963. NYT (Part I).

SMITH, Henry D. *See* Mining Engineers.

SMITH, Hermon Dunlap (1900–   ) (with Mrs. Smith) *See* Adlai E. Stevenson Project.

SMITH, Howard Kingsbury (1914–   ) Journalist.
EISENHOWER ADMINISTRATION
Foreign and domestic policies under Eisenhower; Eisenhower and the press; first Richard Nixon-John Kennedy debate.
44 pp. *Permission required to cite or quote.* 1968.

SMITH, Ira D. *See* Radio Pioneers.

SMITH, Jesse. *See* Air Force Academy.

SMITH, Julian Constable (1885–   ) Marine Corps officer.

Duty in Haiti, Santo Domingo, 1915–16; antibanditry assignments; Bureau of the Budget, 1923–27: disposal of war surplus; Nicaragua, 1930–34; genesis of Fleet Marine Force; WWII: military observer in London, British amphibious operations, establishment of Camp Lejeune, Tarawa and Peleliu operations; CG, Department of the Pacific, 1944–46; Parris Island, 1946–47.
354 pp. *Permission required to cite or quote.* 1968.

SMITH, Merle. *See* Aviation.

SMITH, Merriman (1913–1970) *See* Eisenhower Administration.

SMITH, Oliver Prince (1893–   ) Marine Corps officer.

WWI: Mare Island, Guam; Personnel Section, HQMC, 1924–28; Haiti, 1928–31; USMC Schools, Quantico, 1932–33; WWII: Iceland, Talasea, and Peleliu operations; postwar USMC; unification dispute; Cates Commandancy; CG, 1st Division, 1950–51; Korea: Inchon landing, Chosin reservoir; relations with Gens. Douglas MacArthur, Edward Almond, Lemuel Shepherd; CG, Camp Pendleton, 1951–53.
337 pp. *Open.* 1960.

SMITH, Ralph Bevin (1894–   ) *See* McGraw-Hill.

SMITH, Robert James (1899–   ) *See* Flying Tigers.

SMITH, Ruth Proskauer. *See* Joseph M. Proskauer Project.

SMITH, William J. *See* Eisenhower Administration.

SNAITH, William Theodore (1908–   ) *See* Federated Department Stores.

REFER TO "NOTES ON USE" IN INTRODUCTION

Columbia University

SNEDEKER, Edward Walter (1903–   ) *See* Marine Corps.

SNYDER, Murray (1911–   ) Public relations executive.
EISENHOWER ADMINISTRATION
Experiences as Assistant White House Press Secretary
1953–57; Assistant Secretary of Defense for Public Affairs,
1957–61.
67 pp. *Permission required to cite or quote.* 1967.

SOCIAL SECURITY

This project has the dual aim of presenting personal recollections about the origins and early years of Social Security
in the US, and of exploring the legislative history of Medicare.

Pioneers in the social insurance movement tell about
many who were prominent in its early years, including
John B. Andrews, John R. Commons, and Frances Perkins.
There are descriptions of the activities and personnel of
the American Association for Labor Legislation and the
American Association for Social Security. Special emphasis
is given to experiences with the Committee on Economic
Security and the growth and organization of the Social
Security Board.

Recollections of early attempts to enact government
health insurance, the work on the Committee on Costs
of Medical Care and the Committee on Economic
Security, the National Health Conference of 1938, the
Wagner Bill, 1939, the Wagner-Murray-Dingell Bill, and
the Forand Bill, 1957, provide background about the
precursors of the Medicare program. The bulk of the
Medicare recollections focus on the period 1960–65. Included are memoirs of members of the Social Security
Administration, the Kennedy entourage, organized labor, the National Council of Senior Citizens, the US
Senate, the insurance industry, Blue Cross, the House
Ways and Means Committee, the American Hospital Association, and AMA.

Participants and pages: Arthur Altmeyer, 231 *(permission required to cite
or quote)*; Edward Annis, 84; Barbara Armstrong, 317 *(permission re-*

363

quired); Fred Arner, 47 *(closed during lifetime);* A. Henry Aronson, 173 *(closed during lifetime);* Robert M. Ball, 84 *(permission required);* Frank Bane, 121; Alexander Barkan, 10; Harry Becker, 40 *(closed during lifetime);* Bernice Bernstein, 125; Andrew Biemiller, 49 *(closed during lifetime);* Carter Bradley, 27; Howard Bray, 112 *(closed during lifetime);* James Brindle and Martin Cohen, 35; J. Douglas Brown, 105; Eveline M. Burns, 180; John Byrnes, 51; Winslow Carlton, 55; Blue Carstenson, 227; Ewan Clague, 152; Wilbur J. Cohen, 57; Nelson Cruikshank, 506;

Charles U. Daly, 27; Alvin David, 27 *(closed during lifetime);* Michael M. Davis, 65; Richard Donahue, 74 *(closed during lifetime);* Loula F. Dunn, 73; John Edelman, 99; Martha Eliot, 115 *(closed during lifetime);* Thomas H. Eliot, 81; Katherine Ellickson, 285; Lavinia Engle, 184; Caldwell Esselstyn, 43; Oscar Ewing, 90; Clinton Fair, 75 *(closed during lifetime);* Isidore Falk, 289; Fedele Fauri, 59; Meyer Feldman, 29 *(closed during lifetime);* William K. Fitch, 100; Marion B. Folsom, 207 *(permission required to cite or quote);* Aime Forand, 77; Kathryn Goodwin, 80; Frank P. Graham, 24; William Haber, 78 *(closed during lifetime);* Alvin Hansen, 28; Joseph Harris, 44; Ray Henry, 135 *(closed during lifetime);* Arthur Hess, 102; Jane Hoey, 102 *(permission required to cite or quote);* Reinhard Hohaus, 141 *(closed during lifetime);* Marjorie Hunter, 26; William Hutton, 113;

Leo Irwin, 76; Jacob Javits, 12; Jarold Kieffer, 21; Arlen Large, 66; Arthur Larson, 54; Murray Latimer, 50 *(closed during lifetime);* Katherine Lenroot, 173; Allen Lesser, 46; Leonard Lesser, 78; Manuel Levine, 34; Isidor Lubin, 32; Dorothy McCamman, 79 *(permission required);* Walter McNerney, 34; Mike Manatos, 41 *(closed during lifetime);* Morton D. Miller, 61; William Mitchell, 140; Raymond Moley, 19; Maurine Mulliner, 303; Robert J. Myers, 94 *(permission required to cite or quote);* Robert R. Neal, 46; Ivan Nestingen, 109; Robert Novak, 46 *(closed during lifetime);*

James C. O'Brien, 220; Charles Odell, 117; P. Kenneth O'Donnell, 40 *(permission required);* Michael O'Neill, 60 *(permission required to cite or quote);* Claude D. Pepper, 61; Roswell Perkins, 143; Robert Perrin, 48; Jerome Pollack, 47 *(closed during lifetime);* M. Allen Pond, 88; Jennings Randolph, 15; Paul and Elizabeth Raushenbush, 295 *(permission required to cite or quote);* William Reidy, 101; William A. Reynolds, 61; Elliot Richardson, 57 *(permission required to cite or quote);* Gerel Rubien, 41;

Sidney Saperstein, 122 *(closed during lifetime);* Lisbeth B. Schorr, 105 *(permission required to cite or quote);* Charles Schottland, 167; Harold Sheppard, 104; Anton G. Singsen, 20; Herman M. Somers, 199 *(closed during lifetime);* Sidney Spector, 57; Joseph Stetler, 58; Jack B. Tate, 119; Russell Gordon Wagenet, 108; Elizabeth Wickenden, 211 *(permission required);* Alanson Willcox, 140 *(permission required to cite or quote);* Kenneth Williamson, 240; Edwin Winge, 48; Irwin Wolkstein, 255; Leonard Woodcock, 28.

10,649 pp. *Open except as noted.* 1965–68. Papers. *Underwritten by the Social Security Administration.*

REFER TO "NOTES ON USE" IN INTRODUCTION

SOCIALIST MOVEMENT

This project describes the genesis and development of the Socialist Party, primarily in the words of those actively involved in the Party, past and present. It deals with the relationship of the Socialist Party to unions, the American Labor Party, the Trotskyist movement, the Communist Party, and other groups. Included are analyses of failure of the Socialist Party to thrive in this country, and of the impact of Franklin Roosevelt and the New Deal on the Party. Memoirists also describe the role Socialists have played in civil rights activities. There are recollections about Eugene V. Debs, Samuel Gompers, Upton Sinclair, Norman Thomas, and others.

Participants and pages: Irving Barshop, 27; Daniel Bell, 49; John Bennett, 30; Thomas Clement, 39; Morris L. Ernst, 33; Paul Feldman, 23; Harry Fleischman, 38; Samuel Friedman, 54; Gerry Gelles, 50; Maurice Goldbloom, 37; Eric Hass, 33; Adolph Held, 28; Harry Laidler, 50; Aaron J. Levenstein, 43; David McReynolds, 34; Nathaniel Minkoff, 28; A. J. Muste, 26; Robin Myers, 53; Pauline Newman, 33; D. Ernst Papanek, 62; Joseph Schlossberg, 51; Max Shachtman, 76; Herman Singer, 23; Mark Starr, 42; Seymour Steinsapir, 24; Irwin Suall, 43; Paul Sweezy, 14; Norman Thomas, 25; Gus Tyler, 28; James Weinstein, 45.

1,141 pp. *Permission required to cite or quote.* 1965. *Contributed by Mrs. Betty Yorburg, Pelham, New York.*

SOKOLSKY, George Ephraim (1893–1962) Columnist, author.

Early life on the Lower East Side; Columbia; Russia; China, 1927: militarism, Chinese bandits, arms procurement, Chiang Kai-shek and political-military situation.
126 pp. *Permission required to cite or quote.* 1962. NYT (Part I).

SOLA, Fernando (1906–   ) Lawyer.
ARGENTINA IN THE 1930's

Political cross currents, 1922–43, from vantage point outside the capital: stratification, charges of fraud, role of police, reasons for Peron's rise.
50 pp. *Open.* 1971.

SOLOMON, Sidney L. (1902–   ) *See* Federated Department Stores.

SOMERS, Herman Miles (1911–   ) Economist.
SOCIAL SECURITY
Experiences in Wisconsin with unemployment insurance and public welfare; discussion of Madison group: academic involvement in public affairs, economics as instrument for action; establishment of Social Security, contributions of Arthur Altmeyer and Wilbur Cohen; Medicare debate: proposed legislation, lobbying, AMA reaction; 1961 Task Force on Health and Social Security; White House Conference on Aged. Impressions of Edwin Witte, Paul Raushenbush, Robert Kerr.
199 pp. *Closed during lifetime.* 1968.

SOMMERS, Davidson. *See* World Bank.

SOPWITH, Sir Thomas Octave Murdoch (1888–   ) *See* Aviation.

SOUTHERN INTELLECTUAL LEADERS

This project consists of interviews with intellectual leaders in the South whose work fell predominantly in the period between the two World Wars and who were responsible for bringing a vigorous and modern intellectual life to their region.

Participants and pages: William T. Couch, 571; Jonathan Daniels, 176; Guy B. Johnson, 171; Broadus Mitchell, 165; Arthur Raper, 161; Rupert Vance, 106.

1,350 pp. *Closed pending publication of a study.* 1970–72.
Contributed by Daniel Singal, Durham, North Carolina.

SOWELL, F. C. (1904–   ) *See* Radio Pioneers.

SPAATZ, Carl (1891–   ) *See* Air Force Academy *and* Henry H. Arnold Project.

REFER TO "NOTES ON USE" IN INTRODUCTION

SPAETH, Sigmund (1885–1965) Writer, musician, lecturer.
RADIO PIONEERS
Family background, childhood in Philadelphia; education, Haverford College, Princeton; music critic and sports writer for NY *Evening Mail* and NY *Times*; music and sports programs; reminiscences of broadcasting at various stations in NY and throughout the country from 1921. Impressions of Woodrow Wilson, Fiorello La Guardia, and others.
121 pp. *Permission required to cite or quote.* 1951.
See also Popular Arts.

SPARGO, John (1876–1966) British Socialist, author.

Youth; British Social Democratic Federation; growth and development of the British labor movement; socialism in America; impressions of Daniel DeLeon, William Haywood, Morris Hillquit, Mrs. Rand, Max Eastman, Felix Adler, Victor Berger, Eugene Debs; break with Socialist Party to work with Woodrow Wilson in WWI; Versailles Treaty.
356 pp. *Permission required to cite or quote.* 1950. NYT (Part I).

SPARKMAN, John (1899–   ) *See* Adlai E. Stevenson Project.

SPARKS, Jeff. *See* Radio Pioneers.

SPECTOR, Sidney. *See* Social Security.

SPEED, Keats (1879–1952) Newspaperman.

Newspaper experiences, 1898–1950; Frank Munsey; William Randolph Hearst; career with the NY *Sun*.
64 pp. *Open.* 1950.

SPENCE, Hersey Everett (1882–   ) *See* James B. Duke Project.

SPENCER, Roscoe. *See* Health Science.

SPEWACK, Bella Loebel (1899–) *See* Popular Arts.

SPEWACK, Samuel (1899–) *See* Popular Arts.

SPIEGEL, Mathias L. *See* New York Political Studies.

SPIEGELBERG, George Alfred (1897–) *See* Robert P. Patterson Project.

SPINGARN, Arthur B. (1878–1971) Lawyer.

Early development of NAACP; NAACP president, 1911–40; impressions of Adam Clayton Powell, Roy Wilkins, W. E. B. DuBois, Lewis Gannett, and others.
101 pp. *Closed until December 2, 1976.* 1966.

SPITZ, René. Psychoanalyst.
PSYCHOANALYTIC MOVEMENT
Introduction to psychoanalysis; early career; Vienna, Paris, and US; discussion of theories; research in the nature of the thought process; cross-cultural studies; psychoanalytic groups in the US.
104 pp. *Permission required.* 1965.

SPIVACKE, Harold (1904–) Musicologist.
CARNEGIE CORPORATION
Relationship of Carnegie Corporation and the Music Division of the Library of Congress; impressions of John Lomax and Alan Lomax, Frederick P. Keppel.
76 pp. *Permission required.* 1968.

SPRAGUE, Mansfield Daniel (1910–) Lawyer.
EISENHOWER ADMINISTRATION
Work for Eisenhower in Connecticut, 1952; General Coun-

sel, Department of Defense, 1955–57; Assistant Secretary of Defense, International Security Affairs, 1957–58; Chairman, President's Committee on Information Activities Abroad, 1960; Sprague Report; impressions of Charles E. Wilson, Dwight D. Eisenhower, and others.
57 pp. *Permission required to cite or quote.* 1968. Papers.

SPURR, John C. (1900–   ) *See* McGraw-Hill.

STAATS, Elmer Boyd (1914–   ) Government official.
EISENHOWER ADMINISTRATION

Bureau of the Budget from 1939; Executive Officer, Operations Coordinating Board.
59 pp. *Permission required to cite or quote.* 1967.

STACKPOLE, Stephen. Foundation officer.
CARNEGIE CORPORATION

First contacts with the Carnegie Corporation, 1935; member of Corporation staff from 1940: impressions of office and employees; Army duty, 1940–45; educational testing program, 1946; Corporation's Commonwealth program, 1946–67: travel grants, selection of grantees, political complications, book sets, college and university programs, Anglo-American collaborations in Africa; African education program at TC; evaluation of Commonwealth program; impressions of Frederick Keppel, Charles Dollard, John Gardner, Alan Pifer, and others.
413 pp. *Permission required.* 1967.

STAEHLE, Alfred W. (1895–1972) *See* McGraw-Hill.

STAHL, Jules (1902–   ) Physician.

Alsatian childhood, medical training; US influence, work with Drs. Robert Loeb and Dana Atchley; return to France, 1935; Strasbourg during the German occupation; postwar medical developments. The memoir is in French.
61 pp. *Permission required to cite or quote.*

STAKMAN, Elvin C. (1885–   ) Plant pathologist.

Youth and early education; University of Minnesota: undergraduate, graduate school, and teaching career; Department of Agriculture; barberry eradication program; rust control and other agricultural problems; work in Germany, Mexico, India, Japan, and other countries; effects of WWI, the Depression, and WWII on agriculture; world food and hunger problems; Rockefeller Foundation; *Campaigns Against Hunger;* agricultural science in Russia and other Communist countries; work on numerous scientific boards, commissions, journals; philosophy of education; impressions of prominent plant pathologists and other academic and public figures.
1,687 pp. *Permission required.* 1970.
Underwritten by the Rockefeller Foundation.

STANLEY, Kim (Mrs. Alfred Ryder) (1925–   ) *See* Popular Arts.

STANLEY, Wendell Meredith (1904–   ) *See* Nobel Laureates.

STANS, Maurice Hubert (1908–   ) Investment banker, government official.
EISENHOWER ADMINISTRATION

Post Office Department; Bureau of the Budget; impressions of President Eisenhower, Richard Nixon, Arthur Summerfield.
83 pp. *Closed during lifetime.* 1968.

STANTON, Frank (1908–   ) Broadcasting executive.
AMERICAN CULTURAL LEADERS

Boyhood, Dayton, Ohio; psychology department, Ohio State University, 1931–35; psychological research among radio audiences; Center for Advanced Study in the Behavioral Sciences; Office of Radio Research; experiences as CBS president, 1946–68: corporate organization and executives, news and public affairs programs, "CBS Reports,"

REFER TO "NOTES ON USE" IN INTRODUCTION

Columbia Records, color television, scheduling procedures, public television, broadcast editorials, video recording. Impressions of Paul Lazarsfeld, Fred Friendly, Goddard Lieberson, William Paley, Lyndon Johnson.
330 pp. *Closed pending publication of a study.* 1968.

STAPLETON, Maureen (1925–   ) *See* Popular Arts.

STAPP, John Paul (1910–   ) *See* Aviation.

STARR, Mark (1894–   ) *See* Socialist Movement.

STASSEN, Harold Edward (1907–   ) Lawyer.
EISENHOWER ADMINISTRATION
Governor of Minnesota; drafting Eisenhower for Presidential candidacy; campaigning, 1951–52; appointment as director of MSA; foreign aid.
68 pp. *Closed until 1985.* 1967.

STATES, M. N. *See* American Association of Physics Teachers.

STEELMAN, John Roy (1900–   ) Labor administrator.

Boyhood and education; work as federal conciliator with emphasis on years as Director of US Conciliation Service; relationship of Conciliation Service to the Department of Labor; impressions of Frances Perkins, Isador Lubin, Franklin D. Roosevelt, Harry S. Truman, Thomas G. Corcoran, and others; labor adviser and special assistant to President Truman; Cabinet and White House staff meetings; relations with the leading members of both Houses of Congress; personalities and influences which helped to shape the major decisions of the Truman administration.
378 pp. *Closed until 1985.* 1957.

EISENHOWER ADMINISTRATION
White House staffs under Truman and Eisenhower; transition between administrations; impressions of the two

Presidents, Sherman Adams, Robert A. Taft. 89 pp. *Closed during lifetime.* 1968.

STEFFANSON, Hokan Bjornstrom (1883–1962) Financier and executive.

Early life, education, business experiences in Sweden; travel to US, 1909; business ventures, US and Canada; Kraft pulp, paper mills, oil, investments; business and finance during WWI and Depression; Swedish-American cultural and educational activities; NYC society and social life; experiences on *Titanic*, 1912; Metropolitan Club, Newport and Carlsbad; comments on Wall Street, investments and investing, estate management, Prohibition, antenuptial agreements; Pinchots and US aid to Finland, 1940; impressions of Ivar Kreuger, Oskar Froding, Hjalmar Branting; the Eno family; Mary Eno Steffanson, Carl Milles, George MacDonald, Ignace Paderewski, Axel Wenner-Gren, Edward R. Finch. 1,997 pp. *Permission required.* 1960.

STEIGER, Rod (1925–   ) *See* Popular Arts.

STEIN, Herbert. *See* Federated Department Stores.

STEINBERG, Martin. *See* Mt. Sinai Hospital.

STEINBRINK, Meyer (1880–1967) Lawyer.

Accounts of the Brooklyn bench and bar; NYC politics; notable cases, NY Supreme Court, 1932–50; associates. 234 pp. *Open.* 1955. *Contributed by Mr. Steinbrink's family.*

STEINSAPIR, Seymour. *See* Socialist Movement.

STEPHENS, Lafayette. *See* Weyerhaeuser Timber Company.

REFER TO "NOTES ON USE" IN INTRODUCTION

STEPHENS, Thomas E. (1903–   ) (with Mrs. Stephens)
EISENHOWER ADMINISTRATION
Appointments secretary to Eisenhower as candidate and
President; 1952 campaign; anecdotes and personal obser-
vations.
98 pp. *Closed during lifetime.* 1968.

STERN, Henry R. (–1966) *See* Theodore Roosevelt Association.

STERN, Julius David (1886–1971) Editor, publisher.

Experiences in publishing the New Brunswick *Times*,
1912–47; Springfield *News-Record*, 1914–47; Philadelphia
Record, 1928–47; NY *Post*, 1933–39.
109 pp. *Permission required to cite or quote.* 1954.

STETLER, C. Joseph (1917–   ) *See* Social Security.

STEURT, Marjorie Rankin (1888–   ) *See* China Missionaries.

STEVENS, Arthur Grant (1912–   ) *See* Marshall Plan.

STEVENS, James Floyd (1892–   ) *See* Forest History Society *and* Weyerhaeuser Timber Company.

STEVENSON, Adlai E. III (1930–   ) *See* Adlai E. Stevenson
Project.

STEVENSON, Alexander. *See* World Bank.

STEVENSON, Ed M. *See* Adlai E. Stevenson Project.

STEVENSON, John Fell (1936–   ) *See* Adlai E. Stevenson
Project.

STEVENSON, Nancy Anderson (Mrs. Adlai E. III) *See* Adlai E. Stevenson Project.

ADLAI E. STEVENSON PROJECT

Friends and associates describe Governor Adlai Stevenson's life and career from a number of vantage points. Personal reminiscences and anecdotes recall his wit and contribute fresh material for a study of his personality. Political associates analyze and illuminate his career, particularly as Governor of Illinois (1949–53), as Democratic nominee for the Presidency (1952 and 1956), and as Ambassador to the UN (1961–65).

Participants and pages: Mr. and Mrs. Warwick Anderson, 35; Jacob M. Arvey, 59; William Attwood, 33; Lauren Bacall, 76; George W. Ball, 29; Elizabeth Beale, 36; Robert S. Benjamin, 39; Richard Bentley, 35; William Benton, 40; Barry Bingham, 117; William McCormick Blair, Jr., 94; Joseph E. Bohrer, 46; John Brademas, 23; John Paulding Brown, 24; Mrs. John Carpenter, 14; Marquis W. Childs, 35; Jonathan W. Daniels, 19; Kenneth S. Davis, 91; James Edward Day, 40; Jane Dick, 102; Sherwood Dixon, 87; Carol Evans, 74;

Margaret M. Farwell, 31; Ruth Field, 26; Thomas K. Finletter, 62; Thomas Finney, 33; Walter T. Fisher, 27; Clayton Fritchey, 27; Katherine Clark Gibbons, 73; Richard Graebel, 39; Phyllis Gustafson, 44; John Marshall Harlan, 23; Marian Heiskell, 27; Juanda Higgins, 41; Alicia Hoge, 51; Stephen Y. Hord, 41; Edd Hyde, 24; Lawrence Irvin, 72; Elizabeth Stevenson Ives, 309; Ernest Ives, 36; Walter Johnson, 37; Barbara Kerr, 39; Doris Fleeson Kimball, 22; Louis A. Kohn, 18;

Kathryn Lewis, 55; Glen A. Lloyd and Mrs. Lloyd, 30; Edward McDougal, 67; Katherine McDougal, 42; Nan McEvoy, 42; Carl McGowan, 252; Kay McQuaid, 6; Paul B. Magnuson, 32; Thomas S. Matthews, 39; Maury Maverick, Jr., 24; Loring C. Merwin, 55; Newton Minow, 122; George W. Mitchell, 37; Stephen A. Mitchell, 173; A. S. Mike Monroney, 128; Michael Monroney, 50; Arthur Moore, 13; Theodore Myers, 50; John U. Nef, 20; Richard Nelson, 79; James F. Oates, 20; Elizabeth Paepcke, 46; Howard C. Petersen, 69; Francis T. P. Plimpton, 74;

Viola Reardy, 99; Richard Reed, 22; Mr. and Mrs. Lawrence Rust, 36; Walter V. Schaefer, 78; Arthur M. Schlesinger, Jr., 43; Eric A. Sevareid, 47; John Sharon, 148; Mr. and Mrs. Hermon Dunlap Smith, 58; John Sparkman, 43; Adlai E. Stevenson III, 75; Ed M. Stevenson, 60; John Fell Stevenson, 28; Nancy Anderson Stevenson, 47; Carroll Sudler, 35; Joseph Tally, 13; Chalmer C. Taylor, 41; Marietta Tree, 161; Mr. and Mrs. Clifton Utley, 55; Mrs. A. L. Voigt, 70; Kenneth Walker, 35; James A. Wechsler, 21; Harriet Welling, 26; Franklin Hall Williams, 13; William Willard Wirtz, 87; Samuel W. Witwer, 49; Wilson W. Wyatt, 161.

REFER TO "NOTES ON USE" IN INTRODUCTION

5,326 pp. *Permission required.* 1966–70.
Underwritten by the National Endowment for the Humanities and by friends of Adlai Stevenson.

STEWART, Harold Julian (1896–   ) *See* Health Science.

STEWART, Isabel Maitland (1878–1963) Professor of nursing.

Nursing education in Canada at the end of the 19th century, Winnipeg General Hospital; beginning of graduate nursing education at TC; Lillian Wald; attempts to standardize curricula and improve nursing education; nurses in WWI; travel in Europe and Asia; Goldmark Commission; Rockefeller Commission to investigate curricula in 1927 and subsequently.
459 pp. *Permission required to cite or quote.* 1960. NYT (Part I). Papers.
Underwritten by Teachers College, Columbia University.

STEWART, Joseph L. *See* Marine Corps.

STICHT, J. Paul. *See* Federated Department Stores.

STILLER, Ernest A. (1897–   ) *See* Benedum and the Oil Industry.

STILLMAN, John S. Politician.

NYC and State politics, 1948–50; special election for Congress, 20th Congressional District, NY, 1949.
40 pp. *Permission required to cite or quote.* 1949. NYT (Part I).
See also New York Political Studies.

STILLWELL, James (1906–   ) *See* Marshall Plan.

STIMSON, Henry Lewis (1867–1950) Secretary of War, Secretary of State.

Franklin D. Roosevelt; relations with the press; the atomic bomb.
23 pp. *Permission required to cite or quote.* 1949. NYT (Part I).

STINE, Oscar Clemen (1884–   ) Agricultural economist.

Family and early life; Ohio University; teaching in Ohio; Henry C. Taylor and the University of Wisconsin; Department of Agriculture, WWI; preparing data for national policy in price determination; extension of wheat production; Congressional inquiry into farm situation; BAE; outlook work and price forecasting; farm organizations and agricultural problems in the 1920's; National Agricultural Conference, 1922; International Institute of Agriculture; foreign travel; Department of Commerce and farm marketing problems; McNary-Haugen Bill; Farm Board; Russia, 1934; AAA; Agricultural Act of 1948.
434 pp. *Permission required to cite or quote.* 1952. NYT (Part I).

STINEBOWER, Leroy Dean (1904–   ) *See* Marshall Plan.

STINSON, Katherine. *See* Aviation.

STODDARD, Francis Russell (1877–1957) Lawyer, politician.

Republican Party district leader, Greenwich Village: campaigning, voting procedures; 1921 mayoralty campaign and rise of Fiorello LaGuardia; NY Assemblyman, 1912–15; Deputy Superintendent of Insurance, NY, 1915–21; Superintendent, 1921–24; WWI: anti-aircraft artillery study, 1917; 10th Assembly District leader, 1919–27; military aide to Mayor LaGuardia, WWII. Observations on political leaders, notably Franklin Roosevelt, Thomas E. Dewey, Alfred E. Smith, Charles Whitman, and Nathan Miller.
122 pp. *Open.* 1949.

REFER TO "NOTES ON USE" IN INTRODUCTION

STOLBERG, Benjamin (1891–1951) Author, journalist.

National politics and Communism.
48 pp. *Closed until January 1, 1975. 1950.*

STONE, Frederick Logan (1915–   ) *See* Health Science.

STONE, Irving (1903–   ) *See* Allan Nevins Project.

STONE, Jean (Mrs. Irving) *See* Allan Nevins Project.

STONE, M. Hedley (1897–1970) Labor leader.

Early experiences; International Seaman's Union; National Maritime Union: conditions of employment, hiring halls, injury cases, racial discrimination, dues collection, pensions; contrast between East and West Coast shipping; relations with International Longshoremen's Association; strikes in the 1930's; Congressional investigations; effects of NRA, Wagner Act, New Deal; foreign flag ships; Communist Party and the unions; founding of CIO, merger with AFL; establishment of PAC-CIO. Impressions of Joseph Curran, Harry Bridges, Walter Reuther, John L. Lewis.
411 pp. *Closed until 1988. 1969.*

STOREY, Robert Gerald (1893–   ) *See* Eisenhower Administration.

STRANGMAN, Henry W. *See* Henry H. Arnold Project.

STRAUS, Nathan (1889–1961) Businessman, publisher.

Childhood; early newspaper work on *Puck* and *Literary Digest;* NYC housing (Hillside Homes); NYC and State politics, 1920–33; national politics, 1932–44; USHA.
139 pp. *Open.* 1950. Papers.

STRAUSS, Anna Lord (1899–   ) Civic leader.

Girlhood, NYC; *Century Magazine;* Lucretia Mott and

women's suffrage; NYC and State League of Women Voters, 1934–43; NYC politics; United Aircraft, 1943–44; league positions on Equal Rights Amendment, TVA, Civil Service reform, civil rights; FAO conference, 1945; National League President, 1944–50; foreign affairs programs; Town Meeting of the Air tour, 1949; atomic energy control; International Alliance of Women; Overseas Education Fund; Freedom Agenda; postwar anti-Communist agitation; President Harry Truman's Commission on Internal Security; UN Association; UN delegate, 1951–52; Committee for Economic Development; USIA mission, Africa and Asia; women's position, US and abroad; impressions of colleagues in government and League.

571 pp. *Open.* 1972.
Contributed by Mrs. Walter Gellhorn, New York.

STRAUSS, Lewis Lichtenstein (1896–   ) Government official, financier.

EISENHOWER ADMINISTRATION

Family background; religious upbringing in Richmond, Virginia; shoe salesman in the South; Herbert Hoover and Belgian War Relief, Food Administration, 1917–19; Kuhn, Loeb, 1919–47; Jewish Agricultural Society; Navy, WWII; AEC, 1946–50 and 1953–58: May-Johnson Bill, security problems; Rockefeller Brothers Fund, 1950–53.

177 pp. *Closed until 1985 or death, whichever is later.*

STRAUSS, Morris Lincoln (1877–1953) Lawyer.

Columbia College and Law School; law practice in Queens County; experiences as a trial lawyer; attorney with the NYC Law Department, 1914; Mayor John P. Mitchel; August Belmont and rapid transit; Citizens Water Supply Rate case, 1921; assistant corporation counsel to Mayor John O'Brien; NY bench and bar; commentaries on the American scene.

436 pp. *Permission required to cite or quote.* 1952.

STREIBERT, Theodore. *See* Eisenhower Administration.

REFER TO "NOTES ON USE" IN INTRODUCTION

STROTHER, Dean C. *See* Air Force Academy.

STUMP, Felix Budwell (1894–1972) Naval officer.

Family background; Naval Academy; early cruises, Central and South America; naval aviation training, Pensacola, 1919; aeronautical engineering, 1922–24; shore and sea commands, 1924–40: cruiser duty, dive bombing squadron, war games, Naval Air Maintenance Procurement Division, Bureau of Aeronautics; executive officer, *Enterprise*, 1940: ship organization manual; *Langley*, 1941; WWII: duty in Java, Australia, 1942; Captain of the new *Lexington*, 1943–44; the Marshalls, Truk; Commander, Carrier Division 24, 1944–45: operations in Western Pacific and Philippines areas, Leyte, air strikes; technical training command, Chief of Naval Air Technical Training, 1945–48; Korean War; Commander NATO striking fleet. Comments on naval colleagues, especially Adms. William Halsey, Hart, William Moffett, and Arthur Radford.

364 pp. *Permission required to cite or quote.* 1965.

SUALL, Irwin. *See* Socialist Movement.

SUDLER, Carroll. *See* Adlai E. Stevenson Project.

SULLIVAN, William (1894–   ) Naval officer.

Education, MIT; Naval construction; Annapolis; Navy Yards in US; Philippines; Shanghai, 1934–37; Trans-Siberian Railroad; Model Basin, Washington Naval Gun Factory; salvage and admiralty law; diving; Merritt, Chapman & Scott; San Diego salvage depot; equipment and personnel, procurement problems; Assistant Naval Attaché, London; British WWII salvage operations: training personnel, blocking channels, enemy interference, financial aspects of salvage and marine insurance, rescue tugs; Bureau of Ships, 1941, salvage branch, training personnel; Pearl Harbor: communications problems, Naval districts; salvage off US and Canadian coasts; clearing Cape Cod Canal; Chief of Navy Salvage, WWII; *Normandie* fire and sinking; salvage training exercises and school; divers; civilian training; development of equipment; salvage award claims; clearing Casablanca harbor after North African landings; salvage problems in Mediterranean Theater: Bizerte Channel, Ferryville, Tunis; Operation Husky; landings in Sicily, Salerno, Naples; plans for landing at Kwajalein; London, preparations for D-Day; Normandy landings: demolition teams, artificial harbors, mine-sweeping; operations at LeHavre, Marseilles; clearing Manila Harbor; impressions of Adms. Alan Kirk, John Hall, Ernest King, Benjamin Manseau, and Gens. Dwight Eisenhower and Douglas MacArthur, and many others.

1,784 pp. *Permission required.* 1965.

SULZBURGER, Frank L. (1887–   ) *See* Federated Department Stores.

SUMMERFIELD, Arthur (1899–1972) *See* Eisenhower Administration.

SUTHERLAND, Albert Edward (1897–   ) Director, actor.
POPULAR ARTS

Early career in Hollywood film making; Tommy Meehan; Mack Sennett and the Keystone Film Co.; Charlie Chaplin; Harold Lloyd; careers of many Hollywood celebrities; Buster Keaton; Laurel & Hardy; movie director, stunt man, propman; Ralph Spence; impressions of other comedy writers amd directors; John Ford, Frank Capra; movies as escapism; Bebe Daniels; W. C. Fields; testifying against the Neeley bill before Senate Investigation Committee; Westerns; unions; Douglas Fairbanks, Sr.; *International House.*

188 pp. *Permission required to cite or quote.* 1959.

SWAINE, Philip W. (1889–1958) *See* McGraw-Hill.

SWANSON, Gloria (1899–   ) *See* Popular Arts.

SWEEZY, Paul. *See* Socialist Movement.

REFER TO "NOTES ON USE" IN INTRODUCTION

SWEM, Charles L. (–1956) *See* John Robert Gregg Project.

SWING, Joseph (1894–   ) Army officer.
EISENHOWER ADMINISTRATION

US Immigration Commissioner; illegal immigration from Mexico; Chinese immigration and the "confession program"; immigration legislation; relations with President Eisenhower and with Congress.
76 pp. *Closed during lifetime.* 1967.

SWINYARD, Chester A. *See* Association for the Aid of Crippled Children.

SWOPE, Gerard (1872–1957) Electrical engineer.

Family, youth and education; early work in Chicago; Hull House; work for Western Electric; Gen. George Goethals and the Division of Purchase, Storage and Traffic, 1918; International General Electric.
116 pp. *Permission required to cite or quote.* 1955. NYT (Part I). Papers.

SZENT-GYÖRGYI, Albert (1893–   ) *See* Nobel Laureates.

TABER, Louis John (1878–1960) Past Master National Grange.

Agricultural political problems, 1915–40, and an exposition of personal and official Grange positions on these problems.
437 pp. *Permission required to cite or quote.* 1952. NYT (Part I).
Papers: 78 pp. of supplementary notes.

TABOADA, Diogenes. *See* Argentina in the 1930's.

TAFT, Barbara (Mrs. William H. III) *See* Robert A. Taft Project.

TAFT, Horace (1925–   ) *See* Robert A. Taft Project.

TAFT, Lloyd (1923–   )

ROBERT A. TAFT PROJECT

Childhood in Cincinnati; impressions of Senator and Mrs. Taft and their relatives; family vacations, Murray Bay, Canada; picnics, fishing, daily routine; Yale College; father's political career; Republican Convention, 1952; father's relationship with President Dwight Eisenhower; mother's illness; father's death.
113 pp. *Permission required.* 1970.

TAFT, Seth. *See* Robert A. Taft Project.

ROBERT A. TAFT PROJECT

The life and career of Senator Robert A. Taft (1889–1953) are recounted by colleagues, friends, and family. Interviews describe his legal development and political growth, as a Republican, his activities in Ohio and in Washington, and his family relationships.

Participants and pages: Harold B. Alderson, 27; Leslie C. Arends, 21; Stanhope Bayne-Jones, 62; Jack L. Bell, 22; Mrs. Robert L. Black, 36; Katharine Kennedy Brown, 41; Eugenie Mary Davie, 69; John W. Ewen, 18; Homer Ferguson, 15; L. Richard Guylay, 136; Marjorie Hein, 27; Bourke B. Hickenlooper, 40; John B. Hollister, 58; Edwin A. Lahey, 66; Alfred M. Landon, 43; Harry Maginnis, 17; Helen Taft Manning, 83; L. Randolph Mason, 41; Vernon Romney, 43; Mr. and Mrs. Stanley Rowe, 64; Thomas Shroyer, 36; Barbara Taft, 79; Horace Taft, 81; Lloyd Taft, 113; Seth Taft, 30; Clare M. Torrey, 22; Walter Trohan, 26; Paul Walter, 131; Howard Young, 24.

1,471 pp. *Permission required.* 1967–70.
Underwritten by the Robert A. Taft Institute of Government of New York City.

TALLY, Joseph. *See* Adlai E. Stevenson Project.

TAMIROFF, Akim. *See* Popular Arts.

REFER TO "NOTES ON USE" IN INTRODUCTION

TANENBAUM, Marc Herman (1925–   ) *See* Herbert H. Lehman Project.

TANNER, Frederick Chauncey (1878–1963) Lawyer.

Early background and interest in politics, NY politics; Chairman, NY State Republican Party, 1914–17; impressions of Charles Evans Hughes, Theodore Roosevelt, William Howard Taft, and many other political figures.
299 pp. *Permission required to cite or quote.* 1950. NYT (Part I) Papers.

TANZER, Laurence Arnold (1874–1963) Lawyer.

Columbia Law School and legal practice, NYC: inception of Citizens Union, 1897; charter revision efforts, 1910 and 1936; proportional representation; home rule; legislative drafting for NY Factory Investigation Commission, 1912–13; NY income tax law, 1919; 1945 mayoralty campaign: William O'Dwyer. Observations on NY political leaders, 1900–1949.
73 pp. *Permission required to cite or quote.* 1949. NYT (Part I).

TAPP, Jesse Washington (1900–1967) Agricultural economist.

Agriculture in the South before 1917; Department of Agriculture, 1920–39; agricultural economics since 1920; WFA; Bank of America, 1939–53.
225 pp. *Open.* 1953.

TARR, Frank. *See* Weyerhaeuser Timber Company.

TARRANT, William Theodore (1878–   ) Naval officer.

Naval Academy; Spanish-American War; instructor, Naval Academy; cruises and engineering duty; troop transport, WWI; commands afloat and ashore; adviser to OSS, WWII.
53 pp. *Open.* 1963.

TATE, Allen (1899–) *See* Hart Crane Project.

TATE, Jack Bernard (1902–1968) Lawyer.
SOCIAL SECURITY
Assistant to Chief, later General Counsel, Social Security Board, 1935–39: federal public assistance programs, hiring staff, relations with states, dealings with Congress and FBI; 1939 amendments; General Counsel, Federal Security Agency, 1939–47; development of Social Security. Impressions of Thomas Eliot, Jane Hoey, Arthur Altmeyer, Paul McNutt, Fowler Harper, John Winant, and others.
119 pp. *Open.* 1965.

TATUM, Edward Lawrie (1909–) *See* Nobel Laureates.

TAYLOR, Chalmer C. (with Mrs. Taylor) *See* Adlai E. Stevenson Project.

TAYLOR, CHARLES E. (1883–1967) Farm leader.

Family background; Progressive politics; publisher and editor, Plentywood, Montana, *Producers News*, 1918–31, 1935–37; Nonpartisan League leader, 1918–24; joins Communist Party, 1920; expulsion as a Trotskyite, 1934; Montana State Senator, 1922–30; National Farm Labor Party Convention, 1924; President, United Farmers League, and director, Farmers National Committee of Action, 1932–34.
248 pp. *Closed until July 4, 1976.* 1967.
Contributed by Lowell K. Dyson, Blacksburg, Virginia.

TAYLOR, James Davidson (1907–) *See* Radio Pioneers.

TAYLOR, Henry Charles (1873–1969) Agricultural economist.

Department of Agriculture, 1919–25; appraisal of the work of Henry C. Wallace and Henry A. Wallace in the Department; International Institute of Agriculture.
170 pp. *Closed until April 28, 1974.* 1952. Papers: 8 bound

volumes of an unpublished history of agricultural economics in the US *(open)*.

TAYLOR, John Whitfield (1914–   ) *See* McGraw-Hill.

TAYLOR, Telford (1908–   ) Lawyer.

Early life; Harvard Law School; clerk to Judge Augustus Hand, 1932–33; Department of Interior, 1933–34; AAA, 1934–35; Securities and Exchange Act; associate counsel to the Senate Committee on Interstate Commerce, railroad investigation, 1935–39; FCC, 1940–42.
501 pp. *Closed until 5 years after death.* 1956.
See also James Lawrence Fly Project.

TAYLOR, William L. Civil rights worker.

Experiences on staff of US Commission on Civil Rights, 1961–68.
30 pp. *Permission required.* 1970.
Contributed by Stephen Lawson, New York.

TEAD, Ordway (1891–   ) Editor, teacher.

Experiences on NYC Board of Higher Education: relationship with the mayor's office and State legislature, personnel policies, Bertrand Russell case, Strayer Committee report, curricula; impressions of persons and policies in NYC college system.
212 pp. *Open.* 1960.

TEDESCO, Mariano. *See* Argentina in the 1930's.

TELLER, Ludwig (1911–1965) Lawyer, politician.

Childhood and education; NYU Law School; labor relations, Navy, 1943–45; labor relations specialist, law practice; drafting Taft-Hartley Act; NYC West Side politics: Amsterdam Democratic Club, relationship of clubhouse to

NY County Committee, role and function of district leader, reform movement; State Assemblyman; Congressman. Impressions of Carmine DeSapio.
571 pp. *Open.* 1962.

TENNEY, Charles Henry (1911–) *See* New York Political Studies.

TENNEY, George Clinton (1898–) *See* McGraw-Hill.

THACHER, Thomas Day (1881–1950) Judge.

NY and national bench and bar; Supreme Court; Russia, 1917; work of the Solicitor General, 1928–31; NY politics and charter revision, 1935–38.
108 pp. *Permission required to cite or quote.* 1949. Papers.

THATCHER, Herbert B. *See* Air Force Academy.

THAYER, Robert Helyer (1901–) *See* Eisenhower Administration.

THAYER, Walter Nelson (1910–) Lawyer, banker.
EISENHOWER ADMINISTRATION
1952 Citizens for Eisenhower Committee; 1960 Volunteers for Nixon and National Republican Citizens Committee; relations between President Eisenhower and Richard Nixon in 1960 campaign.
52 pp. *Permission required to cite or quote.* 1967.

THEATER. *See* Popular Arts.

THEILER, Max (1899–1972) *See* Nobel Laureates.

THEOBALD, John J. (1904–) Educator.

Career in public education; professor and Dean of City and

Columbia University

Queens Colleges; Deputy Mayor of NYC; Superintendent of NYC Schools.
229 pp. *Permission required.* 1966. Papers.

THOMAS, G. Harris. *See* Weyerhaeuser Timber Company.

THOMAS, Gerald Carthrae (1894–   ) Marine Corps officer.

Family background, education; WWI service; Haiti, 1919–21; Washington Disarmament Conference; special mission to Middle East with James Roosevelt, 1941: observation of British operations; WWII: Guadalcanal and Bougainville operations; Alexander Vandegrift Commandancy, unification fight; Marine occupation of North China; Chinese Civil War; fighting in Central Korea; Army personalities.
989 pp. *Permission required to cite or quote.* 1966.

THOMAS, Norman Mattoon (1884–1968) Clergyman, politician.

Part I: Detroit Socialist Convention of 1950; autobiographical material; impressions of Franklin D. Roosevelt and Henry A. Wallace and many other contemporaries; Socialist Party politics, 1920–49.
217 pp. *Permission required to cite or quote.* 1950. NYT (Part I).

Part II: Impressions of US Presidents, 1912–65; activities in support of socialist and labor organizations; newspaper career; early political campaigns; work for civil liberties: freedom of speech in Jersey City, sharecropper protection, defense of Japanese-Americans during WWII.
152 pp. *Permission required to cite or quote.* 1965. NYT (Part II).
See also Socialist Movement.

THOMAS, Rolland Jay (1900–1967) Union official.

Early life and experiences as a migrant worker; early days

of the automobile industry; formation of the UAW; politics in election of officers; role of the Communist Party in the UAW; Walter Reuther supporters.
270 pp. *Open.* 1956.

THOMPSON, Frank, Jr. (1918–   ) Congressman.
AMERICAN CULTURAL LEADERS

Boyhood, Trenton, New Jersey; federal support of the arts; Kennedy Center for the Performing Arts; New Jersey Democratic politics, 1928–50; creation of National Foundation on the Arts and the Humanities; impressions of John F. Kennedy, Jacob Javits.
138 pp. *Closed pending publication of a study.* 1967.

THOMPSON, James Stacy (1887–   ) *See* McGraw-Hill.

THOMPSON, Llewellyn (1904–1972) *See* International Negotiations.

THOMPSON, Mrs. Marshall. *See* American Cultural Leaders.

THOMPSON, Ralph (1904–   ) *See* Book-of-the-Month Club.

THORNE, Florence Calvert (1878–   ) Aide to Samuel Gompers.

Education, University of Chicago; AFL and Samuel Gompers; prominent US labor leaders before WWI; growth of the research movement in the AFL, 1920's.
170 pp. *Closed during lifetime.* 1957.

THORNTON, Jessie Willock (Mrs. Dan) (1912–   ) *See* Eisenhower Administration.

THORPE, James. *See* Allan Nevins Project.

REFER TO "NOTES ON USE" IN INTRODUCTION

THYE, Edward (1896–1969) Senator.
EISENHOWER ADMINISTRATION
1952 Republican Convention; Ezra Taft Benson; Republican politics; Northwest Airlines' air rights; Senate committee work.
76 pp. *Permission required to cite or quote.* 1967.

TIBBETS, Paul, Jr. *See* Aviation.

TINKER, Edward Laroque (1881–1968) Author.

Adventures in Mexico with Alvaro Obregon and Pancho Villa; Latin American experiences.
41 pp. *Permission required to cite or quote.* 1964.

TODD, Jane H. (–1966) *See* New York Political Studies.

TODD, Webster Bray (1899–   ) *See* Eisenhower Administration.

TOLLEY, Howard Ross (1889–1958) Agricultural economist.

Early life and teaching in Indiana; Office of Farm Management; development of bureaus in the Department of Agriculture; BAE, 1915–29, 1938–43; Division of Agricultural Engineering; tariff policy; farm organizations; Secretaries Henry A. Wallace and William Jardine; outlook work; Giannini Foundation, University of California, 1930–33, 1935–36; AAA, 1933–35, 1936–38; OPA; interim commission of the FAO.
703 pp. *Open.* 1954.

TOOTELL, George Thomas (1886–   ) *See* China Missionaries.

TOPPING, Norman Hawkins (1908–   ) *See* Health Science.

TOPPING, William Hill (1888–   ) *See* China Missionaries.

TORREY, Clare M. *See* Robert A. Taft Project.

TORREY, Daniel Wellington, Jr. (1904–   ) *See* Marine Corps.

TOWE, Kenneth Crawford (1893–   ) Business executive.
JAMES B. DUKE PROJECT

Family background, childhood in North Carolina; Trinity College; WWI experiences; postwar career; American Cyanamid Co., 1926–58: history of the company, impressions of leading officers; connections with James B. Duke, Duke Endowment, Duke Power Co., Duke University. 175 pp. *Permission required.* 1966.

TRAENDLY, Wallace Francis. (1910–   ) *See* McGraw-Hill.

TRAIN, Harold C. (1887–1967) Naval officer.

Naval Academy; South American cruise; Nicaraguan Revolution, 1912; Navy Department Communications Office, 1916–18; Washington Disarmament Conference, 1921; Geneva Naval Conference, 1927; Herbert Hoover's 1928 tour of Latin America; London Naval Disarmament Conference, 1930; WWII: counter-attack at Pearl Harbor, Director of Naval Intelligence, Commander Southeast Pacific Force and Panama Sea Frontier; Eleanor Roosevelt's Caribbean Cruise; Dumbarton Oaks Conference; 1945 Inter-American Conference; postwar career. Impressions of J. Edgar Hoover, Adms. Hilary P. Jones, H. E. Kimmel, W.S. Pye, Frank H. Scofield, and others.
451 pp. *Permission required to cite or quote.* 1965. NYT (Part II).

TREE, Marietta (Mrs. Ronald) (1917–   ) Civic leader, diplomatic representative.
ADLAI E. STEVENSON PROJECT

Recollections of Adlai Stevenson; appointment to UN Human Rights Commission; US mission to the UN under Stevenson; Democratic Advisory Committee; Stevenson's re-

lationship with Lyndon Johnson; 1952 campaign; press representation during the 1950's; 1956 campaign; Cuba missile crisis; NSC; Marine landing in Dominican Republic; last weeks of Stevenson's life and Stevenson funeral. Impressions of Eleanor Roosevelt, Harry S. Truman, George Ball, John F. Kennedy.
161 pp. *Permission required.* 1967.

TRILLING, Lionel (1905–   ) *See* Columbia Crisis of 1968.

TROHAN, Walter (1903–   ) *See* Robert A. Taft Project.

TROOB, Lester (1912–   ) *See* Book-of-the-Month Club.

TROY, David S. *See* Weyerhaeuser Timber Company.

TRUE, Sybil. *See* Radio Pioneers.

TRUMAN, David Bicknell (1913–   ) *See* Columbia Crisis of 1968.

TRUMAN, Harry S (1884–   ) *See* Journalism Lectures.

TRUMBLE, Thomas. *See* Flying Tigers.

TRUSSELL, Ray Elbert (1914–   ) Physician.

Childhood and education; Hunterdon Medical Center, 1953; problems of medical care and hospital maintenance. 320 pp. *Permission required.* 1966.

TSIANG, Tingfu F. *See* Chinese Oral History.

TSO, Shun-sheng. *See* Chinese Oral History.

TUCKER, Everett, Jr. *See* Eisenhower Administration.

TUGWELL, Rexford Guy (1891–   ) Economist.

The Brain Trust, 1928–33; 1933 banking panic; Department of Agriculture and the NRA.
75 pp. *Permission required to cite or quote.* 1950. NYT (Part I).

TURNER, Joseph. *See* Mt. Sinai Hospital.

TURNER, Justin George (1898–   ) *See* Allan Nevins Project.

TURNER, Roscoe (1895–   ) *See* Aviation.

TUTT, Thayer. *See* Air Force Academy.

TUTTLE, Charles Henry (1879–1971) Lawyer.

Education, early legal and political activities, NYC; appointment, Board of Trustees, CCNY, 1913; US Attorney, Southern District of NY, 1927–30; formation of Board of Higher Education, 1926; NYC higher education in the 1930's: the city colleges, their presidents, relations between the Board, the college presidents, and the city government; tenure, civil service coverage, free tuition. Impressions of John H. Finley, Frederick B. Robinson, Buell Gallagher.
263 pp. *Permission required to cite or quote.* 1964. NYT (Part I).

TUTTLE, Elbert Parr (1897–   ) Federal judge.
EISENHOWER ADMINISTRATION

Georgia Republican Party; national conventions, 1948 and 1952; General Counsel, Treasury Department, 1953–54; decisions of 5th Circuit, US Court of Appeals, 1954–70, especially on civil rights; federal judiciary in the South, 1954–70; history of Republican Party in the South; impressions of colleagues in executive and judiciary branches.
113 pp. *Closed during lifetime.* 1970.

REFER TO "NOTES ON USE" IN INTRODUCTION

TWEED, Harrison (1885–1969) Lawyer.

Education at Harvard College and Law School; practice with various firms, NYC; American Law Institute; Legal Aid Society of NY; impressions of notable members of the NY bench and bar, including George Welwood Murray, Learned Hand and Augustus Hand, and Robert P. Patterson.
128 pp. *Permission required to cite or quote.* 1967. NYT (Part I).

TWINING, Nathan Farragut (1897–   ) Air Force officer.
EISENHOWER ADMINISTRATION
WWII experiences; downed in Coral Sea; dropping the atom bomb; Air Force Chief of Staff; Chairman, Joint Chiefs of Staff, 1957–60; relations with Secretaries of Defense, Congress, and Presidents.
250 pp. *Closed during lifetime.* 1967.
See also Air Force Academy.

TYLER, Gus. *See* Socialist Movement.

TYLER, Ralph Winfred (1902–   ) Educator.
CARNEGIE CORPORATION
First connections with the Corporation, 1934; Eight-Year Study; chairman, Department of Education, University of Chicago, 1938; work for Corporation over the years; Center for Advanced Study in the Behavioral Sciences; Carnegie study of American education. Impressions of various academic figures.
139 pp. *Permission required.* 1967.

TYSON, Edwin Lloyd. *See* Radio Pioneers.

UNDERHILL, James Latham (1891–   ) Marine Corps officer.

Education; sea and barracks duty, 1913–18; China duty; Fleet Marine Force, late 1930's; USMC buildup for war;

393

WWII: Kwajalein, Roi-Namur, Saipan-Tinian operations; President, USMC Postwar Personnel Reorganization Board, 1945–46.
204 pp. *Open.* 1968.

UNITED NATIONS CONFERENCE, SAN FRANCISCO, 1945.

Group discussion among Malcolm W. Davis, William T.R. Fox, Leland Goodrich, Joseph E. Johnson, and Grayson Kirk on such topics as press coverage, language problems, structure of the UN and the Secretariat, Big Five, and the veto.
77 pp. *Open.* 1951.

UNIVERSITY SEMINARS

A description of the origin and purpose of the Columbia University Seminars, together with transcripts of panel discussions in several fields. The Labor Seminar, the most extensive, deals with labor-management relations, automation, the impact of foreign trade on collective bargaining, strikes, and arbitration procedures. Several seminars on the city, technological and social change, American civilization, and mass communications are included.
8,311 pp. *Permission required.* 1961–72.

UPINGTON, Gaylord M. *See* Weyerhaeuser Timber Company.

UPTON, Wayne. *See* Eisenhower Administration.

UREY, Harold Clayton (1893–   ) *See* Nobel Laureates.

UTLEY, Clifton Maxwell (1904–   ) (with Mrs. Utley) *See* Adlai E. Stevenson Project.

UVILLER, Harry. *See* New York Political Studies.

REFER TO "NOTES ON USE" IN INTRODUCTION

VALESH, Eva MacDonald (1874–1956) Journalist, labor leader, civic worker.

Education; labor work and journalism, Minnesota and NY; AFL; Samuel Gompers and the *AFL Magazine;* social work in NY; Democratic National Committee; persons in labor and social work.
228 pp. *Permission required to cite or quote.* 1952. NYT (Part I).

VAN ASCH VAN WIJK, W. *See* Pablo de Azcarate.

VANCE, Rupert B. (1899–   ) Sociologist.
SOUTHERN INTELLECTUAL LEADERS
Childhood; education, Henderson-Brown College; graduate work, Vanderbilt and University of North Carolina; development of social science in the South; Southern race relations; Populist Party; agricultural life; Southern Sociological Society; impressions of the Nashville Agrarians, W. T. Couch, Frank Graham, Charles S. Johnson, Herman C. Nixon, Howard W. Odum, and others.
106 pp. *Closed pending publication of a study.* 1971.

VAN SCHAICK, George S. (1883–1968) Lawyer, public official.

NY State politics; State Insurance Department, 1931–35.
93 pp. *Open.* 1950. Papers: 8 letters (microfilm).

VAN SLYKE, Cassius James (1900–   ) *See* Health Science.

VAN VECHTEN, Carl (1880–1964) Writer, critic.

Childhood and education; Chicago, 1900–06; music criticism, NY *Times;* European travel, 1906–12; drama and literature, 1914–32; Negroes; photography; ballet; impressions of Mabel Dodge Luhan, Gertrude Stein, James Weldon Johnson, F. Scott Fitzgerald, Theodore Dreiser, Thomas Wolfe.
355 pp. *Open.* 1960. Papers.

VARNEY, William Frederick (1884–1960) Prohibitionist.

Social and political aspects of Prohibition; Presidential candidate on Prohibition Party ticket, 1928.
37 pp. *Open.* 1958.

VAUGHAN, George A. *See* Aviation.

VEILLER, Lawrence (1872–1959) Social worker.

Tenement house reform, NYC, 1892–1902; City Club and municipal reform, 1903–06; national movement for housing reform; Hoover Housing Conference, 1931–32; zoning and city planning; initiation of permanent population data in sample NYC blocks; traffic control and rapid transit problems; reforms in NYC courts: Magistrate's, Children's, and Domestic Relations; records systems. Relations with Mayors George McClellan, William Gaynor, and John Hylan, and others.
299 pp. *Open.* 1949.

VELEBIT, Vladimir. *See* International Negotiations.

VERVILLE, Alfred. *See* Aviation.

VICCHI, Adolfo. *See* Argentina in the 1930's.

VICTORY, John Francis (1892–   ) Lawyer.
AIR FORCE ACADEMY

National Advisory Committee for Aeronautics during WWI; Gens. George O. Squier and William Mitchell.
114 pp. *Restriction pending.* 1970.

VIDOR, King Wallis (1895–   ) *See* Popular Arts.

VILARDI, Paul. *See* Columbia Crisis of 1968.

REFER TO "NOTES ON USE" IN INTRODUCTION

VINER, Jacob (1892–1970) Economist.

Treasury Department; recession of 1937–38; State Department; Tariff Commission; USSB; aid to China in WWII. 61 pp. *Open.* 1953.

VISCONTI, Ann. *See* Federated Department Stores.

VIVIAN, John. *See* Flying Tigers.

VOCCO, Rocco (–1960) *See* Popular Arts.

VOGEL, Ezra. *See* International Negotiations.

VOGEL, Peter. *See* Mt. Sinai Hospital.

VOIGT, Mrs. A.L. *See* Adlai E. Stevenson Project.

VOISIN, Gabriel. *See* Aviation.

VOLANDO, Tommy. *See* Popular Arts.

VON BERNUTH, Rudolph Ludwig (1883–1969) Lawyer.

Family background, NYC; Columbia College and Law School; continuing interest and activities in Columbia athletics: Athletic Committee, 1909–51, Baker Field, 1934 Rose Bowl; university administration, trustees, coaches, and athletes. 99 pp. *Open.* 1963.

VON KARMAN, Theodore. *See* Aviation.

VORSE, Mary Heaton (Mrs. Albert White) (1881–1966) Author.

Lawrence strike; Elizabethton textile strike; anarcho-syndicalism; Soviet Russia; IWW. 73 pp. *Open.* 1957.

VOSHMIK, Roy. *See* Weyerhaeuser Timber Company.

WADDELL, Harry W. (1911–) *See* McGraw-Hill.

WADHAMS, William Henderson (1873–1952) Lawyer.

NYC and State and national politics, 1898–1912; League to
Enforce Peace; international law.
118 pp. *Permission required to cite or quote.* 1950. NYT
(Part I).

WADSWORTH, James J. (1905–) Government official.
EISENHOWER ADMINISTRATION

Early career; Economic Cooperation Administration; Civil
Defense; Deputy Representative to the UN; workings of
the UN; International AEC; disarmament conferences; nuclear test ban treaty meetings; relations with Russia; Chief
Delegate to the UN.
248 pp. *Permission required to cite or quote.* 1967.

WADSWORTH, James Wolcott (1877–1953) Congressman.

Childhood and education; rural life in upstate NY; NY State
Assembly, 1905–10; NY politics, 1910–15; US Senate, 1915–27;
Republican National Convention, 1916; WWI; Newton
Baker; European travel; League of Nations and Senate
debate; Warren Harding era; 1920 National Defense Act;
Prohibition; US House of Representatives, 1933–45; vig-
nettes of political contemporaries.
458 pp. *Permission required to cite or quote.* 1952. NYT
(Part II).

WAGENET, Russell Gordon (1890–) Government official.
SOCIAL SECURITY

Professional background; Director, Unemployment Insurance, Social Security, 1935: hiring staff, administration of
law, merit rating, relations with Internal Revenue Service
and state governments; Employment Service; Director,

REFER TO "NOTES ON USE" IN INTRODUCTION

California Employment Agency, 1940. Impressions of Frances Perkins, Arthur Altmeyer.
108 pp. *Open.* 1965.

WAGNER, Hayden. *See* Henry H. Arnold Project.

WAGNER, Robert F. (1910–) *See* New York Political Studies.

WAGONER, Clyde D. (› –1963) *See* Radio Pioneers.

WAHL, John A. *See* Weyerhaeuser Timber Company.

WAINHOUSE, David W. (1900–) *See* Eisenhower Administration.

WALD, Charles. *See* Aviation.

WALD, Jerry (1912–1962) Motion picture producer.
POPULAR ARTS

Warner Brothers Studio; *Twenty Million Sweethearts;* films dealing with current problems; *On the Waterfront;* war films; changes in Hollywood, 1933–59; writing and producing films; *The Man who Came to Dinner;* location shooting; recollections of many Hollywood personalities.
66 pp. *Permission required to cite or quote.* 1959.

WALKER, Edith. *See* Book-of-the-Month Club.

WALKER, Kenneth. *See* Adlai E. Stevenson Project.

WALLACE, Henry Agard (1888–1965) Public official.

Part I: A memoir abundantly supported by diaries and correspondence. Childhood; *Wallace's Farmer;* impressions of Henry Cantwell Wallace; the McNary-Haugen fight; election of 1932; organizing the Department of

Agriculture and AAA; Hugh Johnson, NRA and early New Deal personalities; RA; election of 1936; Supreme Court fight; New Deal and farm problems, 1937; Agricultural Adjustment Act of 1938; "Ever-Normal Granary"; recession, 1937–39; the "purge"; politics and the third term issue; Food Stamp plan; food administration; Forest Service controversy; election of 1940; Mexican trip; WW II; stockpiling; SPAB; BEW; Vice-Presidency; "The Century of the Common Man" speech; US-British relations; invasion of North Africa; Latin American trip, 1943; Britain and Russia in wartime; Democratic Party politics, 1943; trip to Soviet Asia; election of 1944; Department of Commerce; UN; Export-Import Bank; Russia after the war; Palestine; resignation; Bernard Baruch atomic energy plan; *New Republic*; trips abroad; Progressive Party and the election of 1948; policies.

5,197 pp. *Closed until November 18, 1975.* 1951. Papers: 36 items (microfilm).

Part II: Random reflections in answer to questions based chiefly on his editorials in *Wallace's Farmer.*
323 pp. *Closed until November 18, 1975.* 1953.

WALLACE, William Jennings (1895–) *See* Marine Corps.

WALLACH, Eli (1915–) *See* Popular Arts.

WALLANDER, Arthur William (1892–) Police officer.

NYC Police force, 1914–49; work as Commissioner.
41 pp. *Open.* 1950.

WALLERSTEIN, Immanuel. *See* Columbia Crisis of 1968.

WALLIS, Hal Brent (1899–) *See* Popular Arts.

WALLSTEIN, Leonard M. (1884–1968) Lawyer.

NYC politics and public investigations, 1914–40.

REFER TO "NOTES ON USE" IN INTRODUCTION

112 pp. *Permission required to cite or quote.* 1949. NYT (Part I). Papers.

WALTER, Paul. *See* Robert A. Taft Project.

WANZER, C.T. *See* James B. Duke Project.

WARBURG, James Paul (1896–1969) Banker, author.

Family, youth, and education; WWI; banking, 1918–33; a detailed, day by day account of the economic problems and activities of the New Deal in 1933 based on Mr. Warburg's diary and some correspondence.
1,873 pp. *Permission required to cite or quote.* 1952.

WARD, James Truman (1898–   ) *See* Radio Pioneers.

WARD, Robert E. *See* Carnegie Corporation.

WARD, Robertson Dwight (1905–   ) *See* Carnegie Corporation.

WARDWELL, Allen (1873–1953) Lawyer.

Family background; Yale; Harvard Law School; Stetson, Jennings and Russell; WWI financing; impressions of John W. Davis, Charles Evans Hughes, Joseph Choate; Legal Aid Society.
124 pp. *Permission required to cite or quote.* 1952. NYT (Part I).

WARING, Julius Waties (1880–1968) Judge.

Career as attorney in Charleston, South Carolina; appointment to Federal District Court; South Carolina voting, bus segregation, school segregation cases and the community reaction to his decisions; non-racial cases.
449 pp. *Permission required to cite or quote.* 1957. NYT (Part I). Papers.

WARNER, Emily Smith (Mrs. John).

Recollections of father, Alfred E. Smith: boyhood and education, career in NY State Assembly, terms as Governor, 1928 campaign, civil rights stands, Prohibition; Tammany Hall; 1927 Governors' Conference; Smith's differences with Franklin D. Roosevelt. Impressions of Belle Moskowitz, Robert Moses, William Randolph Hearst, and Mayors James Walker and Fiorello LaGuardia.
118 pp. *Permission required to cite or quote.* 1967.

WARNSHUIS, Abbe Livingston (1877–1958) Missionary secretary.

Missionary experiences in Amoy; wartime mission to Switzerland, 1944.
160 pp. *Permission required to cite or quote.* 1952. NYT (Part I).

WARREN, Charles (1868–1954) Lawyer.

Education; teaching; law practice; important law cases in which he was involved. The manuscript includes 17 pp. of impressions of Grover Cleveland written in 1919 by Mr. Warren's father, Winslow Warren (1838–1930).
67 pp. *Open.* The memoir was written by Mr. Warren for Professor Nevins.

WASHBURN, Abbot McConnell (1915–   ) (with Mrs. Washburn).
                        EISENHOWER ADMINISTRATION
Eisenhower campaign, 1951–52; appointment as assistant to C.D. Jackson; USIA; People to People program.
91 pp. *Closed during lifetime.* 1967.

WASHBURN, Benjamin E. (1885–   ) Physician.

Early life, education, University of North Carolina, University of Virginia; internship, private practice; Rockefeller

Sanitary Commission for the Eradication of Hookworm
Disease; International Health Board of the Rockefeller
Foundation, 1915–39; Health Editor, *Progressive Farmer,*
1940–53; District Health Officer, North Carolina, 1941–50.
156 pp. *Permission required to cite or quote.* 1971.
Contributed by the Rockefeller Foundation.

WASHBURN, Stanley (1878–1950) Journalist, businessman.

Republican politics, 1890–1932; Russo-Japanese War; Russian correspondent, London *Times,* 1914–17; Stevens' railroad mission and Elihu Root diplomatic mission to Russia,
1917.
201 pp. *Permission required to cite or quote.* 1950. NYT
(Part I).

WATERS, Gene. *See* Radio Pioneers.

WATKINS, Arthur V. (1886–   ) Government official.
EISENHOWER ADMINISTRATION
Mormon background; Utah; Columbia Law School; US
Senator, 1946–58; Taft-Hartley Act; NATO agreement;
McCarran Act, immigration problems; censure of Senator
Joseph McCarthy; projects for water development,
Colorado River; head of Indian Claims Commission, 1959;
Navajo School, Brigham City; Mexican wetbacks.
98 pp. *Closed during lifetime.* 1968.

WATSON, Goodwin (1899–   ) Educator.

Childhood and education, Wisconsin; early teaching experiences; University of Wisconsin; Director of Religious
Education, Denver and NYC; TC and Union Theological
Seminary; interest in psychology and psychoanalysis; socialist orientation; New College; Foreign Broadcast Intelligence Service under FCC, 1941; Martin Dies Committee;
Bureau of Applied Social Research, 1943–44; World Study
tours; psychology of social change; National Training
Laboratories; Newark State College; National Institute of

Labor Education. Impressions of William H. Kilpatrick, George Counts, George Strayer, John Dewey, Edward Thorndike, and James Russell and William Russell. 237 pp. *Permission required to cite or quote.* 1963. NYT (Part I).

WATSON, Robert Briggs (1903–   ) Physician.

Family background; education; medical officer, Norris Dam Project, TVA; malaria control in Tennessee Valley; malaria control in WWII; use of anti-malarial drugs in Pacific Theater; field staff of Rockefeller Foundation, 1946; travels in Latin America; work with Chinese government on malaria control from 1946; Taiwan, 1948; work in Japan, Korea, Philippines, Macao; medical education in India and public health problems; work in Brazil and South America; fellowships and policy; training teachers for medical schools; role of foundations. 375 pp. *Permission required to cite or quote.* 1968. *Underwritten by the Rockefeller Foundation.*

WATSON-WATT, Sir Robert Alexander (1892–   ) Radio physicist, meteorologist.

Part I: Childhood and education, Scotland; meteorological work, WWI; radio and static studies, direction finders; Department of Scientific and Industrial Research; studies of nature of atmospherics; simultaneity of technical developments; memorandum on detection of radiation, 1935; Baudsie Manor, training observers, operation research; political pressures; Air Ministry staff, 1936; airborne radar; recruiting young scientists; US interest in radar; planned position indicator; target finding, H_2S; "Window"; interallied intelligence missions; secondary radar devices; Telecommunications Research Establishment; V-1 and V-2 raids; Royal Commission on awards to inventors; impressions of many political and military figures, notably Winston Churchill, Clement Attlee, Stafford Cripps, Frederick Lindemann, Henry Tizard, Ernest Rutherford, Arthur Balfour, Richard Haldane. 568 pp. *Permission required.* 1961.

REFER TO "NOTES ON USE" IN INTRODUCTION

Part II: Consulting with US military leaders during WWII; post-war activities in civil aviation, marine navigation; scientific adviser to British government ministries; Pugwash conferences; travel; writings; Center for Study of Democratic Institutions.
121 pp. *Permission required.* 1964.

WEAVER, Warren (1894–   ) Mathematician, foundation executive.

Childhood and family background, Wisconsin; education, University of Wisconsin; WWI Signal Corps; graduate work and teaching; views on home, family, work, religion, collecting *Alice in Wonderland;* Division of Natural Sciences, Rockefeller Foundation, 1932; experimental biology programs; Paris office, Rockefeller Foundation; European travel; detailed discussion of foundation programs and procedures; WWII: NDRC, 1940–46: range finders, fuses, bomb sights, gun directors, electrical predictors, computers; Applied Mathematics Panel; England, 1941; sequential testing; machine translations; Rockefeller agricultural work in Latin America and India; European refugee scientists; Vice President for Natural and Medical Sciences; Sloan-Kettering Institute; Sloan Foundation; security problems and procedures; science writing and reporting; impressions of Robert Millikan, Max Mason, John D. Rockefeller, Jr., Raymond Fosdick, Linus Pauling, George W. Beadle, Harold Urey, Ernest Lawrence, Henry Tizard, John Cockcroft, Norbert Wiener, Niels Bohr, Alfred P. Sloan.
783 pp. *Open, except for specified pages.* 1961. *Underwritten by the Rockefeller Foundation.*

WEBER, Max (1881–1961) Artist.

Career as a painter; studies with Arthur Dow, Jean Laurens, and Henri Matisse; travel in Europe; experiences with Alfred Stieglitz; art critics, juries, and galleries in US; views on paintings and painters, past and present.
520 pp. *Open.* 1958. Papers: illustrations and other supporting material; correspondence with Leonard Van

Noppen, Pascin, Stieglitz, Grierson, Pablo Picasso, Henri Rousseau, Arthur Davies, George Gershwin, and others; exhibition catalogues; Weber's writings and speeches, including his unpublished poetry (225 pp.).

WEBSTER, Bethuel Matthew (1900–   ) *See* Carnegie Corporation.

WEBSTER, David Locke (1888–   ) *See* American Association of Physics Teachers.

WECHSLER, James A. (1915–   ) *See* Adlai E. Stevenson Project.

WEDEMEYER, Albert C. (1897–   ) *See* Air Force Academy.

WEEKS, Sinclair (1893–1972) Secretary of Commerce.
                                    EISENHOWER ADMINISTRATION

Finance Chairman, Republican National Committee; 1952 campaign; Secretary of Commerce, 1953–58: departmental operations and Cabinet meetings.
172 pp. *Permission required.* 1967.

WEIDIG, William J. (1884–   ) *See* McGraw-Hill.

WEINSTEIN, James. *See* Socialist Movement.

WEIR, Irvin Reed (1897–   ) *See* Radio Pioneers.

WELLE, John E. (1898–1962) *See* McGraw-Hill.

WELLER, Donald M. (1908–   ) Marine Corps officer.

USS *Arkansas,* 1932–33; early artillery training, 1934–36; USS *Tuscaloosa,* 1937–39; WWII: Bougainville, Guam, Iwo

Jima operations; USMC Schools, Quantico, 1946–49; Naval War College, 1949–50; Chief of Staff, USMC Schools, 1954–56; CG, 3d Marine Division, 1960–61; contingency planning for Southeast Asia operations; Deputy CG, Fleet Marine Force, Pacific, 1961–63.
In process.

WELLING, Harriet (Mrs. John) *See* Adlai E. Stevenson Project.

WELLS, John A. *See* New York Political Studies.

WERT, Robert Joseph (1922–   ) College president.
CARNEGIE CORPORATION

Graduate student, Stanford University; Carnegie Corporation staff, 1954–59; relations with college and university administrators; programs; report on education in the South; relations with other foundations and with Carnegie affiliates; "The American Shelf"; Committee on Education; return to Stanford. Impressions of various Corporation officers.
200 pp. *Permission required.* 1968.

WESSLER, Harry. *See* Mt. Sinai Hospital.

WEYERHAEUSER, C.D. *See* Weyerhaeuser Timber Company.

WEYERHAEUSER, Frederick King (1895–   ) Industrialist.
WEYERHAEUSER TIMBER COMPANY

Historical data on formation of Mississippi River Logging Company and related lumber companies in Wisconsin and Minnesota, 1871–1890's; Weyerhaeuser Timber Company, 1900, and related firms in the Northwest; life in lumber camps; policies and personalities; competitive factors in the lumber industry.
167 pp. *Permission required.* 1956.

WEYERHAEUSER, John Philip, Jr. (1899–1956) *See* Weyerhaeuser Timber Company.

WEYERHAEUSER TIMBER COMPANY

Materials on the development of the lumbering industry and the lumber regions based upon the recollections of executives and employees of the Weyerhaeuser Timber Company and of others in the industry.

Descriptions of lumbering practices include accounts of life in the Minnesota and Wisconsin woods; labor problems; immigrants; religious practices and conflicts (including some account of the Ku Klux Klan in Washington); camp sports; camp safety practices; fire-fighting in camp, mill and forest; CCC; reforestation, homesteading and land claims in Idaho about 1900; timber speculation; cooperation in the development of white and ponderosa pine stands in Idaho, Oregon, and Washington; and methods of forest transportation.

Corporate developments are described in accounts of early days of the Weyerhaeuser Timber Company and the Weyerhaeuser Sales Company, the Potlatch Lumber Company, and other related or competing firms, market changes and sales problems, advertising and public relations, exploitation of the Eastern market, development of intercoastal shipping and of Baltimore and other terminals for Eastern distribution, effects of the change from rail to truck lots in local sales.

There are impressions of members of the Weyerhaeuser and Denkmann families, George S. Long, William Deary, and others prominent in lumbering.

Participants and pages: Vol. I: A.E. Aitchison, 85; John Aram, 98; David H. Bartlett, 59; Jack Bishop, 32; Ralph Boyd, 26; Hugh B. Campbell, 32; Norton Clapp, 32; R. V. Clute, 65; T. S. Durment, 45; O. D. Fisher, 73; A. N. Frederickson, 71; John H. Hauberg, 126; E. F. Heacox, C. S. Martin and C. D. Weyerhaeuser, 98; F. W. Hewitt, 66; Robert W. Hunt, 85; C. H. Ingram, 12; R. E. Irwin, 40; S. P. Johns, Jr., 46; Don Lawrence, 66; George S. Long, Jr., 46; R. R. Macartney, 44; Charles J. McGough, 66; William L. Maxwell, 112; Howard Morgan, 54; C. R. Musser, 27; Leonard H. Nygaard, 49; Harold H. Ogle, 47; Arthur Priaulx and James Stevens, 75; Al Raught, 54; Otto C. Schoenwerk, 40; A. O. Sheldon, 41; H.C. Shellworth, 77; Frank Tarr, 17; G. Harris Thomas, 63; David S. Troy, 36; Roy Voshmik, 16; John A. Wahl, 18; Frederick K. Weyerhaeuser, 167; J. Philip Weyerhaeuser, 41; Maxwell W. Williamson, 38.

Vol. II: Earl R. Bullock, 32; Albert B. Curtis, 103; Wells Gilbert, 26; Roy Huffman, 68; W. K. McNair, 33; Leslie Mallory, 13; S. G. and C. D. Moon, 32; Jack Morgan, 43; J. J. O'Connell, 77; R. E. Saberson, 81; Hugo Schlenck, 113; Gaylord M. Upington and Lafayette Stephens, 75.

2,981 pp. *Permission required.* 1956.
Underwritten by the Weyerhaeuser Timber Company.

WEYLAND, Otto P. (1902–   ) *See* Aviation.

WHALEN, Grover A. (1886–1962) *See* Radio Pioneers.

WHEATON, Anne W.

EISENHOWER ADMINISTRATION

Assistant chief of press relations and head of publicity for the women's division, Republican National Committee, 1939–57; 1952 convention and campaign; associate press secretary to the President; Eisenhower's press conferences; Cabinet meetings; impressions of the Eisenhowers; White House staff.

178 pp. *Permission required to cite or quote.* 1968.

WHEELER, Bert. *See* Popular Arts.

WHEELER, Burton Kendall (1882–   ) Senator.

Montana politics, 1920; Nonpartisan League; Anaconda Company; US Senator, 1923–47: committee assignments, Teapot Dome investigations, silver bills, court-packing issue, war preparations; accounts of Democratic conventions and campaigns, 1924, 1932, 1940, 1944; European trip, 1945. Impressions of Franklin Roosevelt, Harry S. Truman; Senators William Borah, George Norris, Huey Long, and Thomas Walsh.

161 pp. *Closed during lifetime.* 1969.

The Oral History Collection

WHEELER, Leslie Allen (1899–   ) Agriculturist.

Childhood and education; Department of Commerce, 1923–26; BAE, 1926–40; Foreign Agricultural Service, Office of Foreign Agricultural Relations, 1940–47; US Foreign Service, 1948–51.
532 pp. *Closed until 5 years after death.* 1952.

WHEELER, Raymond A. *See* World Bank.

WHEELOCK, John Hall (1886–   ) Author.

Family history and childhood; Harvard College; work on literary publications; career as editor for Charles Scribner's Sons, 1926–57: clients and staff; career as poet: influences, publications, evaluations of his own and others' work; anecdotes concerning Zoe Akins, Van Wyck Brooks, Vachel Lindsay, Edgar Lee Masters, Maxwell Perkins, Edwin Arlington Robinson, the Charles Scribner family, Edward Sheldon, Sara Teasdale, Oscar Williams, Thomas Wolfe, and many others.
478 pp. *Closed until January 1, 1990.* 1967.

WHITE, F. Clifton (1918–   ) Politician.

Early political interests; Young Republican Clubs; candidacy of Senator Barry Goldwater in 1964: primaries and state conventions, San Francisco convention, campaign and election; vignettes of Republican leaders.
222 pp. *Permission required.* 1964.
Contributed by James Cannon, New York.

WHITE, Ivan Bertis (1907–   ) *See* Marshall Plan.

WHITE, John Campbell (1884–1967) Diplomat.

Diplomatic service in Russia, 1915–16; Royalist-Venizelist controversy, Greece, 1916–17; Far East; Poland, 1919–21: food distribution, Bolshevik advance on Warsaw; oil ex-

Columbia University

ploration rights in Venezuela, 1921–23; Argentina, 1928–33:
President Herbert Hoover's 1928 visit, 1930 revolution;
Nazi Germany, 1933–35; consular duty, Calcutta, 1936–40;
Ambassador to Haiti, 1940–43, Peru, 1944–45. Impressions
of many statesmen.
139 pp. *Permission required to cite or quote.* 1953. NYT
(Part I).

WHITE, John Francis (1917–   ) *See* Children's Television
Workshop.

WHITE, Lawrence Grant (1887–1956) Architect.

Early life, family history, and education; experiences in
World Wars I and II; career with McKim, Mead & White;
interest in aviation; literary activities; personal anecdotes
of many well-known figures.
161 pp. *Permission required to cite or quote.* 1956. NYT
(Part I).

WHITE, Rex G. (–1951) *See* Radio Pioneers.

WHITE, Robert M. (1924–   ) *See* Aviation.

WHITE, Sam. *See* Alaskan Pioneers.

WHITE, Thomas D. *See* Aviation.

WHITE, William Cummings. *See* Radio Pioneers.

WHITNEY, George (1885–1963) Banker.

Childhood, Boston; Groton and Harvard; private banking
firms; partnership in J.P. Morgan firm, 1920; financing foreign and domestic loans; impressions of prominent bankers and financiers.
82 pp. *Permission required to cite or quote.* 1963. NYT
(Part I).

411

WHITTEN, George Easton (1896–   ) *See* Federated Department Stores.

WICKARD, Claude Raymond (1893–1967) Government official.

Early life in Indiana; education; farming; observation of the farm revolt and the McNary-Haugen movement in the 1920's; election to the Indiana Senate, 1932; Corn and Hogs Section of the AAA; Agricultural Conservation Program; the Depression and the Department of Agriculture; experience as Under Secretary, 1940, and Secretary, 1940–45, of Agriculture; WWII; Lend-Lease; inter-American conferences on agriculture; work with the REA.
3,992 pp. *Permission required to cite or quote.* 1953.

WICKENDEN, Elizabeth.

SOCIAL SECURITY

Education, Vassar; FERA, 1933; medical programs; representative for American Public Welfare Association; public welfare philosophy; social insurance legislation; interaction with politicians; consultant on health insurance to Adlai Stevenson, John F. Kennedy, Lyndon Johnson, and others; Medicare and AMA; insurance companies; senior citizens in politics, 1950's and '60's. Impressions of Wilbur Cohen, Nelson Cruikshank, Francis Townsend, James O'Brien, Charles Odell, Zalman Lichtenstein, Marjorie Shearon, and others.
211 pp. *Permission required.* 1966.

WICKENS, Aryness Joy (Mrs. David L.) (1901–   ) Government official, economist.

Department of Labor, Coolidge to Eisenhower; Bureau of Labor Statistics and its relation to the labor movement.
94 pp. *Permission required to cite or quote.* 1957. NYT (Part I).

WICKER, Tom. *See* Journalism Lectures.

REFER TO "NOTES ON USE" IN INTRODUCTION

WIEDEMER, Charles. *See* Federated Department Stores.

WIEN, Noel. *See* Aviation.

WIENER, Jan.

Experiences in Czechoslovakia during WWII; escape, service in Allied forces; life in occupied countries.
58 pp. *Permission required to cite or quote.*

WIESEMAN, Frederick L. (1908–) Marine Corps officer.

USS *Minneapolis,* 1934–35; USS *Yorktown,* 1937–39; WWII: Guadalcanal, Bougainville, Guam operations; postwar duty in China, 1946–48; USMC Schools, 1949–52; 3d Marine Division, Camp Pendleton and Japan, 1952–54; Fiscal Director, HQMC, 1955–59; CG, 1st Marine Brigade, 1959; CG, 2d Marine Division, 1961–63; Commandant, USMC Schools, 1963–66.
In process.

WIGHT, Joseph V. *See* McGraw-Hill.

WIGNER, Eugene Paul (1902–) *See* Nobel Laureates.

WILCOCKSON, A.S. *See* Aviation.

WILCOX, Francis O. *See* Eisenhower Administration.

WILEY, Alexander (1884–1967) Senator.

Childhood, education; political experience; election to US Senate; WWII; Senator Joseph McCarthy.
63 pp. *Open.* 1964.

WILEY, Bell Irvin (1906–) *See* Civil War Centennial.

WILEY, Martha. *See* China Missionaries.

WILHELM, John Remsen (1916–) *See* McGraw-Hill.

WILKINS, Raymond Sanger (1891–1971) *See* Robert P. Patterson Project.

WILKINS, Roy (1901–) Publicist, administrator.

Family background, childhood, education, St. Paul and Minneapolis; job discrimination; journalism, Kansas City *Call;* discrimination in Kansas City; NAACP; Walter White; housing, NYC; travel; labor problems in the South; *The Crisis;* Negroes in government; anti-lynching bills; industrial integration; 1941 March on Washington; FEPC; Supreme Court desegregation decision, 1954.
130 pp. *Permission required to cite or quote.* 1960. NYT (Part I).
See also Herbert H. Lehman Project.

WILLCOX, Alanson Work (1901–) Lawyer.
SOCIAL SECURITY

Drafting Social Security Act, 1935–36; legal adviser, Social Security Board, 1938; General Counsel, Federal Security Agency, 1947; Murray-Wagner-Dingell bill; philosophy of social security; evaluation of legislation; Medicare: positions of AMA, Blue Cross, and American Hospital Association. Impressions of Jack Tate, Tom Eliot, Wilbur Cohen, and others.
140 pp. *Open except for specified pages.* 1966.

WILLIAMS, Alex, Sr. *See* Marine Corps.

WILLIAMS, Edward Eugene (1892–) *See* James B. Duke Project.

WILLIAMS, E. Grainger. *See* Eisenhower Administration.

REFER TO "NOTES ON USE" IN INTRODUCTION

WILLIAMS, Franklin Hall (1917–) *See* Adlai E. Stevenson Project.

WILLIAMS, Henry (1877–) Naval officer.

Naval Academy; Spanish-American War; graduate course in naval architecture, Paris, 1899–1901; naval construction specialist, 1901–33: launching problems, development of plastic ship bottom paint, submarine rescue chamber; Army Industrial College, 1933; administrative officer, Bureau of Ships, and later for Secretary of Navy, WWII; Munitions Board; Maritime Commission; allocation of strategic materials, laying up surplus vessels, disposal of shipyards. Accounts of Theodore Roosevelt, Charles Edison, Frank Knox, and Adms. William Sims, Henry Taylor, Samuel Robinson, and Emory Land.
251 pp. *Permission required to cite or quote.* 1963. NYT (Part I).

WILLIAMS, James Thomas, Jr. (1881–1969) Editor.

Background; education; reporter in Washington for Columbia, South Carolina *State*, AP, and Boston *Evening Transcript*, 1902–08; Theodore Roosevelt and his Cabinet; 1908 election; Arizona cure; Frank Blighton libel case; Arizona statehood; Republican conventions of 1912 and 1920; campaigns of 1912, 1916, 1920, 1936; Boyd-Adair; Leonard Wood; Boston police strike; Warren Harding; Calvin Coolidge; Philippines, Nicaragua; Mexico; Herbert Hoover and the Crash; William R. Hearst organization; Franklin D. Roosevelt; J. Reuben Clark; Josephus Daniels; WWII; George C. Marshall, Harry S. Truman; Sacco-Vanzetti Case.
966 pp. *Permission required to cite or quote.* 1953. NYT (Part I).

WILLIAMS, Mrs. John. *See* James B. Duke Project.

WILLIAMS, T. Harry (1909–) *See* American Historians *and* Civil War Centennial.

415

WILLIAMS, W. Walter (1894–   ) Banker.
EISENHOWER ADMINISTRATION

Chairman, Committee for Economic Development; Citizens for Eisenhower; Under Secretary of Commerce.
103 pp. *Closed during lifetime.* 1967.

WILLIAMSON, Kenneth.

SOCIAL SECURITY

California health insurance program, 1930–33; work with Blue Cross and American Hospital Association; impressions of AMA leaders; Wagner-Murray bill; work with federal government, 1945–67; HEW; Public Health Service; Forand bill; Medicare; President John F. Kennedy's concern for health programs and aid to the aged; Special Committee on Aging. Impressions of Nelson Cruikshank, Andrew Biemiller, Nelson Rockefeller, Wilbur Cohen, Wilbur Mills, Alanson Willcox, and others.
240 pp. *Open.* 1967.

WILLIAMSON, Maxwell W. (1884–   ) *See* Weyerhaeuser Timber Company.

WILLIS, Charles Fountain, Jr. (1918–   ) Airline executive.
EISENHOWER ADMINISTRATION

Citizens for Eisenhower; Special Assistant, White House staff; presidential appointments.
50 pp. *Permission required to cite or quote.* 1968.

WILLIS, Harold B. *See* Aviation.

WILLSON, Meredith (1902–   ) *See* Popular Arts.

WILSON, Carey (1889–1962) *See* Popular Arts.

WILSON, Comar (–1961) *See* Mining Engineers.

WILSON, Dean. *See* Marine Corps.

REFER TO "NOTES ON USE" IN INTRODUCTION

WILSON, Eugene Edward (1887–   ) Naval aviator, industrialist.

Childhood and education, Montana; US Naval Academy; Navy Rifle Teams; engineering and gunnery service at sea; Engineering School, Columbia; WWI experiences with Grand Fleet at Scapa Flow; Aviation Mechanics School at Great Lakes; Bureau of Aeronautics; pilot training; Aircraft Squadrons Battle Fleet, 1927; development of carrier task force; resignation from Navy, 1929; United Aircraft Corporation; aircraft industry developments and problems; air-cooled engine; controllable angle propeller; new types of planes; helicopter; airmail contract cancellations; aircraft industry through WWII; postwar industry problems. Impressions of industrial, political, naval, and military leaders, notably Adms. William A. Moffett, Ernest J. King, and Joseph M. Reeves, Gen. William Mitchell, Chance M. Vought, Charles A. Lindbergh, Thomas F. Hamilton, Frederick B. Rentschler, Igor Sikorsky, William Boeing, and James Forrestal.

974 pp. *Permission required to cite or quote.* 1962. NYT (Part I).

WILSON, Gill Robb (1893–1966) See Aviation.

WILSON, John C. *See* Federated Department Stores.

WILSON, Luke. *See* La Follette Civil Liberties Committee.

WILSON, Milburn Lincoln (1885–1969) Agriculturist.

Childhood, education; early farming experiences in Nebraska and Montana; dry-farming; Nonpartisan League; grain cooperatives; McNary-Haugen Bill; Fairway Farms Corporation; Department of Agriculture, 1924; advisory trip to Russia, 1929; extension service; Grange, Farmers' Union; BAE; domestic allotment plans, writing agricultural speeches for Franklin D. Roosevelt, 1932; first hundred days; AAA; land resettlement, use of submarginal land; Division of Subsistence Homesteads in Interior

Department, 1933; Arthurdale project; Cuban sugar survey; Assistant Secretary of Agriculture, 1934; shelter belts; FSA; Roerich expedition, Wallace mysticism; visits of George Russell; Dust Bowl and land use; Department of Agriculture purge; RSA; soil conservation; 1936 campaign; Under Secretary of Agriculture, 1937; impressions of many prominent New Deal figures, especially Henry A. Wallace, Rexford Tugwell, Chester Davis.

2,095 pp. *Permission required to cite or quote.* 1956.

WINANS, Pearl Fosnot (1891–   ) *See* China Missionaries.

WINCHELL, Constance Mabel (1896–   ) Librarian.

Education; early library experiences; NY Public Library School, 1919; University of Michigan, 1920–23; reference work, inter-library loans; American Library in Paris, 1924; Columbia University Library from 1925: Reference Department, move from Low Library to Butler Library; library school; *Guide to Reference Books;* American Library Association. Impressions of Miss Isadore G. Mudge, President Nicholas Murray Butler.

246 pp. *Permission required to cite or quote.* 1963. NYT (Part I).

WINCHELL, Oscar (1903–   ) Pilot.

ALASKAN PIONEERS

Flying at fairs in South Dakota; Pioneer Airlines and flying school; bush pilot in Alaska, 1931–52; description of planes, equipment, landing fields. Impressions of life among Alaskan miners.

159 pp. *Open.* 1965.

WINDELS, Paul (1885–1967) Corporation counsel.

NY State Bridge and Tunnel Commission; Holland Tunnel; NY Port Authority; NYC politics; LaGuardia administration; Committee of Fifteen and NY transit; Rapp-Coudert Committee.

REFER TO "NOTES ON USE" IN INTRODUCTION

178 pp. *Permission required to cite or quote.* 1950. NYT (Part I).

Fiorello H. LaGuardia.
24 pp. *Permission required to cite or quote.* 1953. NYT (Part I).

WINGE, Edwin. *See* Social Security.

WINKELSTEIN, Ashe. *See* Mt. Sinai Hospital.

WINSTON, Garrard Bigelow (1882–1955) Lawyer.

Impressions of Andrew Mellon.
13 pp. *Open.* 1949.

WINTER, Keyes (1878–1960) Judge.

NYC party politics, 1920–33.
259 pp. *Closed until 2010.* 1950.

WIRTA, Harvey. *See* Flying Tigers.

WIRTH, Conrad Louis (1899–   ) *See* Jackson Hole Preserve.

WIRTZ, William Willard (1912–   ) *See* Adlai E. Stevenson Project.

WITHERSPOON, Frances (1886–   ) and MYGATT, Tracy (1885–   ) Pacifists.

Girlhoods in New England and the South; education, Bryn Mawr College; support of pacifism and racial equality; opposition to US participation in WWI; War Resisters' League; *The Glorious Company;* NY Bureau of Legal Advice and defense of conscientious objectors and persons charged under the Espionage Act.

53 pp. *Permission required to cite or quote.* 1966. NYT (Part I). Papers.

WITHERSPOON, Milton E. *See* Benedum and the Oil Industry.

WITMARK, Julius. *See* Popular Arts.

WITWER, Samuel Weiler (1908–) Lawyer.
ADLAI E. STEVENSON PROJECT
Stevenson as Governor of Illinois; state constitutional reform under Stevenson.
49 pp. *Permission required.* 1969.

WOHLFORTH, Robert. *See* La Follette Civil Liberties Committee.

WOLFE, Kenneth B. (1896–1971) *See* Henry H. Arnold Project.

WOLKSTEIN, Irwin.
SOCIAL SECURITY
Assistant Chief, Coverage and Disability Branch, Social Security; early health insurance bills; development of legislation; background of Medicare; Subcommittee on the Aged; consultant to Senator Patrick McNamara; speechwriting; 1960 election; John F. Kennedy's stand on Medicare; relations with HEW, Ways and Means Committee, AFL-CIO, White House staff, Blue Cross, AMA; Congressional hearings. Impressions of Wilbur Cohen, Wilbur Mills, Abraham Ribicoff, and others.
255 pp. *Open.* 1968.

WOLMAN, Leo (1890–1961) Economist.

Boyhood, Baltimore; education, Johns Hopkins; work as economist in federal agencies, WWI; negotiator and economist, 1920's; impressions of New School faculty members,

1920's; joining a government agency during the early days of the New Deal.
316 pp. *Open.* 1960. Papers.

WOMBLE, Bunyan Snipes (1882–   ) *See* James B. Duke Project.

WOOD, Benjamin De Kalbe (1894–   ) College professor, author.

CARNEGIE CORPORATION

Educational background; teaching at Columbia College; NY experiment with modern language tests, 1925–27; Pennsylvania Study, 1927; Educational Records Bureau; Frederick Keppel and other Corporation officers; educational testing programs.
123 pp. *Permission required.* 1967. Papers.

WOOD, James Madison (1875–1958) Educator.

Childhood and early experiences in the Ozarks; teaching; interest in farming and extension; Stephens Junior College, 1912–47: concept of junior college, analysis of women's activities, change in direction, trips, publicity, recruiting, faculty, finances; Women's Foundation; Junior College Association, 1920; women's rights movement; Rockefeller Foundation support; accreditation of junior colleges; Edward Bok and *Ladies Home Journal.* Impressions of many prominent educators.
387 pp. *Open.* 1954.
Contributed by W. H. Cowley of Stanford, California.

WOOD, John Edmund Fitzgerald (1903–   ) Lawyer.

CARNEGIE CORPORATION

Experiences as the Carnegie Corporation's Counsel; interpretation of the charter.
52 pp. *Permission required.* 1968.

WOOD, Meredith (1895—   ) *See* Book-of-the-Month Club.

WOOD, Robert E. (1879–1969) Executive, government official.

Family background, West Point; Philippines, 1901–02; Panama Canal, 1905–15; DuPont, General Asphalt; WWI: shipbuilding program, Army Transport Service, Acting Quartermaster General; Montgomery Ward, 1919–24: establishment of retail stores; Sears, Roebuck, 1924–61: shopping centers, profit sharing, Allstate; New Deal; America First; supply problems in WWII: labor relations.
110 pp. *Permission required to cite or quote.* 1961. NYT (Part I).

WOODCOCK, Leonard (1911–   ) *See* Social Security.

WOODS, Louis Ernest (1895–1971) Marine Corps officer.

Education, Syracuse University, 1913–17; sea duty; Haiti, 1924–26, 1933–34; Marine aviation in the 1920's and '30's: amphibious warfare doctrine, close air support concepts; WWII: Guadalcanal and Solomon operations, air operations against Japan; return of prisoners of war; occupation of North China; CG, Marine Corps Air Station, Cherry Point, 1949–51; USMC air operations in Korea.
354 pp. *Open.* 1968.

WOODS, Mark (1901–   ) Advertising executive.
RADIO PIONEERS

Broadcasting department, NY Telephone Company, 1922; early days at Broadcasting Corporation of America and NBC; administrative view of broadcasting; first commercials; division of NBC into two networks; formation of ABC; President of ABC; future of radio and television. Impressions of various figures in radio.
120 pp. *Open.* 1951.

WOODWARD, Joanne (Mrs. Paul Newman) (1930–   ) *See* Popular Arts.

REFER TO "NOTES ON USE" IN INTRODUCTION

WOODWARD, C. Vann (1908–   ) *See* American Historians.

WORLD BANK

Interviews with officers of the International Bank for Reconstruction and Development detail its history and operations from the 1944 Bretton Woods Conference. Organization, development of policies, management practices, personnel, and the relationship of directors and staff during the presidencies of Eugene Meyer, John McCloy, and Eugene Black are described.

The functions of the World Bank are analyzed, including policy formulation and supervision of end-use of funds, project appraisal, creditworthiness, administration and significance of loans, government banks, equity investment and venture capital, bond issues and corollary legislation, and foreign and domestic bond marketing. The relationship of the Bank to the International Monetary Fund and to other financing institutions is explored. There are interesting descriptions of individual projects in various parts of the world, particularly flood protection, railway rehabilitation, the Indus Basin Settlement Plan, the Mekong River Survey, and the Suez Canal.

Participants and pages: Siem Aldewereld, 31; Gerald Alter, Harold Larsen, and John de Wilde, 32; Eugene R. Black, 62 *(open)*; Robert W. Cavanaugh, 90; Sidney Raymond Cope, 54; Daniel Crena de Iongh, 47; Richard H. Demuth, 91 *(certain pages closed)*; William Diamond and Michael Hoffman, 37 *(open)*; Donald Fowler, 44; Robert L. Garner, 100 *(open)*; William F. Howell, 37 *(open)*; Sir William Iliff, 76; Andrew Kamarck, 22; J. Burke Knapp, 76;

Harold Larsen, 32; Ansel F. Luxford, 61 *(open)*; Luis Machado, 35; George Martin and Emil Pattberg, 25 *(open)*; Morton Mendels, 76; Lester Nurick, 35 *(closed during lifetime)*; Hoyt Peck, 35; Hugh Ripman, 29; Leonard B. Rist, 62 *(open)*; Paul Rosenstein-Rodan, 51 *(closed during lifetime)*; Orvis A. Schmidt, 23; Davidson Sommers, 74; Alexander Stevenson, 28; Raymond A. Wheeler, 27 *(open)*.

1,392 pp. *Permission of individual contributor required to cite or quote, except as noted.* 1961.
Underwritten by the International Bank for Reconstruction and Development, Washington, D.C. Also available at the Brookings Institution.

WORNHAM, Thomas Andrew (1903–   ) Marine Corps officer.

Naval Academy, 1922–26; early assignments; China, 1927–29; Haiti, 1930–33; instructor, USMC Schools, 1936–39; WWII: HQMC Personnel Department, 1941–44, Iwo Jima operation; occupation of Japan; USMC training, interwar period; CO, 1st Marines, Korea, 1951; Chief of Staff, Fleet Marine Force, Pacific, 1951–52; CG, USMC Recruit Depot, San Diego, 1956–59.
127 pp. *Open.* 1968.

WORTON, William Arthur (1897–   ) Marine Corps officer.

Family background; Massachusetts Naval Militia; Quantico; WWI: Verdun, Belleau Wood; Santo Domingo; Chinese language officer, Peking and Tientsin, 1920's; WWII: defense of Iceland, preparation for amphibious assaults; Japanese surrender of North China, occupation of Peking, 1945; Washington during unification discussions, 1947; retirement, 1949; Los Angeles Police Chief. Impressions of Chiang Kai-shek, Madame Chiang, Chou En-lai, and many US military officers.
328 pp. *Permission required.* 1967.

WRATHER, William Embry (1883–1963) *See* Mining Engineers.

WRAY, Lawrence (1899–   ) *See* McGraw-Hill.

WRIGHT, Frank Lloyd (1869–1959) Architect.

Opinions on religion, politics, and architecture in two television interviews with Mike Wallace.
45 pp. *Open.* 1957.

WRIGHT, James. *See* Poets on their Poetry.

WRIGHT, Teresa (1918–   ) *See* Popular Arts.

REFER TO "NOTES ON USE" IN INTRODUCTION

WRISTON, Henry Merritt (1889–) Educator.
CARNEGIE CORPORATION

Relations between the Carnegie Foundation for the Advancement of Teaching and the Carnegie Corporation; trustee of the Foundation, 1933–55; President of Lawrence College, 1925–37, and of Brown University, 1937–50; Frederick Keppel; functions of the Corporation; evaluation of programs and studies; Pennsylvania Study; study in applied mathematics; Alger Hiss case; Harvard Russian Research Center. Impressions of Foundation and Corporation officers and trustees.
219 pp. *Permission required.* 1967.
EISENHOWER ADMINISTRATION

Dwight Eisenhower at Columbia University; Council on Foreign Relations; American Assembly; Goals Commission and other appointments under President Eisenhower.
51 pp. *Permission required to cite or quote.* 1968.

WU, K.C. *See* Chinese Oral History.

WYATT, Wilson Watkins (1905–) Lawyer.
ADLAI E. STEVENSON PROJECT

First meetings with Adlai Stevenson; nomination of Stevenson at 1952 convention; 1952 campaign: television, Harry Truman's role, Stevenson fund; Elks Club; prison riot; 1956 campaign: choice of a running mate, issues; 1960 convention, Mrs. Eleanor Roosevelt; Stevenson's influence on John F. Kennedy and feelings about UN. Impressions of various aides and politicians.
161 pp. *Permission required.* 1969.

WYNKOOP, Norman Osborne (1893–) *See* McGraw-Hill.

WYZANSKI, Charles Edward, Jr. (1906–) Judge.

Family and early childhood; Harvard College and Law School; private practice with Ropes, Gray; General Counsel at Department of Labor; Solicitor General and Social Security cases; NLRB cases; delegate to ILO; private practice; National Defense Mediation Board. 321 pp. *Closed until 5 years after death.* 1954. Papers: memoranda on Schechter case and on immigration and naturalization problems.

YALE, William (1887–   ) Middle East specialist.

Travel in Middle East for Standard Oil Co., WWI era; special agent, US State Department, Near East, WWI; Versailles Peace Conference; King-Crane Commission; Yale Plan.
83 pp. *Permission required.* 1969.
Contributed by Garé Le Compte, Old Saybrook, Connecticut.

YANG, Chen Ning (1922–   ) *See* Nobel Laureates.

YATES, Charles Richardson (1913–   ) *See* Eisenhower Administration.

YATES, William R. *See* Radio Pioneers.

YEAGER, Charles. *See* Aviation.

YEE, Chiang. *See* Chinese Oral History.

YELLEN, Jack. *See* Popular Arts.

YOKEL, Mike. *See* Jackson Hole Preserve.

YOUEL, Harlan. *See* Occupation of Japan.

YOUNG, Donald Ramsey (1898–   ) *See* Carnegie Corporation.

YOUNG, Howard. *See* Robert A. Taft Project.

REFER TO "NOTES ON USE" IN INTRODUCTION

YOUNG, Mahonri Mackintosh (1877–1957) Sculptor, painter.

Early life in Salt Lake City; art education; early experiences as an artist; study in Europe; experiences as a professional painter and sculptor; illustrations of his work. 127 pp. *Permission required to cite or quote.* 1956. NYT (Part I).

YOUNG, Milton R. (1897–   ) Senator.

EISENHOWER ADMINISTRATION

Senate Agricultural Committee; 1952 Republican campaign; President Eisenhower's agricultural policy; Ezra Taft Benson. 30 pp. *Closed during lifetime.* 1967.

YOUNGSTEIN, Max Emanuel (1913–   ) *See* Popular Arts.

ZAFRULLA KHAN, Sir Muhammed (1893–   ) Jurist.

Education and legal training; government service in India before independence; Round Tables; Muslim League; Indian independence and partition; service in Pakistani Cabinet, High Court; service in UN as delegate and President of the General Assembly, 1947–54, 1961–64; International Court of Justice; Discussion of life in India and Pakistan: religion, social customs, economics, education. Impressions of figures such as Mohandas Gandhi, Jawaharlal Nehru, Sir Fazle Husain, Winston Churchill, Lord Willingdon, and Lord Templewood. 488 pp. *Permission required to cite or quote.* 1963. NYT (Part I).

ZEITZ, Abraham. *See* New York Political Studies.

ZORACH, William (1887–1966) Sculptor, painter.

Early life in Cleveland; study at the National Academy and in Europe; return to NY and first work in stone; commissioned monuments; citizenship difficulties; interview with

Mrs. Marguerite Zorach; plate-by-plate discussion of Paul Wingert's *The Sculpture of William Zorach;* work habits; artistic philosophy.
348 pp. *Closed until 1977.* 1957.

ZUKOR, Adolph (1873–   ) *See* Popular Arts.

Index

PART II: BIOGRAPHICAL

The Oral History Collection

Baker, Newton D.: ISAACS, Stanley Myer; WADSWORTH, James Wolcott
Bakhmeteff, Boris: COUDERT, Frederic Rene
Balanchine, George: RODGERS, Richard
Baldwin, C. B.: ALEXANDER, Will Winton
Baldwin, Roger: ASCHER, Charles
Balfour, Arthur: WATSON-WATT, Sir Robert Alexander
Ball, George: TREE, Marietta (Mrs. Ronald)
Bane, Frank: CLAGUE, Ewan; ENGLE, Lavinia
Barcelo, Alberto: HABIAGUE, Esteban
Barnes, William: O'BRIAN, John Lord
Barrett, Edward W.: INTERNATIONAL NEGOTIATIONS
Barton, Bruce: DURSTINE, Roy Sarles
Baruch, Bernard: LAND, Emory Scott; WALLACE, Henry Agard
Bateson, William: DUNN, Leslie Clarence
Beachey, Lincoln: BELL, Lawrence Dale
Beadle, George W.: WEAVER, Warren
Beard, Charles A.: KNOPF, Alfred A.
Becker, Carl: NEVINS, Allan
Beecher, Henry: CHURCHILL, Edward Delos
Belding, Milo: ASSOCIATION FOR THE AID OF CRIPPLED CHILDREN
Belmont, August: HETTRICK, John T.; STRAUSS, Morris Lincoln
Benchley, Robert: GILMAN, Mildred
Benedum, Michael Late: BENEDUM AND THE OIL INDUSTRY
Benes, Eduard: PAPANEK, Jan
Benson, Ezra Taft: BUTZ, Earl Lauer; PAARLBERG, Don; THYE, Edward; YOUNG, Milton R.
Benton, William: BOWLES, Chester; BOWLES, Dorothy Stebbins; HUTCHINS, Robert Maynard
Berenson, Bernard: KINKAID, Thomas Cassin
Berger, Victor: SPARGO, John
Bergson, Henri: COUDERT, Frederic Rene
Bernhardt, Sarah: DOWLING, Eddie
Bertram, James: CARNEGIE CORPORATION
Biddle, Francis: EMERSON, Thomas Irwin
Biemiller, Andrew: CRUIKSHANK, Nelson Hale; WILLIAMSON, Kenneth
Bingham, Hiram: GIESECKE, Albert Anthony
Black, Eugene: WORLD BANK
Blair, William McCormick, Jr: IVES, Elizabeth Stevenson (Mrs. Ernest); MINOW, Newton Norman
Bleriot, Louis: BROWNE, Ross
Blighton, Frank: WILLIAMS, James Thomas, Jr.
Bloch, Ernest: SESSIONS, Roger Huntington
Bloom, Andrew: MAXWELL, William L.
Blossom, Virgil: FAUBUS, Orval Eugene
Boas, Franz: BOAS, Franziska
Boeing, William: WILSON, Eugene Edward
Bohr, Niels: RABI, Isidor Isaac; WEAVER, Warren
Bok, Edward: WOOD, James Madison
Bonaparte, Marie: LOEWENSTEIN, Rudolph Maurice
Boothby, Walter: BERRY, Frank Brown

434

Index

435

The Oral History Collection

Carmichael, Oliver C.: CARNEGIE CORPORATION
Carnegie, Andrew: ANDERSON, Florence; HASKINS, Caryl Parker; HEN-
DRICK, Burton Jesse
Carnegie, Mrs. Andrew: HALL, Samuel Stickney, Jr.
Carpender, Arthur: FIFE, James
Carrel, Alexis: COUDERT, Frederic Rene
Carr, William: NORTON, John Kelley
Carson, Clarence: COUCH, William Terry
Carson, John: MULLINER, Maurine
Carstenson, Blue: HENRY, Ray; O'BRIEN, James Cuff; ODELL, Charles
Cartwright, Morse: CAPERS, Roberta; LLOYD, Trevor; RUSSELL, John
McFarlane
Cashmore, John: NEW YORK POLITICAL STUDIES
Castle, William: DUNN, Leslie Clarence
Castro, Fidel: BARCO, James William; CHERNE, Leo; EISENHOWER,
Milton Stover; MANN, Thomas Clifton
Cates, Clifton: MASTERS, John H.
Cather, Willa: KNOPF, Alfred A.
Chambers, Whittaker: GISSEN, Max
Chandler, Harry: DOUGLAS, Donald Wills
Chaplin, Charlie: SUTHERLAND, Albert Edward
Charters, W. W.: COWLEY, William Harold
Chase, Harry Woodburn: COUCH, William Terry
Chase, William: DICKINSON, Edwin Walter
Chennault, Claire: ALISON, John Richardson; FLYING TIGERS; FRILL-
MAN, Paul W.
Childs, John: KILPATRICK, William Heard
Choate, Joseph: WARDWELL, Allen
Churchill, Edward: AUB, Joseph Charles
Churchill, Sir Winston: BUTLER, Richard Austen; EAKER, Ira C.; FECH-
TELER, William Morrow; HAGERTY, James C.; MERCHANT, Living-
ston Tallmadge; ZAFRULLA KHAN, Sir Muhammed
Ciano, Galeazzo: KINKAID, Thomas Cassin
Clark, J. Reuben: WILLIAMS, James Thomas, Jr.
Clay, Alexander Stephen: CLAY, Lucius DuBignon
Clay, Lucius D.: CLAY, Lucius DuBignon, Jr.
Clayton, Will: BENTON, William; MARSHALL PLAN
Cleveland, Grover: BENNET, William Stiles; WARREN, Charles
Clifford, Cornelius: COUDERT, Frederic Rene
Cockcroft, John: WEAVER, Warren
Cocteau, Jean: BARZUN, Jacques
Coffin, Henry Sloane: GIVENS, Willard Earl
Cohen, Morris Raphael: KLEIN, Joseph J.
Cohen, Wilbur: ALTMEYER, Arthur Joseph; BURNS, Eveline Mabel;
CRUIKSHANK, Nelson Hale; ODELL, Charles; PERKINS, Roswell Bur-
chard; REIDY, William; SAPERSTEIN, Sydney; SCHOTTLAND,
Charles Irwin; SHEPPARD, Harold; SOMERS, Herman Miles; WICK-
ENDEN, Elizabeth; WILLCOX, Alanson Work; WILLIAMSON,
Kenneth; WOLKSTEIN, Irwin
Cohn, Edwin: CHURCHILL, Edward Delos
Cohn, Harry: RAPHAELSON, Samson

Index

Index

439

The Oral History Collection

aulkner, William: COMMINS, Dorothy Berliner; KLOPFER, Donald
  Simon
Fejos, Paul: GIESECKE, Albert Anthony
Ferenczi, Sandor: RADO, Sandor
Fermi, Enrico: RAMSEY, Norman
Fields, W. C.: POPULAR ARTS PROJECT; SUTHERLAND, Albert Edward
Finch, Edward R.: STEFFANSON, Hokan Bjornstrom
Finley, John H.: TUTTLE, Charles Henry
Fischer, John: ALEXANDER, Will Winton
Fitzgerald, F. Scott: VAN VECHTEN, Carl
Fleet, James Van: ROYALL, Kenneth Claiborne
Flexner, Simon: COUDERT, Frederic Rene; FLEXNER, Abraham
Flynn, Edward: O'DWYER, William
Fohl, Theodore: CURTIS, Albert B.
Folsom, Marion: SCHOTTLAND, Charles Irwin
Ford, Henry: DAVIS, Elmer Holmes; KELLAND, Clarence Budington
Ford, John: SUTHERLAND, Albert Edward
Foreman, Clark: DURR, Virginia Foster
Forrestal, James V.: CLARK, Joseph James; HART, Thomas Charles; HOL-
  LOWAY, James Lemuel, Jr.; ROYALL, Kenneth Claiborne; WILSON,
  Eugene Edward
Fosdick, Harry Emerson: GIVENS, Willard Earl
Fosdick, Raymond: RHIND, Flora Macdonald; WEAVER, Warren
Foster, William Z.: BROPHY, John
Fox, William: SINCLAIR, Upton
Franco, Francisco: LODGE, John Davis
Frankfurter, Felix: CHILDS, Marquis William; GREENBAUM, Edward
  Samuel; HAND, Learned; JACKSON, Gardner; LANDIS, James McCau-
  ley; MORSE, David A.
Frank, Jerome: COBB, Cully Alton; JACKSON, Gardner
Franks, Robert: CARNEGIE CORPORATION
Fraser, Phyllis: CERF, Bennett Alfred
Freeman, Douglas Southall: GALLUP, George Horace; MITCHELL, Broa-
  dus
Freeman, Edward M.: HARRAR, J. George
Freud, Anna: HOFFER, Willi; SANDLER, Joseph
Freud, Sigmund: BERNAYS, Edward L.; GLOVER, Edward; HOFFER,
  Willi; KARDINER, Abram; PSYCHOANALYTIC MOVEMENT; REIK,
  Theodor
Freund, Paul: MORSE, David A.
Friendly, Fred: STANTON, Frank
Frink, W. H.: KARDINER, Abram
Froding, Oskar: STEFFANSON, Hokan Bjornstrom
Frost, Robert: BAKER, Dorothy; BRAITHWAITE, William Stanley Beau-
  mont
Fry, Luther: LAZARSFELD, Paul Felix
Gallagher, Buell: TUTTLE, Charles Henry
Gandhi, Mohandas: ROUNDS, Frank W., Jr.; ZAFRULLA KHAN, Sir Mu-
  hammed
Gannett, Lewis: SPINGARN, Arthur B.
Garbo, Greta: MAMOULIAN, Rouben

440

Index

alley, Rudolph: NEW YORK POLITICAL STUDIES
Hall, John: SULLIVAN, William
Hall, Leonard: ALCORN, Hugh Meade, Jr.; FOLGER, John Clifford
Halsey, William: CARNEY, Robert Bostwick; PECK, DeWitt; ROUNDS,
    Frank W., Jr.; STUMP, Felix Budwell
Halsted, William: FLEXNER, Abraham
Hamilton, Thomas F.: WILSON, Eugene Edward
Hammarskjold, Dag: AGHNIDES, Thanassos; BARCO, James William;
    CORDIER, Andrew Wellington; EVANS, Luther Harris
Hammerstein, Oscar, II: RODGERS, Richard
Hand, Augustus: HAND, Learned; TAYLOR, Telford; TWEED, Harrison
Hand, Learned: TWEED, Harrison
Hanna, Marcus A.: GRISCOM, Lloyd Carpenter
Harding, Warren G.: ALBRIGHT, Horace Marden; ANSORGE, Martin
    Charles; KIRK, Alan Goodrich; MEYER, Eugene; WADSWORTH, James
    Wolcott; WILLIAMS, James Thomas, Jr.
Harper, Fowler: TATE, Jack Bernard
Harrar, J. George: RHIND, Flora Macdonald
Harriman, W. Averell: BUSH, Prescott; COSTIKYAN, Edward; FELD-
    MAN, Justin N.; GOLDBERG, Arthur Joseph
Hart, Larry: MYERS, Henry
Hart, Lorenz: RODGERS, Richard
Hartmann, Heinz: LOEWENSTEIN, Rudolph Maurice
Hart, Thomas: FIFE, James; FOSTER, Paul F.; HALL, John Lesslie Jr.
Harvey, George: COBB, Candler
Hauge, Gabriel: ADAMS, Sherman; BENEDICT, Stephen
Hauptmann, Bruno Richard: DELONG, Edmund
Hawthorne, Charles W.: DICKINSON, Edwin Walter
Hays, Brooks: FAUBUS, Orval Eugene
Haywood, William D.: BALDWIN, Roger Nash; SPARGO, John
Hearst, William Randolph: BOWERS, Claude Gernade; SPEED, Keats;
    WARNER, Emily Smith (Mrs. John); WILLIAMS, James Thomas, Jr.
Heiser, Victor: GRANT, John B.
Henry, Ray: O'BRIEN, James Cuff
Hepburn, Arthur: FIFE, James; HART, Thomas Charles
Herbert, Victor: POPULAR ARTS PROJECT
Hergesheimer, Joseph: KNOPF, Alfred A.
Herter, Christian: DILLON, Clarence Douglas
Hewitt, H. Kent: BALLENTINE, John Jennings; MOORE, Charles J.
Hill, George Washington: LASKER, Albert Davis
Hill, Jerome: CLAYTON, William Lockhart
Hill, John A.: McGRAW-HILL
Hill, Patty: GARRISON, Charlotte
Hillman, Sidney: ALEXANDER, Will Winton; BROPHY, John; KAZAN,
    Abraham; POTOFSKY, Jacob Samuel; PRESSMAN, Lee
Hillquit, Morris: McLAURIN, Benjamin.; SPARGO, John
Hiss, Alger: FRANK, Jerome New; JACKSON, Gardner; JOSEPHS, Deve-
    reux Colt; OSBORN, Frederick; WRISTON, Henry Merritt
Hitler, Adolf: DENNIS, Lawrence; GAY, Luis F.; KALTENBORN, Hans
    V.
Hobby, Oveta Culp: PERKINS, Roswell Burchard; SCHEELE, Leonard
    Andrew; SCHOTTLAND, Charles Irwin

Index

Hodge, William: GORDON, Richard
Hoey, Jane: TATE, Jack Bernard
Hoffman, Abby: SACKS, Herbert
Ho, Franklin L.: CHINESE ORAL HISTORY
Hollander, Jacob: MITCHELL, Broadus
Holland, Mildred: GORDON, Richard
Holmes, Oliver W.: LANDIS, James McCauley; O'BRIAN, John Lord
Hoover, Herbert C.: ALBRIGHT, Horace Marden; BUNDY, Harvey Hollister; CHAMBERLAIN, Thomas Gassner; DORR, Goldthwaite Higginson; FREY, John Philip; GALPIN, Perrin Comstock; HOLMAN, Charles William; MEYER, Eugene; REYNOLDS, Jackson E.; SMITH, H. Alexander; STRAUSS, Lewis Lichtenstein; TRAIN, Harold C.; WHITE, John Campbell; WILLIAMS, James Thomas, Jr.
Hoover, J. Edgar: TRAIN, Harold C.
Hoover, John: CUSTER, Benjamin Scott
Hopkins, Harry: ALISON, John Richardson; BANE, Frank; CLAY, Lucius DuBignon; DICKERMAN, Marion; DUNCAN, Donald; EVANS, Luther Harris; FALK, Isidore Sydney; FRANK, Jerome New; LAND, Emory Scott; LENROOT, Katharine Fredrica
Houdini, Harry: CANE, Melville Henry
Hough, Henry Beetle: ASCHER, Charles
Hoving, Walter: LUSK, William
Howe, Harold, II: CHILDLAW, Benjamin W.
Howe, Louis: DICKERMAN, Marion
Hughes, Charles Evans: TANNER, Frederick Chauncey; WARDWELL, Allen
Hughes, Emmett: ADAMS, Sherman
Hughes, Howard: COCHRAN, Jacqueline; DOUGLAS, Donald Wills
Hull, Cordell: BALLANTINE, Joseph; BRADEN, Spruille
Humphrey, George: DILLON, Clarence Douglas; JACOBY, Neil H.
Humphrey, Hubert H.: ANNIS, Edward Roland; IVES, Elizabeth Stevenson (Mrs. Ernest); McGOWAN, Carl
Hurley, Patrick: ROBERTSON, Walter Spencer
Husain, Sir Fazle: ZAFRULLA KHAN, Sir Muhammed
Hutchins, Robert M.: COUCH, William Terry; COWLEY, William Harold
Huxley, Aldous: CANFIELD, Cass
Huxley, Julian: ASCHER, Charles; CANFIELD, Cass
Hylan, John: PECORA, Ferdinand; VEILLER, Lawrence
Ickes, Harold: ALBRIGHT, Horace Marden; ASCHER, Charles; CLAY, Lucius DuBignon
Impellitteri, Vincent: MAX, Pearl (Mrs. Louis W.); McLAUGHLIN, Frederick Charles
Ives, Charles: COWELL, Henry
Ives, Irving: ISAACS, Stanley Myer
Ivy, James W.: SCHUYLER, George Samuel
Jackson, C. D.: BENEDICT, Stephen; WASHBURN, Abbot McConnell
Jackson, Gardner: BLEDSOE, Samuel B.
Jackson, Robert H.: CHILDS, Marquis William; DEAN, Gordon Evans
James, Henry: CASWELL, Hollis; COLLINS, Joseph; DUER, Caroline King; RAUP, R. Bruce
Jansen, William: McLAUGHLIN, Frederick Charles
Jardine, William: TOLLEY, Howard Ross

443

The Oral History Collection

Javits, Jacob: THOMPSON, Frank, Jr.
Jerome, William Travers: SCHIEFFELIN, William Jay
Jessel, George: RAPHAELSON, Samson
Jessup, Philip: BARCO, James William
Jessup, Walter A.: CARNEGIE CORPORATION; CARTWRIGHT, Morse
  Adams; LESTER, Robert MacDonald
Johnson, Allen: MALONE, Dumas
Johnson, Charles S.: VANCE, Rupert B.
Johnson, Hiram: ALBRIGHT, Horace Marden
Johnson, Hugh: DORR, Goldthwaite Higginson; FRANK, Jerome New;
  WALLACE, Henry Agard
Johnson, James Weldon: SCHUYLER, George Samuel; VAN VECHTEN,
  Carl
Johnson, John B.: O'DWYER, William
Johnson, Lyndon B.: ANNIS, Edward Roland; EISENHOWER, Milton
  Stover; EVANS, Luther Harris; GOLDWATER, Barry Morris; HARDE-
  MAN, D. B.; IVES, Elizabeth Stevenson (Mrs. Ernest); MINOW, Newton
  Norman; SHARON, John; STANTON, Frank; TREE, Marietta (Mrs.
  Ronald); WICKENDEN, Elizabeth
Jolson, Al: RAPHAELSON, Samson
Jones, Hilary P.: TRAIN, Harold C.
Jones, Jesse: CLAYTON, William Lockhart; LAND, Emory Scott
Jones, W.A. (Pete): ROBERTS, Clifford
Josephs, Devereux: CARTWRIGHT, Morse Adams; DOLLARD, Charles;
  HASKINS, Caryl Parker; HERRING, Edward Pendleton; LESTER, Rob-
  ert MacDonald
Joyce, James: COLLINS, Joseph; HUEBSCH, Ben W.
Judson, Arthur: BARLOW, Howard
Jung, Carl: GLOVER, Edward
Justo, Agustin P.: PENA, Jose Luis; SARACHAGA, Dario
Kades, Charles: OCCUPATION OF JAPAN
Kalbfuss, Edward: MOORE, Charles J.
Keaton, Buster: SUTHERLAND, Albert Edward
Kefauver, Estes: BINGHAM, Barry; BROWNING, Gordon; HARDEMAN,
  D. B.; O'DWYER, William; SHARON, John
Keller, John W.: HETTRICK, John T.
Kelley, Florence: ALGER, George William
Kelley, Nicholas: CARNEGIE CORPORATION
Kelly, Frank: NEW YORK POLITICAL STUDIES
Kelly, Howard: FLEXNER, Abraham
Kendrick, John B.: O'MAHONEY, Joseph Christopher
Kennan, George: ROUNDS, Frank W., Jr.
Kennedy, Jacqueline: CANFIELD, Cass
Kennedy, John F.: ANNIS, Edward Roland; BINGHAM, Barry; BOWLES,
  Chester; CRUIKSHANK, Nelson Hale; IVES, Elizabeth Stevenson (Mrs.
  Ernest); JOURNALISM LECTURES; JUDD, Walter H.; McGOWAN,
  Carl; MONRONEY, Almer Stillwell Mike; NESTINGEN, Ivan Arnold;
  NEUSTADT, Richard Elliott; ODELL, Charles; SHARON, John; SMITH,
  Howard Kingsbury; THOMPSON, Frank, Jr.; TREE, Marietta (Mrs. Ro-
  nald); WICKENDEN, Elizabeth; WILLIAMSON, Kenneth; WOLK-
  STEIN, Irwin; WYATT, Wilson Watkins

444

Index

The Oral History Collection

Ted; DEWEY, Thomas Edmund; DRESSLER, David; EARLE, Genevieve Beavers; GOLDSTEIN, Jonah J.; ISAACS, Julius; ISAACS, Stanley Myer; KUPER, Theodore Fred; LaGUARDIA, Marie M. (Mrs. Fiorello H.); LANDIS, James McCauley; LAZARUS, Reuben Avis; MACK, Walter Staunton, Jr.; MAX, Pearl (Mrs. Louis W.); MORRIS, Newbold; NEW YORK POLITICAL STUDIES; O'DWYER, Paul; O'DWYER, William; SPAETH, Sigmund; STODDARD, Francis Russell; WARNER, Emily Smith (Mrs. John); WINDELS, Paul
Laird, Allison W.: MAXWELL, William L.
Lamas, Carlos Saavedra: BRADEN, Spruille
Lamont, Thomas W.: CARNEGIE CORPORATION
Land, Emory: WILLIAMS, Henry
Lane, Franklin K.: ALBRIGHT, Horace Marden
Langdell, C. C.: FRANKFURTER, Felix
Langdon, Harry: POPULAR ARTS PROJECT
Langmuir, Irving: HULL, Albert Wallace
Lansing, Robert: COUDERT, Frederic Rene; DULLES, Eleanor Lansing
Latimer, Murray: BROWN, James Douglas
Lattimore, Owen: BALLANTINE, Joseph; EMERSON, Thomas Irwin
Laurens, Jean: WEBER, Max
Lawrence, D. H.: HUEBSCH, Ben W.
Lawrence, Ernest: WEAVER, Warren
Lawrence, Gertrude: RODGERS, Richard
Lawrence, T. E.: CURTIS, James Freeman
Lazarsfeld, Paul: STANTON, Frank
Lazarus, Fred, Jr.: FEDERATED DEPARTMENT STORES
Leahy, William: FIFE, James; HART, Thomas Charles
Learned, William S.: CARNEGIE CORPORATION
Leary, Fairfax: FIFE, James
LeCorbusier, Charles: GREENSTEIN, Robert
Lee, Don: PALEY, William S.
Lee, Stephen D.: COBB, Cully Alton
Leffingwell, Robert: HISS, Alger
Leffingwell, Russell C.: CARNEGIE CORPORATION; OSBORN, Frederick
LeHand, Marguerite: DICKERMAN, Marion
Lehman, Hartley: GOELL, Theresa
Lehman, Herbert: COSTIKYAN, Edward; DAVIS, William Hammatt; DRESSLER, David; FELDMAN, Justin N.; GOLDSTEIN, Jonah J.; JESSUP, Philip Caryl
Lenroot, Katherine: SCHOTTLAND, Charles Irwin
Lester, Robert: CAPERS, Roberta
Levant, Oscar: GOLENPAUL, Dan
Lewis, Edwin O.: INDEPENDENCE NATIONAL HISTORICAL PARK
Lewis, John L.: BROPHY, John; DAVIS, William Hammatt; DURR, Virginia Foster; FREY, John Philip; HAYES, Albert John; JACKSON, Gardner; LAHEY, Edwin A.; LANDIS, James McCauley; PRESSMAN, Lee; SHISHKIN, Boris Basil; STONE, M. Hedley
Lewis, Sinclair: CANE, Melville Henry
Lichtenstein, Zalman J.: HENRY, Ray; WICKENDEN, Elizabeth
Lie, Trygve: AGHNIDES, Thanassos; CORDIER, Andrew Wellington; GROSS, Ernest A.

446

Index

447

The Oral History Collection

JESSUP, Philip Caryl; KIMBALL, Arthur Alden; KNOWLAND, William Fife; LAMONT, Corliss; McCARDLE, Carl Wesley; McGOWAN, Carl; RAMSEY, Norman; WATKINS, Arthur V.; WILEY, Alexander
McClellan, George: VEILLER, Lawrence
McCloy, John: WORLD BANK
McClure, Robert A.: JESSUP, Frederick P.
McClure, S. S.: HENDRICK, Burton Jesse
McCone, John: FOSTER, Paul F.
McCooey, John: NEW YORK POLITICAL STUDIES
McCullers, Carson BAKER, Dorothy
MacDonald, George: STEFFANSON, Hokan Bjornstrom
McGraw, James H.: McGRAW-HILL
McGregor, Tracy: McGREGOR, James Murray; NORTON, William John
McKellar, Kenneth: BROWNING, Gordon
McKinley, William: BIRD, Hobart Stanley
McLain, George: ODELL, Charles
MacLeish, Archibald: EVANS, Luther Harris
McMurrin, Sterling: IANNI, Francis A. J.
McNamara, James: FREY, John Philip
McNamara, Patrick: SHEPPARD, Harold; WOLKSTEIN, Irwin
McNamara, Robert: KRULAK, Victor Harold; REIDY, William
McNary, Charles: FARLEY, James Aloysius
McNutt, Paul: TATE, Jack Bernard
McPeak, William: ASSOCIATION FOR THE AID OF CRIPPLED CHILDREN
McPherson, Aimee Semple: HOOVER, Herbert Clark
MacVeagh, Franklin: CURTIS, James Freeman
Macy, George: MACY, Helen (Mrs. George).
Magnes, Judah: RICHARDS, Bernard G.
Mann, Thomas: KNOPF, Alfred A.
Mansfield, Katherine: KNOPF, Alfred A.
Manseau, Benjamin: SULLIVAN, William
Mara, Tim: DOWLING, Eddie
Marcantonio, Vito: DURR, Virginia Foster; O'DWYER, Paul
Markham, Edwin: HILL, Frank Ernest
Marks, Herbert: MORSE, David A.
Marquand, J. P.: GISSEN, Max
Marquis, Don: HILL, Frank Ernest
Marshall, George C.: ANDERSON, Orvil A.; ARNOLD, Eleanor; BENEDICT, Stephen; BUNDY, Harvey Hollister; CLAYTON, William Lockhart; EAKER, Ira C.; EISENHOWER, Dwight David; ROBERTSON, Walter Spencer; ROYALL, Kenneth Claiborne; WILLIAMS, James Thomas, Jr.
Marshall, Louis: PROSKAUER, Joseph M.; RICHARDS, Bernard G.
Martin, Glenn: BELL, Lawrence Dale; DOUGLAS, Donald Wills
Mason, Max: WEAVER, Warren
Masters, Edgar Lee: MASTERS, Ellen Coyne (Mrs. Edgar Lee); WHEELOCK, John Hall
Matisse, Henri: WEBER, Max
Matthews, T. S.: GISSEN, Max
Matthiessen, F.O.: BAKER, Dorothy

Index

Mayer, Louis B.: DOWLING, Eddie; POPULAR ARTS PROJECT
Meany, George: CRUIKSHANK, Nelson Hale; DAVIS, William Hammatt
Meara, Frank S.: GUION, Connie Myers
Medalie, George Z.: DEWEY, Thomas Edmund
Medina, Harold: SACHS, Walter Edward
Meehan, Tommy: SUTHERLAND, Albert Edward
Meighan, Thomas: GORDON, Richard
Mellon, Andrew: COBB, Candler; WINDELS, Paul
Mencken, H. L.: FOREST HISTORY SOCIETY; GILMAN, Mildred;
   HUEBSCH, Ben W.; KNOPF, Alfred A.; MASTERS, Ellen Coyne (Mrs.
   Edgar Lee); MENCKEN, August; OWENS, J. Hamilton; SCHUYLER,
   George Samuel
Menon, Krishna: BALDWIN, Roger Nash; COOK, Charles D.; KAUL, Brij
   Mohan.
Meyer, Eugene: WORLD BANK
Michelson, Charles: PROSKAUER, Joseph M.
Miles, Milton: MASTERS, John H.
Miles, Vincent: ARONSON, A. Henry; HOHAUS, Reinhard Arthur ; MUL-
   LINER, Maurine
Millay, Edna St. Vincent: CANFIELD, Cass
Miller, Nathan: STODDARD, Francis Russell
Miller, Robert E.: CHORLEY, Kenneth
Milles, Carl: STEFFANSON, Hokan Bjornstrom
Millikan, Robert: WEAVER, Warren
Mills, Ogden: ISAACS, Stanley Myer
Mills, Wilbur: SAPERSTEIN, Sydney; WILLIAMSON, Kenneth; WOLK-
   STEIN, Irwin
Mitchel, John Purroy: COUDERT, Frederic Rene; CRUGER, Bertram
   D.; PERKINS, Frances; PINK, Louis Heaton; STRAUSS, Morris Lin-
   coln
Mitchell, Dr. Wesley Clair: MITCHELL, Lucy Sprague
Mitchell, George S.: MITCHELL, Broadus
Mitchell, Morris: MITCHELL, Broadus
Mitchell, Samuel Chiles: MITCHELL, Broadus
Mitchell, William: AVIATION; CLARK, Joseph James; HENRY H. AR-
   NOLD PROJECT; HUNSAKER, Jerome Clarke; VICTORY, John Fran-
   cis; WILSON, Eugene Edward
Mitchell, William W.: ARNOLD, Eleanor
Mitscher, Marc: CLARK, Joseph James; READ, William Augustus, Jr.
Moffett, William A.: CLARK, Joseph James; HUNSAKER, Jerome Clarke;
   STUMP, Felix Budwell; WILSON, Eugene Edward
Moley, Raymond: BERLE, Adolf Augustus
Molotov, Vyacheslav: FOSTER, Paul F.; MERCHANT, Livingston Tall-
   madge
Montgomery, Bernard: GAVIN, James M.
Mooney, Thomas: BROWDER, Earl; FREY, John Philip
Moore, Louis: LUSK, William
Morgan, J. P.: BAKHMETEFF, Boris Alexander; SCHIEFFELIN, William
   Jay
Morgan, Thomas H.: DOBZHANSKY, Theodosius; DUNN, Leslie Clarence
Morgenthau, Henry: DOWLING, Eddie

449

The Oral History Collection

Morgenthau, Henry, Sr.: GREENBAUM, Edward Samuel
Morgenthau, Robert: FELDMAN, Justin N.
Morison, Samuel E.: PARKER, Ralph Chandler
Morrill, J. L.: COWLEY, William Harold
Morris, Newbold: ISAACS, Stanley Myer; O'DWYER, William
Morrissett, Lloyd: CREMIN, Lawrence Arthur
Morrow, Dwight: BAKHMETEFF, Boris Alexander; BRANCH, Hilarion
    Noel; RUBLEE, George
Morse, Josiah: MITCHELL, Broadus
Moses, Robert: ISAACS, Stanley Myer; KAZAN, Abraham; O'DWYER,
    Paul; O'DWYER, William; PROSKAUER, Joseph M.; WARNER, Emily
    Smith (Mrs. John)
Mosher, Frederic A.: CARNEGIE CORPORATION
Moskowitz, Belle: WARNER, Emily Smith (Mrs. John)
Moss, Maximilian: O'DWYER, William
Mossadegh, Mohammed: MARCUS, Morris M.
Mott, Lucretia: STRAUSS, Anna Lord
Mountin, Joseph: GRANT, John B.
Moyne, Lord: LANDIS, James McCauley
Mudge, Isadore G.: WINCHELL, Constance Mabel
Muller, H. J.: DUNN, Leslie Clarence
Mumford, Lewis: ASCHER, Charles
Munsey, Frank: NEVINS, Allan; SPEED, Keats
Murnau, Frederic: POPULAR ARTS PROJECT
Murphy, Charles F.: KROCK, Arthur; PECORA, Ferdinand; PELL, Her-
    bert Claiborne
Murphy, Frank: DEAN, Gordon Evans
Murray, George Welwood: TWEED, Harrison
Murray, James: REIDY, William
Murray, Philip: BROPHY, John; LAHEY, Edwin A.; PRESSMAN, Lee
Musica, Philip: DELONG, Edmund
Mussolini, Benito: DENNIS, Lawrence; GAY, Luis F.; KINKAID, Thomas
    Cassin
Muste, A. J.: SHACHTMAN, Max
Muzzey, David: JABLONOWER, Joseph
Myrdal, Gunnar: JOHNSON, Guy Benton; RAPER, Arthur Franklin
Nathan, George Jean: DOWLING, Eddie; KNOPF, Alfred A.
Nathanson, Ira: AUB, Joseph Charles
Nehru, Jawaharlal: BALDWIN, Roger Nash; BARCO, James William;
    BINGHAM, Barry; BOWLES, Chester; KAUL, Brij Mohan.; ROBERT-
    SON, Walter Spencer; ZAFRULLA KHAN, Sir Muhammed
Nelson, Donald: BOWLES, Chester
Nestingen, Ivan: CARSTENSON, Blue
Nevins, Allan: HILL, Frank Ernest; PAULEY, Edwin Wendell
Nimitz, Chester: ANDERSON, Walter Stratton; BALLENTINE, John Jen-
    nings; CARNEY, Robert Bostwick; CLARK, Joseph James; FIFE, James;
    HART, Thomas Charles; HILL, Harry W.; MOORE, Charles J.; PARKER,
    Ralph Chandler; PFEIFFER, Omar Titus
Nixon, Herman C.: COUCH, William Terry; VANCE, Rupert B.
Nixon, Richard M.: ABEL, Elie; ALCORN, Hugh Meade, Jr.; BEHRENS,
    Earl C.; BENEDICT, Stephen; DRUMMOND, Roscoe; EISENHOWER,

Index

The Oral History Collection

Pauli, Wolfgang: RABI, Isidor Isaac
Pauling, Linus: WEAVER, Warren
Pavlov, Ivan: AUB, Joseph Charles
Peabody, Endicott: FUESS, Claude Moore
Pearson, Drew: JACKSON, Gardner
Peek, George: FRANK, Jerome New; HENSHAW, Frederick W.; JONES, Marvin
Pelliot, Paul: GOODRICH, Luther Carrington
Pendergast, Thomas J.: COMBS, George Hamilton, Jr.
Penrose, Boies: CURTIS, James Freeman
Perkins, Frances: ALTMEYER, Arthur Joseph; ARMSTRONG, Barbara; BANE, Frank; BROPHY, John; CLAGUE, Ewan; FREY, John Philip; MULLINER, Maurine; SOCIAL SECURITY; STEELMAN, John Roy
Perkins, James: JACKSON, Frederick Herbert; PIFER, Alan
Perkins, Maxwell: WHEELOCK, John Hall
Perkins, Milo: ROSENTHAL, Morris Sigmund
Perkins, William: PERKINS, Thomas Lee
Peron, Juan D.: ARGENTINA IN THE 1930'S; BONILLA, Lucio
Pershing, John J.: GIESECKE, Albert Anthony
Peyton, Corse: GORDON, Richard
Piaget, Jean: MATTHEWS, Geoffrey
Picasso, Pablo: WEBER, Max
Pifer, Alan: ANDERSON, Florence; DE KIEWIET, Cornelis Willem; SINGER, Arthur; STACKPOLE, Stephen
Pinchot, Gifford: ALBRIGHT, Horace Marden
Post, C. W.: POST, Marjorie Merriweather
Post, Langdon W.: ABRAMS, Charles
Post, Wiley: BRUNO, Harry A.
Potofsky, Jacob: KAZAN, Abraham
Pound, Roscoe: LANDIS, James McCauley; MADDEN, Joseph Warren
Powell, Adam Clayton: BROWNELL, Herbert; FELDMAN, Justin N.; SPINGARN, Arthur B.
Pratt, Ruth: ISAACS, Stanley Myer
Pressman, Lee: BROPHY, John; LAHEY, Edwin A.
Pritchett, Henry: CARNEGIE CORPORATION
Pupin, Michael: FONDILLER, William
Pye, W.S.: TRAIN, Harold C.
Quill, Michael: O'DWYER, William
Quinn, John: HUEBSCH, Ben W.
Rabi, I. I.: RAMSEY, Norman
Radford, Arthur: CLARK, Joseph James; STUMP, Felix Budwell
Randolph, A. Philip: McLAURIN, Benjamin; SCHUYLER, George Samuel
Rank, Otto: KARDINER, Abram; REIK, Theodor
Raskob, J. J.: DOWLING, Eddie
Raushenbush, Paul: SOMERS, Herman Miles
Rayburn, Sam: CLAY, Lucius DuBignon; HARDEMAN, D. B.
Reece, J. Carroll: CARNEGIE CORPORATION
Reed, William: O'DWYER, William
Reeves, Joseph M.: WILSON, Eugene Edward
Reid, Clement: ASSOCIATION FOR THE AID OF CRIPPLED CHILDREN

WARNER, Emily Smith (Mrs. John); WHEELER, Burton Kendall; WILLIAMS, James Thomas, Jr.; WILSON, Milburn Lincoln
Roosevelt, Franklin, Jr.: FELDMAN, Justin N.
Roosevelt, James: THOMAS, Gerald Carthrae
Roosevelt, Theodore: ALGER, George William; DAVENPORT, Frederick Morgan; DORR, Goldthwaite Higginson; FREY, John Philip; GRISCOM, Lloyd Carpenter; HART, Thomas Charles; HETTRICK, John T.; ISAACS, Stanley Myer; LAND, Emory Scott; O'BRIAN, John Lord; PRENDERGAST, William Ambrose; ROBINSON, Beverley Randolph; TANNER, Frederick Chauncey; THEODORE ROOSEVELT ASSOCIATION; WILLIAMS, Henry; WILLIAMS, James Thomas, Jr.
Root, Elihu: O'BRIAN, John Lord; WASHBURN, Stanley
Rose, Arnold: MYRDAL, Gunnar Karl
Rose, Billy: RODGERS, Richard
Rose, Wickliffe: GRANT, John B.
Rosenberg, Anna: BENTON, William; BROWNELL, Herbert; ENGLE, Lavinia
Rosenberg, Julius: BROWNELL, Herbert
Rosenthal, Julius: KLEIN, Joseph J.
Rosenwald, Julius: ALEXANDER, Will Winton; BARKER, James Madison
Rostow, Walt: JESSUP, Frederick P.
Rousseau, Henri: WEBER, Max
Rowntree, Seebohm: LASKER, Bruno
Rubicam, Raymond: GALLUP, George Horace
Rubin, Jerry: SACKS, Herbert
Rugg, Harold: KILPATRICK, William Heard; RAUP, R. Bruce
Ruml, Beardsley: CARNEGIE CORPORATION; RHIND, Flora Macdonald
Rusk, Dean: GROSS, Ernest A.; RHIND, Flora Macdonald
Rusk, Howard: ASSOCIATION FOR THE AID OF CRIPPLED CHILDREN
Russell, Bertrand: TEAD, Ordway
Russell, Charles M.: EDWIN, Edward S.
Russell, George: WILSON, Milburn Lincoln
Russell, James E.: CARNEGIE CORPORATION; GARRISON, Charlotte; JERSILD, Arthur T.; KILPATRICK, William Heard; WATSON, Goodwin
Russell, John: PARKIN, George Raleigh
Russell, William F.: CASWELL, Hollis; CARNEGIE CORPORATION; JERSILD, Arthur T.; KILPATRICK, William Heard; WATSON, Goodwin
Rutherford, Ernest: WATSON-WATT, Sir Robert
Sachs, Hans: LOEWENSTEIN, Rudolph Maurice; REIK, Theodor
Said, Boris: DOWLING, Eddie
Salter, William: AUB, Joseph Charles
Sandburg, Carl: HILL, Frank Ernest
Sanger, Margaret: BALDWIN, Roger Nash
Sarnoff, David: LANG, Chester Henry
Sarton, May: BAKER, Dorothy
Saulnier, Raymond: JACOBY, Neil H.
Scherman, Harry: BOOK-OF-THE-MONTH CLUB
Schlesinger, Arthur: JACKSON, Gardner
Schlesinger, Arthur, Jr.: MINOW, Newton Norman
Schroeder, Theodore: BALDWIN, Roger Nash

Index

The Oral History Collection

Stark, Harold: HART, Thomas Charles
Stassen, Harold: ALCORN, Hugh Meade, Jr.; BISSELL, Richard Mervin, Jr.
Stearns, Alfred: FUESS, Claude Moore
Stedman, Alfred: HENSHAW, Frederick W.
Steelman, John: CLAGUE, Ewan
Steffanson, Mary Eno: STEFFANSON, Hokan Bjornstrom
Stein, Clarence: ASCHER, Charles
Stein, Gertrude: VAN VECHTEN, Carl
Sterner, Richard: MYRDAL, Gunnar Karl
Stettinius, Edward: CLAYTON, William Lockhart
Stettinius, Edward, Sr.: BAKHMETEFF, Boris Alexander
Stevenson, Adlai E.: ADLAI E. STEVENSON PROJECT; BOWLES, Chester; CANFIELD, Cass; COOK, Charles D.; COSTIKYAN, Edward; COWAN, Louis G.; HODGES, Luther Hartwell; HODGINS, Eric; MERRIAM, Robert Edward; SHIVERS, Alan; WICKENDEN, Elizabeth
Stewart, Irvin: CARNEGIE CORPORATION
Stewart, Walter: JACOBY, Neil H.
Stieglitz, Alfred: WEBER, Max
Stimson, Henry L.: BUNDY, Harvey Hollister; CHURCHILL, Edward Delos; DORR, Goldthwaite Higginson; FRANKFURTER, Felix; FUESS, Claude Moore; O'BRIAN, John Lord; PRENDERGAST, William Ambrose
Stone, Harlan F.: ASCHER, Charles; BERLE, Adolf Augustus; CHILDS, Marquis William; GELLHORN, Walter
Stouffer, Samuel: LAZARSFELD, Paul Felix
Stouffer, Samuel A.: CARNEGIE CORPORATION
Strauss, Lewis L.: BEACH, Edward Latimer; FOSTER, Paul F.; RAMSEY, Norman
Stravinsky, Igor: SESSIONS, Roger Huntington
Strayer, George: CASWELL, Hollis; JANSEN, William; NORTON, John Kelley; WATSON, Goodwin
Strong, William: SCHIEFFELIN, William Jay
Strunsky, Morris: ABRAMS, Charles
Strunsky, Simeon: NEVINS, Allan
Sturtevant, A. H.: DOBZHANSKY, Theodosius
Sukarno, Achmed: BARCO, James William
Sullivan, John L.: CLARK, Joseph James
Summerfield, Arthur: STANS, Maurice Hubert
Sutherland, Anne: GORDON, Richard
Swain, George F.: BARKER, James Madison
Swope, Herbert B.: NEVINS, Allan
Sydensticker, Edgar: FALK, Isidore Sydney
Symington, Stuart: ROYALL, Kenneth Claiborne
Szilard, Leo: BAINBRIDGE, Kenneth Tompkins
Taft, Robert A.: BENTON, William; BUSH, Prescott; CAKE, Ralph Harlan; DANIELS, Jonathan Worth; DAVIS, William Hammatt; EISENHOWER, Dwight David; GOLDWATER, Barry Morris; GUYLAY, L. Richard; HOLLISTER, John Baker; LAHEY, Edwin A.; LEE, Joseph Bracken; ROBERT A. TAFT PROJECT; STEELMAN, John Roy
Taft, William Howard: BROWN, Sevellon Ledyard; CHAMBERLAIN,

Index

Thomas Gassner; COBB, Candler; CURTIS, James Freeman; DORR, Goldthwaite Higginson; DURSTINE, Roy Sarles; FREY, John Philip; TANNER, Frederick Chauncey

Talbot, Harold: LAWRENCE, William Howard

Tannenbaum, Frank: ALEXANDER, Will Winton

Tarbell, Ida: HENDRICK, Burton Jesse

Tate, Jack: BERNSTEIN, Bernice; WILLCOX, Alanson Work

Taussig, Charles W.: BERLE, Adolf Augustus

Taylor, Henry: WILLIAMS, Henry

Taylor, Henry C.: STINE, Oscar Clemen

Teasdale, Sara: BRAITHWAITE, William Stanley Beaumont; WHEE-LOCK, John Hall

Teller, Edward: RAMSEY, Norman

Templewood, Lord: ZAFRULLA KHAN, Sir Muhammed

Terman, Lewis: NORTON, John Kelley

Thalberg, Irving: POPULAR ARTS PROJECT

Thant, U: AGHNIDES, Thanassos; CORDIER, Andrew Wellington

Theobald, John: McLAUGHLIN, Frederick Charles

Thomas, J. Parnell: MEYNER, Robert Baumle

Thomas, Norman: SHACHTMAN, Max; SOCIALIST MOVEMENT

Thorndike, Edward Lee: JERSILD, Arthur T.; KILPATRICK, William Heard; RAUP, R. Bruce; WATSON, Goodwin

Thorndike, Joseph J.: JENSEN, Oliver

Till, Emmett: BROWNELL, Herbert

Tiomkin, Dmitri: MYERS, Henry

Tizard, Henry: WATSON-WATT, Sir Robert; WEAVER, Warren

Tobin, Maurice: BROPHY, John; SHISHKIN, Boris Basil

Tolley, Howard: HENSHAW, Frederick W.

Towers, John H.: CLARK, Joseph James; READ, William Augustus, Jr.

Townsend, Francis: WICKENDEN, Elizabeth

Tramonti, Antonio: RODRIGUEZ, Juan

Trees, Joseph Clifton: BENEDUM, Michael Late; BENEDUM AND THE OIL INDUSTRY

Trotsky, Leon: CANFIELD, Cass; HARDMAN, J.B.S.; SHACHTMAN, Max

Truman, Harry S.: BOWLES, Chester; CLAGUE, Ewan; DANIELS, Jonathan Worth; DORR, Goldthwaite Higginson; EISENHOWER, Dwight David; EISENHOWER, Milton Stover; ELSON, Edward Lee Roy; FOLLIARD, Edward Thomas; GRAY, Gordon; HOLLOWAY, James Lemuel, Jr.; LANG, Chester Henry; MITCHELL, Stephen Arnold; PAULEY, Edwin Wendell; PERKINS, Frances; PFEIFFER, Omar Titus; ROYALL, Kenneth Claiborne; SHARON, John; STEELMAN, John Roy; STRAUSS, Anna Lord; TREE, Marietta (Mrs. Ronald); WHEELER, Burton Kendall; WILLIAMS, James Thomas, Jr.; WYATT, Wilson Watkins

Truscott, Lucian: JESSUP, Frederick P.

Tugwell, Rexford Guy: ALEXANDER, Will Winton; ASCHER, Charles; BERLE, Adolf Augustus; FRANK, Jerome New; WILSON, Milburn Lincoln

Turkus, Burton: KLEIN, Solomon A.

Turner, Richmond: BALLENTINE, John Jennings; HILL, Harry W.; HOGABOOM, Robert Edward; PECK, DeWitt

Urey, Harold: WEAVER, Warren

Valentine, Louis: DRESSLER, David
Valentino, Rudolph: POPULAR ARTS PROJECT
Van Hise, Charles: ALLEN, William Harvey
Van Loon, Hendrik Willem: HUEBSCH, Ben. W.
Van Noppen, Leonard: WEBER, Max
Van Wyck, Robert: HETTRICK, John T.
Vance, Cyrus: GOLDBERG, Arthur Joseph
Vandegrift, Alexander: BURGER, Joseph Charles; CURTIS, Donald; MAS-
    TERS, John H.
Vandenburg, Arthur: BENTON, William
Vanderbilt, Arthur T.: MEYNER, Robert Baumle
Vavilov, Nikolai: DUNN, Leslie Clarence
Veblen, Thorstein: LUBIN, Isador
Velde, Harold: RAMSEY, Norman
Vest, John: CUSTER, Benjamin Scott
Videla, Ricardo: JOFRE, Emilio
Villa, Pancho: TINKER, Edward Laroque
Villard, Oswald Garrison: NEVINS, Allan
Vincent, George: RHIND, Flora Macdonald
Vought, Chance M.: WILSON, Eugene Edward
Wagner, Robert F.: DAVIS, William H.; GOLDSTEIN, Jonah J.; MUL-
    LINER, Maurine
Wagner, Robert F., Jr.: CARMAN, Harry; COSTIKYAN, Edward; FELD-
    MAN, Justin; McLAUGHLIN, Frederick Charles; MAX, Pearl (Mrs. Louis
    W.)
Wald, Lillian: ALGER, George William; LEHMAN, Herbert Henry; STEW-
    ART, Isabel Maitland
Walker, James: ALLEN, William Harvey; BATTLE, Samuel J.; GOLD-
    STEIN, Jonah J.; LAZARUS, Reuben Avis; NEW YORK POLITICAL
    STUDIES; PECORA, Ferdinand; PERKINS, Frances; WARNER, Emily
    Smith (Mrs. John)
Walker, Madame C.J.: RANDOLPH, Asa Philip
Wallace, Henry A.: ALEXANDER, Will Winton; APPLEBY, Paul Henson;
    BALDWIN, Calvin Benham; BLEDSOE, Samuel B.; BLIVEN, Bruce
    Ormsby; CLAYTON, William Lockhart; COBB, Cully Alton; EZEKIEL,
    Mordecai Joseph Brill; FRANK, Jerome New; HENSHAW, Frederick W.;
    JACKSON, Gardner; JONES, Marvin; LeCRON, James D.; PAULEY,
    Edwin Wendell; ROSENTHAL, Morris Sigmund; TAYLOR, Henry
    Charles; THOMAS, Norman Mattoon; TOLLEY, Howard Ross; WILSON,
    Milburn Lincoln
Wallace, Henry Cantwell: TAYLOR, Henry Charles; WALLACE, Henry
    Agard
Wallace, Mike: WRIGHT, Frank Lloyd
Walsh, Thomas: WHEELER, Burton Kendall
Warburg, Felix: GOLDSTEIN, Jonah J.; KLEIN, Joseph J.
Warren, Earl: ADAMS, Sherman; BEHRENS, Earl C.; KNIGHT, Goodwin
Warren, Robert Penn: BAKER, Dorothy
Warren, Winslow: WARREN, Charles
Washington, Booker T.: DU BOIS, William Edward Burghardt
Wavell, Archibald: FIFE, James
Weeks, Sinclair: ASTIN, Allen Varley

Index

Weizmann, Chaim: PROSKAUER, Joseph M.
Welch, Roy: SESSIONS, Roger Huntington
Welch, William: FLEXNER, Abraham
Welles, Sumner: BRADEN, Spruille; CANFIELD, Cass; DICKERMAN, Marion
Wells, H. G.: HUEBSCH, Ben W.
Wenner-Gren, Axel: FEJOS, Paul; GIESECKE, Albert Anthony; STEFFANSON, Hokan Bjornstrom
Werfel, Franz: HUEBSCH, Ben W.
Westover, Wendell: ARNOLD, Eleanor
Weyerhaeuser, Charles A.: MAXWELL, William L.
Weyerhaeuser, J. P.: CURTIS, Albert B.
Wharton, Arthur: HAYES, Albert John
Wharton, Edith: CANFIELD, Cass; DUER, Caroline King
Wheeler, Benjamin Ide: DRURY, Newton Bishop
White, Harry Dexter: BENEDICT, Stephen
White, Thomas D.: CRABB, Jarred V.
White, Walter: SCHUYLER, George Samuel; WILKINS, Roy
Whitehead, Ennis C.: CRABB, Jarred V.
Whitlock, Brand: GALPIN, Perrin Comstock
Whitman, Charles S.: CHANDLER, George Fletcher; STODDARD, Francis Russell
Whitman, Walt: RODGERS, Cleveland
Whitney, Courtney: OCCUPATION OF JAPAN
Whitney, Willis R.: HULL, Albert Wallace
Wickard, Claude: BLEDSOE, Samuel B.; EZEKIEL, Mordecai Joseph Brill; HAMILTON, Carl; JACKSON, Gardner; JONES, Marvin; PARISIUS, Herbert W.
Wiener, Norbert: WEAVER, Warren
Wilbur, C. Martin: CHINESE ORAL HISTORY
Wilder, Billy: RAPHAELSON, Samson
Wilder, Thornton: LESSER, Sol
Wilkins, Roy: SCHUYLER, George Samuel; SPINGARN, Arthur B.
Willcox, Alanson: WILLIAMSON, Kenneth
Williams, Oscar: WHEELOCK, John Hall
Williams, Tennessee: DOWLING, Eddie
Willingdon, Lord: ZAFRULLA KHAN, Sir Muhammed
Williston, Samuel: FRANKFURTER, Felix; LANDIS, James McCauley
Willkie, Wendell L.: FARLEY, James Aloysius; PRESSMAN, Lee; PROSKAUER, Joseph M.
Willoughby, Charles: OCCUPATION OF JAPAN
Wilson, Charles E.: ABEL, Elie; SPRAGUE, Mansfield Daniel
Wilson, Edmund: GISSEN, Max
Wilson, Francis: GORDON, Richard
Wilson, Henry: HOOVER, John Howard
Wilson, William B.: BROPHY, John
Wilson, Woodrow: ALBRIGHT, Horace Marden; BAKHMETEFF, Boris Alexander; BENEDUM AND THE OIL INDUSTRY; BRECKINRIDGE, Henry; COUDERT, Frederic Rene; GERARD, James Watson; HOLMAN, Charles William; PAGE, Arthur Wilson; PARSONS, Geoffrey; SAYRE, Francis Bowes; SPAETH, Sigmund; SPARGO, John

459

The Oral History Collection

Winant, John: ARONSON, A. Henry; BANE, Frank; BERNSTEIN, Bernice; BURNS, Eveline Mabel; CLAGUE, Ewan; EMERSON, Thomas Irwin; HOHAUS, Reinhard Arthur; LORWIN, Lewis L.; MULLINER, Maurine; TATE, Jack Bernard
Wing, Daniel G.: BARKER, James Madison
Wingate, Orde: ALISON, John Richardson
Wingert, Paul: ZORACH, William
Wirtz, Willard: IVES, Elizabeth Stevenson (Mrs. Ernest); MINOW, Newton Norman
Wise, Stephen S.: PROSKAUER, Joseph M.; RICHARDS, Bernard G.
Wislocki, George: AUB, Joseph Charles
Witte, Edwin: ALTMEYER, Arthur Joseph; ARMSTRONG, Barbara; BROWN, James Douglas; BURNS, Eveline Mabel; LENROOT, Katharine Fredrica; SOMERS, Herman Miles
Wolfe, Thomas: CANE, Melville Henry; DANIELS, Jonathan Worth; VAN VECHTEN, Carl; WHEELOCK, John Hall
Wolkstein, Irwin: SAPERSTEIN, Sydney
Woll, Matthew: SHISHKIN, Boris Basil
Wood, Ida: COX, Joseph Aloysius
Wood, Leonard: MARVIN, Langdon Parker; WILLIAMS, James Thomas, Jr.
Wood, Robert E.: BARKER, James Madison; BENTON, William; HUTCHINS, Robert Maynard
Woodberry, George: PROSKAUER, Joseph M.
Woodward, Ellen: MULLINER, Maurine
Wright, Henry L.: ASCHER, Charles
Wright, Orville: HENRY H. ARNOLD PROJECT
Wright, Wilbur: BROWNE, Ross; LOENING, Grover
Wyck, Robert Van: HETTRICK, John T.
Yamamoto, Isoroku: READ, William Augustus, Jr.
Yarnell, Harry Ervin: HART, Thomas Charles
Young, Owen D.: LANG, Chester Henry
Yu, Frederick T. C.: INTERNATIONAL NEGOTIATIONS
Zangwill, Israel: RICHARDS, Bernard G.
Ziegfeld, Florenz: RODGERS, Richard
Zimbalist, Efrem: CURTIS, James Freeman
Zukor, Adolph: PALEY, William S.
Zweig, Stefan: HUEBSCH, Ben W.